The Variety of Fiction

A CRITICAL ANTHOLOGY

The Variety of Fiction

A CRITICAL ANTHOLOGY

Edward A. Bloom / Lillian D. Bloom

The Odyssey Press, New York

ACKNOWLEDGMENTS

"The Outing," by James Baldwin. Reprinted from *Going to Meet the Man* (copyright © 1948, 1951, 1957, 1958, 1960, 1965 by James Baldwin), by permission of the publisher, The Dial Press, Inc.

"Coming Home," by Elizabeth Bowen. Reprinted from *Early Stories* (copyright 1950 by Elizabeth Bowen), by permission of Alfred A. Knopf, Inc.

"Growing Up," by Joyce Cary. Reprinted from *Spring Song and Other Stories* (copyright © 1956 by Arthur Lucius Michael Cary and David Alexander Ogilvie, executors of the Estate of Joyce Cary), by permission of Harper & Row, Publishers, Inc., and Curtis Brown Ltd.

"The Biggest Band," by Verlin Cassill. Reprinted from *The Father and Other Stories* (copyright © 1956 by R. V. Cassill), by permission of Simon and Schuster, Inc.

"The Secret Sharer," by Joseph Conrad. Reprinted from *'Twixt Land and Sea* (copyright, the Trustees of the Joseph Conrad Estate), by permission of J. M. Dent and Sons Ltd.

"Dry September," by William Faulkner (copyright 1930; renewed 1958 by William Faulkner). Reprinted from *The Collected Stories of William Faulkner,* by permission of Random House, Inc.

"The Lost Decade," by F. Scott Fitzgerald (copyright 1939 Esquire, Inc.; renewal copyright © 1967 Frances Scott Fitzgerald Lanahan). Reprinted by permission of Charles Scribner's Sons from *The Short Stories of F. Scott Fitzgerald.*

"The Curate's Friend," by E. M. Forster. Reprinted from *The Collected Tales of E. M. Forster* (1947), by permission of Alfred A. Knopf, Inc., and Sidgwick and Jackson Ltd.

"The Consummation," reprinted from *A Motley* by John Galsworthy (copyright 1910 Charles Scribner's Sons; renewal copyright 1938 Ada Galsworthy). Reprinted by permission of Charles Scribner's Sons, and by William Heinemann Ltd. (publishers of *The Caravan* by John Galsworthy).

"Message in a Bottle," by Nadine Gordimer. Reprinted from *Not for Publication and Other Stories* (copyright © 1962 by Nadine Gordimer), by permission of The Viking Press, Inc.

"Old Man at the Bridge," by Ernest Hemingway (copyright 1938 Ernest Hemingway; renewal copyright © 1966 Mary Hemingway). Reprinted from *The Short Stories of Ernest Hemingway,* by permission of Charles Scribner's Sons.

"Hubert and Minnie," by Aldous Huxley. Reprinted from *Collected Short Stories* by Aldous Huxley (copyright 1924, 1952 by Aldous Huxley), by permission of Harper and Row, Publishers, Inc., Chatto and Windus Ltd, and Mrs. Laura Huxley.

"The Liar," by Henry James. Reprinted from *The Nation,* in *The Novels and Tales of Henry*

James, Volume XII (Charles Scribner's Sons, 1908).

"The Dead," by James Joyce. Reprinted from *The Dubliners* (originally published by B. W. Huebsch, Inc., 1916), by permission of The Viking Press, Inc. All rights reserved.

"The Rocking Horse Winner," by D. H. Lawrence. Reprinted from *The Complete Short Stories of D. H. Lawrence* (copyright 1933 by the Estate of D. H. Lawrence; renewal copyright © 1961 by Angelo Ravagli and C. Montague Weekley, Executors of the Estate of Frieda Lawrence Ravagli), by permission of The Viking Press, Inc.

"The Nuisance," by Doris Lessing. Reprinted from *African Stories* (copyright © 1951, 1953, 1954, 1957, 1958, 1962, 1963, 1964, 1965 by Doris Lessing), by permission of Simon and Schuster, Inc. Reprinted from *This Was the Old Chief's Country,* by permission of Curtis Brown Ltd.

"Angel Levine," by Bernard Malamud. Reprinted from *The Magic Barrel* (copyright © 1955, 1958 by Bernard Malamud), by permission of Farrar, Straus and Giroux, Inc.

"Signs and Symbols," by Vladimir Nabokov (copyright 1948 by Vladimir Nabokov). Reprinted from *Nabokov's Dozen,* by permission of Doubleday and Company, Inc.

"The Comforts of Home," by Flannery O'Connor. Reprinted from *Everything that Rises Must Converge* (copyright © 1960, 1965 by the Estate of Mary Flannery O'Connor), by permission of Farrar, Straus and Giroux, Inc.

"Mother and Son," by Liam O'Flaherty. Reprinted by permission of the Devin-Adair Company.

"In Dreams Begin Responsibilities," by Delmore Schwartz. Reprinted from *The World Is a Wedding* (copyright 1948 by Delmore Schwartz), by permission of New Directions Publishing Corporation.

"The Followers," by Dylan Thomas. Reprinted from *Adventures in the Skin Trade* (copyright 1955 by New Directions, by permission of New Directions Publishing Corporation. Reprinted from *The Prospect of the Sea,* by permission of J. M. Dent and Sons Ltd. and the Trustees for the Copyrights of the late Dylan Thomas.

"The Facts Concerning the Recent Carnival of Crime in Connecticut," by Mark Twain. Reprinted from *Tom Sawyer Abroad and Other Stories,* by permission of Harper and Row, Publishers, Inc.

"A & P," by John Updike (copyright 1962 by John Updike). Reprinted from *Pigeon Feathers and Other Stories,* by permission of Alfred A. Knopf, Inc. First appeared in *The New Yorker.*

"The Use of Force," by William Carlos Williams. Reprinted from *The Farmers' Daughters* (copyright 1938 by William Carlos Williams) by permission of New Directions Publishing Corporation.

"The String Quartet," by Virginia Woolf. Reprinted from *A Haunted House* (copyright 1944 by Harcourt, Brace & World, Inc.), by permission of Harcourt, Brace & World, Inc., The Hogarth Press Ltd., and Leonard Woolf.

Extract from *Art and Reality,* by Joyce Cary (copyright 1958). Reprinted by permission of Curtis Brown Ltd., and Harper & Row, Publishers, Inc.

"Preface" to *Charley Is My Darling* (Carfax ed., 1951), by Joyce Cary. Reprinted by permission of Curtis Brown Ltd., and Harper & Row, Publishers, Inc.

Extract from the "Preface to 'The Shorter Tales,'" in *Last Essays,* by Joseph Conrad (copyright, Trustees of Conrad Estate). Reprinted by permission of J. M. Dent and Sons Ltd.

Extract from *Old Times in the Faulkner Country* (Chapel Hill, 1961), by John B. Cullen. Reprinted by permission of the University of North Carolina Press.

Extracts from *Aspects of the Novel,* by E. M. Forster. Reprinted by permission of Edward Arnold (Publishers) Ltd., and Harcourt, Brace & World, Inc.

Extracts from Gwynn and Blotner, eds., *Faulkner in the University* (Charlottesville, 1959). Reprinted by permission of the University of Virginia Press.

Extracts from *The Collected Letters of D. H. Lawrence*, ed. by Harry T. Moore (copyright 1932 by the Estate of D. H. Lawrence; renewal copyright © 1960 by Angelo Ravagli and C. Montague Weekley). Reprinted by permission of The Viking Press, Inc.

Extract from "No Plot, My Dear, No Story," by Katherine Anne Porter. Reprinted from *The Days Before* (copyright 1952 by Katherine Anne Porter), by permission of Cyrilly Abels.

Extracts from Mark Schorer, ed., *The Story: A Critical Anthology*, 2nd ed. (copyright © 1967). Reprinted by permission of Prentice Hall, Inc., Englewood Cliffs, N.J.

Extract from "The Reading and Writing of Short Stories," by Eudora Welty. Reprinted from *The Atlantic Monthly*, No. CLXXXIII (copyright 1949 by Eudora Welty), by permission of Russell & Volkening, Inc.

Extract from "The Supernatural in Fiction," by Virginia Woolf. Reprinted from *Granite and Rainbow* (1958), by permission of the Hogarth Press, Leonard Woolf, and Harcourt, Brace & World, Inc.

PREFACE

"The deep motive" of authorship, according to the British critic Walter Allen, is "in the instinct which urges us not to be alone. A writer is essentially a man who will not be resigned to solitude. Each of us is like a desert, and a literary work is like a cry from the desert, or like a pigeon let loose with a message in its claws, or like a bottle thrown into the sea. The point is: to be heard—even if by one single person. And the point is that our thoughts and, if we are novelists [or short story writers], our characters should be understood and loved and welcomed by other intelligences and other hearts. An author who assures you that he writes for himself alone and that he does not care whether he is heard or not is a boaster and is deceiving either himself or you. Every man suffers if he is alone, and the artist is the man for whom and in whom this suffering takes a physical form. Baudelaire was right when he called artists *beacons*. They light a great fire in the darkness, and they set light to themselves so as to attract the greatest number of their fellow-beings to them."

Each of the authors to be presented in this volume seems to us an exemplification of Walter Allen's argument. Each, in his own way, is that metaphoric *beacon* signalling to the world at large for attention. Despite the variety of their thematic and artistic concerns, the short story writers in this collection have in common a desire—it is not too strong to say, a *need*—to make themselves heard by their fellow-men. The measure of their distinction is the way in which they send out their signals; the way in which they command attention. This appears to connote evaluative conclusions, implicit in which is conscious critical preparation on the part of the audience. It is altogether possible, of course, to read and enjoy stories without the advantage of technical training. And this is how a good many readers go about the business of extracting enjoyment from fiction. We have no quarrel with this approach, but we think there are better and longer lasting ones. Whatever innate taste we may have gains solidity and substance from the development and exercise of judgment. In the present context, that is another way of saying that literature improves for us in the process of our acquiring critical standards by which we learn to value and discriminate.

Our aim here is to provide a variety of stories which lend themselves to certain critical problems and solutions. At the same time we wish to leave as clear a field as possible for the pleasure to be derived from these stories. Study, in short, does not have to be a bar to pleasure. Hence, we have attempted to array our own critical apparatus unobtrusively, letting the fiction dominate. We have also—aware always that we must not interfere with the narratives—frequently given the authors themselves an opportunity to account for what they are about. Whosoever the critical voice, however, we have made every effort to keep it in a lower register than that of the fictional voice. The commentaries and expository matters are naturally brief, thus. But for those who may wish fuller critical documentation, we have in this book followed the organization of an earlier volume: *The Order of Fiction* (Odyssey Press, 1964). In that volume, the principles merely hinted or outlined now may be found in elaborated form. The two volumes may be used in complementary fashion, but they may also be used independently of each other.

CONTENTS

Setting   149

Categories of Order

The Narrator's Focus

Content and Purpose

THE VARIETY OF FICTION

Introduction

The word *fiction* is a generic term which, for all its dimension and ambiguity, usually connotes a prose narrative. It embraces such types as the short story, the novella or novelette, and the novel itself. Yet these three types of storytelling differ from each other not only in physical size but in far less tangible intention and structure and goal. This is not to say that any one form is superior to the other two, even though short story writers from Washington Irving to Frank O'Connor have bestowed the laurel upon their own product.

In a letter to Henry Brevoort 11 December 1824, Washington Irving said:

For my part, I consider a story merely as a frame on which to stretch my materials. It is the play of thought, and sentiment, and language; the weaving in of characters, lightly, yet expressively delineated; the familiar and faithful exhibition of scenes in common life; and the half concealed vein of humor that is often playing through the whole,—these are among what I aim at, and upon which I felicitate myself in proportion as I think I succeed. I have preferred adopting the mode of sketches and short tales rather than long works, because I choose to take a line of writing peculiar to myself, rather than fall into the manner or school of any other writer; and there is a constant activity of thought and a nicety of execution required in writings of the kind, more than the world appears to imagine. It is comparatively easy to swell a story to any size when you have once the scheme and the characters in your mind; the mere interest of the story, too, carries the reader on through pages and pages of careless writing, and the author may often be dull for half a volume at a time, if he has some striking scene at the end of it; but in these shorter writings, every page must have its merit. The author must be continually piquant; woe to him if he makes an awkward sentence or writes a stupid page; the critics are sure to pounce upon it. Yet if he succeed, the very variety and piquancy of his writings—nay, their very brevity, make them frequently recurred to, and when the mere interest of the story is exhausted, he begins to get credit for his touches of pathos or humor; his points of wit or turns of language.

More than one hundred years later Frank O'Connor was similarly self-congratulatory when he argued that "the storyteller differs from the novelist in this: he must be much more of a writer, much more of an artist—perhaps . . . more of a dramatist."

William Faulkner, who has worked successfully in the short story and in the novel, supports the claims of Irving and O'Connor. Once, when asked whether it is easier to write a novel than a short story, he answered in the affirmative. "You can be more careless," he said, "you can put more trash in it and be excused for it. In a short story that's next to the poem, almost every word has got to be almost exactly right. In the novel you can be careless but in the short story you can't. I mean by that the good short stories like Chekhov wrote. That's why I rate that second—it's because it demands a nearer absolute exactitude. You have less room to be slovenly and careless. There's less room in it for trash."*

*_Faulkner in the University,_ ed. Frederick L. Gwynn and Joseph L. Blotner (Charlottesville, Virginia, 1959), p. 207.

At the same time, however, he argued that form, whether it be the short story or the novel, must be self-determined and devoted to the exploration of truth; it must emerge from the materials of the fiction and the craft of the teller. In his own practice, composition began

sometimes with a person, sometimes with an anecdote, but the short story is conceived in the same terms that the book is. The first job the crafts-man faces is to tell this as quickly and as simply as I can, and if he's good, if he's of the first water, like Chekhov, he can do it every time in two or three thousand words, but if he's not that good, sometimes it takes him eighty thousand words. But they are similar, and he is simply trying to tell something which was true and moving in the shortest time he can, and then if he has sense enough stop. That is, I don't believe the man or woman sits down and says, Now I'm going to write a short story, or Now I'm going to write a novel. It's an idea that begins with the thought, the image of a character, or with an anecdote, and even in the same breath, almost like lightning, it begins to take shape that he can see whether it's going to be a short story or a novel. Sometimes, not always. Sometimes he thinks it'll be a short story and finds that he can't. Sometimes it looks like it's to be a novel and then after he works at it, he sees that it's not, that he can tell it in two thousand or five thousand words. No rule to it.*

Despite wrangling over comparative merit and even over the dif-ferences which separate the short story, the novella, and novel, there are certain elements which they share. They all have, for example, plot, character, and setting. They all emanate, if they are creatively successful, from an artist-author who believes that man's joys and frustrations, his triumphs and defeats, transcend the limitations of time and place to acquire a universal relevance. And further he is a creator who assumes the need to translate or interpret this belief into language which makes disparate experiences similar, foreign experi-ences familiar, particularized experiences shared. What all good fiction has in common "is a realization of ourselves not as (possibly) immortal beings but as people living here and now amid neighbours who are 'such creatures as we are, in such a world as the present one'

*Ibid., pp. 48–9.

whom we would wish to understand, like, and, no doubt, for such is human nature, judge."*

The short story, our major concern in this anthology, is like the novella and the novel in that each is a unified, organically inevitable composition in which all parts, influences, and attitudes function as segments of the whole. It is for this reason that the good storyteller never lets his attention wander from the total design of his work. To be sure, he is aware of the working parts of his art, but they are made subordinate to and absorbed into the ultimate concept and technique. Even digressions, secondary plots, and peripheral or minor characters are contrived with the same respect for the artistic totality.

One capacity or quality or ingredient—more than any other—blends all the parts into a satisfactory whole. This is the author's imagination without which there could be no fiction. It is from this inventive source that a short story is born; it is from this that the materials are selected, ordered, and interpreted; it is from this that emerges an artistic oneness combining the aesthetic and the intellectual, the matter and the form. Imagination is of course not unique to the artist; in varying degrees it is present in everyone. But the artist's imagination is more refined than that of most men, and at the same time it is usually disciplined to work through reason toward a controlled end. Indeed, it is closely allied to common sense, that quality which we sometimes dismiss too quickly as mundane. For example, Elizabeth Bowen in writing to a fellow artist, V.S. Pritchett, asserts: "I don't think you and I ought to ignore our own commonsense, of which we have the ordinary human modicum. It appears in our writing because it appears in us; but because it is mixed with vision, or whatever else one calls imaginative perception, it sounds Delphic."**

Many short stories may and do grow out of actuality, events experienced or observed by the writer. But these specifics or particularities, no matter how "true" or verifiable, become the proper materials of fiction only as they undergo change by the artist who

*London *Times Literary Supplement* (8 June 1962).

***Why Do I Write? An Exchange of Views between Elizabeth Bowen, Graham Greene and V. S. Pritchett* (London, 1948), p. 26.

is concerned less with their authenticity than with *his* judgment of them. The matter of a short story need not derive exclusively or absolutely from the writer's exposure to the immediate and the real. It may emerge primarily from his own sense of invention, his urge to fabricate. That is to say, he may create rather than reproduce data. Approaching art from this direction, he still does not ignore experience; rather, he reshapes it. Art thus becomes an act of substitution in which what is imagined gives a new or fresh appearance to reality. By this means also—that is, through the transfiguring imagination—he is able to give a tangible dimension to his vision or his commonsense interpretation of human behavior.

It does not matter to us as readers whether the matter of fiction is empirically or imaginatively established. We do not care whether an author has transformed it from other artists who have gone before him in a long chain of creative endeavor. We insist only that it be within the realm of the believable, that it be *credible.* In this way we can accept situations, events, problems, and the like, as being true while admitting that they need not have happened in fact. A work of fiction has credibility when its author allows his material to achieve its own structure and meaning, his characters their own destiny, his plot its own end, without making us feel uncomfortable because we are conscious of his manipulation or interference.

It is through the blending of elements as disparate as the imaginative and the realistic that the writer of fiction establishes his identity. Every short story—and this is true for all other types of fiction—must prove itself as the individual experience of an individual creator. And yet paradoxically the artist usually submerges his personality, permitting the characters and what they experience to transmit his meaning. He is the inventive source, the energizer —the fabulous artificer in Joyce's idiom—but his hand is hidden and his voice is rarely distinct among the others in the work of art. In fact, the reader is not often interested in the author of a short story, only in his masks—the characters—through whom he speaks. The artistic experience, in other words, is between the written word and the reader; the short story or the novel functions as the instrument for the communication and evalution of a complex body of ideas, attitudes, values, people, and events—the "stuff of existence."

However self-effacing a writer may be in what he produces, he is nevertheless always present within the product as the invisible but creative agent. And however instinctive or intuitive the source of his talent, it is subject to a remarkable discipline. He has not merely the vision but the craft with which to translate the vision into verbal form. It is technique which enables him to articulate and evaluate through characters and their behavior, through precise word and exact symbols, the concept or dream which first drove him to create. It is technique which, according to Sherwood Anderson, is so long in being born. "For such men as myself you must understand there is always a great difficulty about telling the tale after the scent has been picked up. The tales that continually came to me . . . could of course not become tales until I clothed them. Having, from a conversation overheard or in some other way, got the bone of a tale, I was like a woman who has just become impregnated. Something was growing inside me. At night while I lay in my bed, I could feel the heels of the tale kicking against the walls of my body. Often as I lay thus every word of the tale came to me quite clearly but when I got out of bed to write it down the words would not come. . . ."*

In the pages which follow we present twenty-eight short stories and novellas in sections which coincide with various problems in technique. As we analyze the means by which authors probe, develop, and realize their material, we silently but firmly insist upon the organicism of all successful fiction.

*A Story Teller's Story (New York, 1924), p. 358.

Character

We believe that "art is an illusion of reality somehow founded upon the facts of experience, and projected in such a way as to make the illusion credible or probable."* This is the point from which we begin our over-all discussion of technique, and specifically that of characterization.

When we pick up a short story to read, we want to know about people who are involved—for good or bad—with other people in a situation or in a related series of events. When we read, we expect to confront various *characters* who are engaged in movement more or less complex, in action which progresses from its initiation to its necessary conclusion. Moreover, we expect that these personalities and their destinies must be worked out in physical time and place, in a setting which is recognizable, or at least credible.

*Edward A. Bloom, *The Order of Fiction* (New York, 1964), p. 19.

According to Arnold Bennett, "the foundation of good fiction is character-creating and nothing else.... Style counts; plot counts; originality of outlook counts. But none of these counts anything like so much as the convincingness of the characters. If the characters are real the novel will have a chance; if they are not, oblivion will be its portion." Bennett is perhaps overly simple in his statement. We know that it is impossible to separate the characters of a piece of fiction from what happens to them (the *plot*), from the way in which they speak (*dialogue*), from the environment and time (*setting*) in which they live. Moreover, the concept of what is "real" varies frequently among readers as well as authors. Certainly the credible characters of Bennett differ from the equally credible characters of Joyce and Virginia Woolf and even those of Faulkner and Hemingway. Still in emphasizing the function of characterization, Bennett is correctly isolating that element of fiction which is indispensable and most readily intriguing; that element which in fact creates a liaison of understanding between reader and writer.

No two men are alike. This truth is a constant source of fascination to the writer of fiction. He wants to catch these human differences in words, wants to analyze their interaction, wants above all else to produce—as Bennett argued—real and convincing characters. As a rule, that is, the short story teller tries to fix in his primary, focal personalities traits and responses which will give them the verisimilitude of completeness. In E. M. Forster's more specific terminology, he intends them to be "round" or three-dimensional and organic rather than "flat" or two-dimensional and static.

Even characters drawn along a plane surface, however, may be consciously and artistically valuable. Consider that the allegorist usually creates so-called "flat" characters to function as agents for specific concepts. They "stand for" certain ideas or values, or even situations. They are deliberately made to be stereotypes rather than give the individuality which might detract from their intended symbolic meaning. We find characters like these in the work of Melville and Hawthorne, for example. We do not see either Ethan Brand or Bannadonna as complex and variable human beings. Instead they move as symbols, as representations of such individuals who in their pride and lust for power are heartlessly indifferent to their fellow men. Wantonly they intrude upon God's dominion only to be destroyed for their effort.

The modern short story writer (with a rare, brilliant exception like Kafka) tends to avoid such characterization even as he tends to avoid those who might be labelled "hero" or "villain." In a world of increasing mechanization, of IBM cards, of push-button death and brain-washing, there is little room for individuals who possess superhuman strength or a spectacular capacity for good or evil. When, therefore, a writer conceives of his characters, he thinks of a protagonist and an antagonist (although his own terms may be different) who are life-size but no larger than that. He thinks of his dominant characters as *dynamic,* as standing in opposition to one another and so providing the movement and conflict of the story; he thinks of them as essentially three-dimensional figures with the comprehensively human qualities admired by Forster.

While we as readers allow our attention to be captured by the protagonist and/or the antagonist, those who advance the action of a story or promote its complications, we are also aware that in most short stories there are also other necessary characters who are *static.* They themselves may not take a significant part in the movement of a story or contribute to it directly. Instead they function primarily as a presence to create effects, to add to the texture of the plot, to illuminate the personalities of the leading characters, perhaps to help enforce the narrative oppositions. It is hard to believe that Capadose in "The Liar" is a static character. Yet that is precisely what he is: he undergoes no change; he is himself in conflict with no one. Yet he is the catalyst for the tension between his wife and the artist or the "I" of the fiction. It is his presence and his affliction which drive Oliver Lyon to seek his exposure.

Briefly, then, we have suggested that characters may be usefully distinguished according to whether they are "round" or "flat," performing fictional roles which are either dynamic or static. Characters acquire further interest when we become aware of the perspectives from which they are drawn. In explicit characterizations, thus, the individual is revealed at close range through external details. The reader is told how he looks, thinks, feels, dresses, and moves. Implicit characterization, on the other hand, is achieved through the longer range of indirection and nuance. It therefore imposes a greater burden on the reader, who must discover depths of personality through the assistance of subtle hints, a bit of conversation, an unexplained movement, and so on.

None of this, however, need convince us that one method is better or more effective than the other; nor, for that matter, that the two modes are mutually exclusive. Elizabeth Bowen's technique in "Coming Home," for example, is to depict her childish protagonist mainly through externalization. Rosalind takes us into her confidence, as it were, almost as if she were addressing herself to us directly and candidly. As a result, we see within a fairly narrow compass the shifting moods of her self-centered personality. We see these overtly, and yet we are still allowed to reflect upon implied associations between the girl and her mother. Joyce Cary likewise treats the introspective world of children, but through the vision of an adult whose reactions become the measure of his personality. But whereas Miss Bowen opens doors for us steadily and progressively, Cary tends to keep us suspended on the threshold of his protagonist's discovery—his adult becomes the startled onlooker, the perplexed and saddened witness of the separation between himself and his daughters. Both authors say essentially the same thing but from opposed points of view. Cary provides us with an implicit characterization but without denying himself the use of exterior details. This is a reversal of Miss Bowen's technique, to be sure; each, however, has its artistic and thematic validity.

The Liar
Henry James

I

The train was half an hour late and the drive from the station longer than he had supposed, so that when he reached the house its inmates had dispersed to dress for dinner and he was conducted straight to his room. The curtains were drawn in this asylum, the candles were lighted, the fire was bright, and when the servant had quickly put out his clothes the comfortable little place became suggestive—seemed to promise a pleasant house, a various party, talks, acquaintances, affinities, to say nothing of very good cheer. He was too occupied with his profession to pay many country visits, but he had heard people who had more time for them speak of establishments where "they do you very well." He foresaw that the proprietors of Stayes would do him very well. In his bedroom at a country house he always looked first at the books on the shelf and the prints on the walls; he considered that these things gave a sort of measure of the culture and even of the character of his hosts. Though he had but little time to devote to them on this occasion a cursory inspection assured him that if the literature, as usual, was mainly American and humorous the art consisted neither of the water-color studies of the children nor of 'goody' engravings. The walls were adorned with old-fashioned lithographs, principally portraits of country gentlemen with high collars and riding gloves: this suggested—and it was encouraging—that the tradition of portraiture was held in esteem. There was the customary novel of Mr. Le Fanu, for the bedside; the ideal reading in a country house for the hours after midnight. Oliver Lyon could scarcely forbear beginning it while he buttoned his shirt.

Perhaps that is why he not only found every one assembled in the hall when he went down, but perceived from the way the move to dinner was instantly made that they had been waiting for him. There was no delay, to introduce him to a lady, for he went out in a group of unmatched men, without this appendage. The men, straggling behind, sidled and edged as usual at the door of the dining-room, and the *dénouement* of this little comedy was that he came to his place last of all. This made him think that he was in a sufficiently distinguished company, for if he had been humiliated (which he was not), he could not have consoled himself with the reflection that such a fate was natural to an obscure, struggling young artist. He could no longer think of himself as very young, alas, and if his position was not so brilliant as it ought to be he could no longer justify it by calling it a struggle. He was something of a celebrity and he was apparently in a society of celebrities. This idea added to the curiosity with which he looked up and down the long table as he settled himself in his place.

It was a numerous party—five and twenty people; rather an odd occasion to have proposed to him, as he thought. He would not be surrounded by the quiet that ministers to good work; however, it had never interfered with his work to see the spectacle of human life before him in the intervals. And though he did not know it, it was never quiet at Stayes. When he was working well he found himself in that happy state—the happiest of all for an artist—in which things in general contribute to the particular idea and fall in with it, help it on and justify it, so that he feels for the hour as if nothing in the world can happen to him, even if it come in the guise of disaster or suffering, that will not be an enhancement of his subject. Moreover there was an exhilaration (he had felt it before) in the rapid change of scene—the jump, in the dusk of the afternoon, from foggy London and his familiar studio to a centre of festivity in the middle of Hertfordshire and a drama half acted, a drama of pretty women and noted men and wonderful orchids in silver jars. He observed as a not unimportant fact that one of the pretty women was beside him: a gentleman sat on his other hand. But he went into his neighbours little as yet: he was busy looking out for Sir David, whom he had never seen and about whom he naturally was curious.

Evidently, however, Sir David was not at dinner, a circumstance sufficiently explained by the other circumstance which constituted our friend's principal knowledge of him—his being ninety years of age. Oliver Lyon had looked forward with great pleasure to the chance of painting a nonagenarian, and though the old man's absence from table was something of a disappointment (it was an opportunity the less to observe him before going to work), it seemed a sign that he was rather sacred and perhaps therefore an impressive relic. Lyon looked at his son with the greater interest —wondered whether the glazed bloom of his cheek had been transmitted from Sir David. That would be jolly to paint, in the old man —the withered ruddiness of a winter apple, especially if the eye were still alive and the white hair carried out the frosty look. Arthur Ashmore's hair had a midsummer glow, but Lyon was glad his commission had been to delineate the father rather than the son, in spite of his never having seen the one and of the other being seated there before him now in the happy expansion of liberal hospitality.

Arthur Ashmore was a fresh-coloured, thick-necked English gentleman, but he was just not a subject; he might have been a farmer and he might have been a banker: you could scarcely paint him in characters. His wife did not make up the amount; she was a large, bright, negative woman, who had the same air as her husband of being somehow tremendously new; a sort of appearance of fresh varnish (Lyon could scarcely tell whether it came from her complexion or from her clothes), so that one felt she ought to sit in a gilt frame, suggesting reference to a catalogue or a price-list. It was as if she were already rather a bad though expensive portrait, knocked off by an eminent hand, and Lyon had no wish to copy that work. The pretty woman on his right was engaged with her neighbour and the gentleman on his other side looked shrinking and scared, so that he had time to lose himself in his favourite diversion of watching face after face. This amusement gave him the greatest pleasure he knew, and he often thought it a mercy that the human mask did interest him and that it was not less vivid than it was (sometimes it ran its success in this line very close), since he was to make his living by reproducing it. Even if Arthur Ashmore would not be inspiring to paint (a certain anxiety rose in him lest if he should make a hit with her father-in-law Mrs. Arthur should take it into her head that he had now proved himself worthy to *aborder* her husband); even if he had looked a little less like a page (fine as to print and margin) without punctuation, he would still be a refreshing, iridescent surface. But the gentleman four persons off—what was he? Would he be a subject, or was his face only the legible door-plate of his identity, burnished with punctual washing and shaving—the least thing that was decent that you would know him by?

This face arrested Oliver Lyon: it struck him at first as very handsome. The gentleman might still be called young, and his features were regular: he had a plentiful, fair moustache that curled up at the ends, a brilliant, gallant, almost adventurous air, and a big shining breastpin in the middle of his shirt. He appeared a fine satisfied soul, and Lyon perceived that wherever he rested his friendly eye there fell an influence as pleasant as the September sun—as if he could make grapes and pears or even human affection ripen by looking at them. What was odd in him was a certain mixture of the correct and the extravagant: as if he were an adventurer imitating a gentleman with rare perfection or a gentleman who had taken a fancy to go about with hidden arms. He might have been a dethroned prince or the war-correspondent of a newspaper: he represented both enterprise and tradition, good manners and bad taste. Lyon at length fell into conversation with the lady beside him—they dispensed, as he had had to dispense at dinner-parties before, with an introduction—by asking who this personage might be.

'Oh, he's Colonel Capadose, don't you know?' Lyon didn't know and he asked for further information. His neighbour had a sociable manner and evidently was accustomed to quick transitions; she turned from her other interlocutor with a methodical air, as a good cook lifts the cover of the next saucepan. 'He has been a great deal in India—isn't he rather celebrated?' she inquired. Lyon confessed he had never heard of him, and she went on, 'Well, perhaps he isn't; but he says he is, and if you think it, that's just the same, isn't it?'

'If *you* think it?'

'I mean if he thinks it—that's just as good, I suppose.'

'Do you mean that he says that which is not?'

'Oh dear, no—because I never know. He is exceedingly clever and amusing—quite the cleverest person in the house, unless indeed you are more so. But that I can't tell yet, can I? I only know about the people I know; I think that's celebrity enough!'

'Enough for them?'

'Oh, I see you're clever. Enough for me! But I have heard of you,' the lady went on. 'I know your pictures; I admire them. But I don't think you look like them.'

'They are mostly portraits,' Lyon said; 'and what I usually try for is not my own resemblance.'

'I see what you mean. But they have much more colour. And now you are going to do some one here?'

'I have been invited to do Sir David. I'm rather disappointed at not seeing him this evening.'

'Oh, he goes to bed at some unnatural hour—eight o'clock or something of that sort. You know he's rather an old mummy.'

'An old mummy?' Oliver Lyon repeated.

'I mean he wears half a dozen waistcoats, and that sort of thing. He's always cold.'

'I have never seen him and never seen any portrait or photograph of him,' Lyon said. 'I'm surprised at his never having had anything done—at their waiting all these years.'

'Ah, that's because he was afraid, you know; it was a kind of superstition. He was sure that if anything were done he would die directly afterwards. He has only consented to-day.'

'He's ready to die then?'

'Oh, now he's so old he doesn't care.'

'Well, I hope I shan't kill him,' said Lyon. 'It was rather unnatural in his son to send for me.'

'Oh, they have nothing to gain—everything is theirs already!' his companion rejoined, as if she took his speech quite literally. Her talkativeness was systematic—she fraternised as seriously as she might have played whist. 'They do as they like—they fill the house with people—they have *carte blanche*.'

'I see—but there's still the title.'

'Yes, but what is it?'

Our artist broke into laughter at this, whereat his companion stared. Before he had recovered himself she was scouring the plain with her other neighbour. The gentleman on his left at last risked an observation, and they had some fragmentary talk. This personage played his part with difficulty: he uttered a remark as a lady fires a pistol, looking the other way. To catch the ball Lyon had to bend his ear, and this movement led to his observing a handsome creature who was seated on the same side, beyond his interlocutor. Her profile was presented to him and at first he was only struck with its beauty; then it produced an impression still more agreeable—a sense of undimmed remembrance and intimate association. He had not recognised her on the instant only because he had so little expected to see her there; he had not seen her anywhere for so long, and no news of her ever came to him. She was often in his thoughts, but she had passed out of his life. He thought of her twice a week; that may be called often in relation to a person one has not seen for twelve years. The moment after he recognised her he felt how true it was that it was only she who could look like that: of the most charming head in the world (and this lady had it) there could never be a replica. She was leaning forward a little; she remained in profile, apparently listening to some one on the other side of her. She was listening, but she was also looking, and after a moment Lyon followed the direction of her eyes. They rested upon the gentleman who had been described to him as Colonel Capadose—rested, as it appeared to him, with a kind of habitual, visible complacency. This was not strange, for the Colonel was unmistakably formed to attract the sympathetic gaze of woman; but Lyon was slightly disappointed that she could let *him* look at her so long without giving him a glance. There was nothing between them to-day and he had no rights, but she must have known he was coming (it was of course not such a tremendous event, but she could not have been staying in the house without hearing of it), and it was not natural that that should absolutely fail to affect her.

She was looking at Colonel Capadose as if she were in love with him—a queer accident for the proudest, most reserved of women. But doubtless it was all right, if her husband liked it or didn't notice it: he had heard indefinitely, years before, that she was married, and he took for granted (as he had not heard that she had become a widow) the presence of the happy man on whom she had conferred what she had refused to *him,* the poor art-student at Munich. Colonel Capadose appeared to be aware of nothing, and this circumstance, incongruously enough, rather irritated Lyon than gratified him. Suddenly the lady turned her head, showing her full face to our hero. He was so prepared with a greeting that he instantly smiled, as a shaken jug overflows; but she gave him no response, turned away again and sank back in her chair. All that her face said in that instant was, 'You see I'm as handsome as ever.' To which he mentally subjoined, 'Yes, and as much good it does me!' He asked the young man beside him if he knew who that beautiful being was—the fifth person beyond him. The young man leaned forward, considered and then said, 'I think she's Mrs. Capadose.'

'Do you mean his wife—that fellow's?' And Lyon indicated the subject of the information given him by his other neighbour.

'Oh, is *he* Mr. Capadose?' said the young man, who appeared very vague. He admitted his vagueness and explained it by saying that there were so many people and he had come only the day before. What was definite to Lyon was that Mrs. Capadose was in love with her husband; so that he wished more than ever that he had married her.

'She's very faithful,' he found himself saying three minutes later to the lady on his right. He added that he meant Mrs. Capadose.

'Ah, you know her then?'

'I knew her once upon a time—when I was living abroad.'

'Why then were you asking me about her husband?'

'Precisely for that reason. She married after that—I didn't even know her present name.'

'How then do you know it now?'

'This gentleman has just told me—he appears to know.'

'I didn't know he knew anything,' said the lady, glancing forward.

'I don't think he knows anything but that.'

'Then you have found out for yourself that she is faithful. What do you mean by that?'

'Ah, you mustn't question me—I want to question you,' Lyon said. 'How do you all like her here?'

'You ask too much! I can only speak for myself. I think she's hard.'

'That's only because she's honest and straightforward.'

'Do you mean I like people in proportion as they deceive?'

'I think we all do, so long as we don't find them out,' Lyon said. 'And then there's something in her face—a sort of Roman type, in spite of her having such an English eye. In fact she's English down to the ground; but her complexion, her low forehead and that beautiful close little wave in her dark hair make her look like a glorified *contadina*.'

'Yes, and she always sticks pins and daggers into her head, to increase that effect. I must say I like her husband better: he is so clever.'

'Well, when I knew her there was no comparison that could injure her. She was altogether the most delightful thing in Munich.'

'In Munich?'

'Her people lived there; they were not rich—in pursuit of economy in fact, and Munich was very cheap. Her father was the younger son of some noble house; he had married a second time and had a lot of little mouths to feed. She was the child of the first wife and she didn't like her stepmother, but she was charming to her little brothers and sisters. I once made a sketch of her as Werther's Charlotte, cutting bread and butter while they clustered all round her. All the artists in the place were in love with her but she wouldn't look at "the likes" of us. She was too proud—I grant you that; but she wasn't stuck up nor young ladyish; she was simple and frank and

kind about it. She used to remind me of Thackeray's Ethel Newcome.
She told me she must marry well: it was the one thing she could do
for her family. I suppose you would say that she *has* married well.'

'She told *you?*' smiled Lyon's neighbour.

'Oh, of course I proposed to her too. But she evidently thinks so
herself!' he added.

When the ladies left the table the host as usual bade the gentlemen draw together, so that Lyon found himself opposite to Colonel
Capadose. The conversation was mainly about the 'run,' for it had
apparently been a great day in the hunting-field. Most of the gentlemen communicated their adventures and opinions, but Colonel
Capadose's pleasant voice was the most audible in the chorus. It was
a bright and fresh but masculine organ, just such a voice as, to
Lyon's sense, such a 'fine man' ought to have had. It appeared from
his remarks that he was a very straight rider, which was also very
much what Lyon would have expected. Not that he swaggered, for
his allusions were very quietly and casually made; but they were all
too dangerous experiments and close shaves. Lyon perceived after a
little that the attention paid by the company to the Colonel's remarks was not in direct relation to the interest they seemed to offer;
the result of which was that the speaker, who noticed that *he* at least
was listening, began to treat him as his particular auditor and to fix
his eyes on him as he talked. Lyon had nothing to do but to look
sympathetic and assent—Colonel Capadose appeared to take so
much sympathy and assent for granted. A neighbouring squire had
had an accident; he had come a cropper in an awkward place—just
at the finish—with consequences that looked grave. He had struck
his head; he remained insensible, up to the last accounts: there had
evidently been concussion of the brain. There was some exchange of
views as to his recovery—how soon it would take place or whether
it would take place at all; which led the Colonel to confide to our
artist across the table that *he* shouldn't despair of a fellow even if
he didn't come round for weeks—for weeks and weeks and weeks—
for months, almost for years. He leaned forward; Lyon leaned forward to listen, and Colonel Capadose mentioned that he knew from
personal experience that there was really no limit to the time one
might lie unconscious without being any the worse for it. It had

happened to him in Ireland, years before; he had been pitched out of a dogcart, had turned a sheer somersault and landed on his head. They thought he was dead, but he wasn't; they carried him first to the nearest cabin, where he lay for some days with the pigs, and then to an inn in a neighbouring town—it was a near thing they didn't put him under ground. He had been completely insensible— without a ray of recognition of any human being—for three whole months; had not a glimmer of consciousness of any blessed thing. It was touch and go to that degree that they couldn't come near him, they couldn't feed him, they could scarcely look at him. Then one day he had opened his eyes—as fit as a flea!

'I give you my honour it had done me good—it rested my brain.' He appeared to intimate that with an intelligence so active as his these periods of repose were providential. Lyon thought his story very striking, but he wanted to ask him whether he had not shammed a little—not in relating it, but in keeping so quiet. He hesitated however, in time, to imply a doubt—he was so impressed with the tone in which Colonel Capadose said that it was the turn of a hair that they hadn't buried him alive. That had happened to a friend of his in India—a fellow who was supposed to have died of jungle fever—they clapped him into a coffin. He was going on to recite the further fate of this unfortunate gentleman when Mr. Ashmore made a move and every one got up to adjourn to the drawing-room. Lyon noticed that by this time no one was heeding what his new friend said to him. They came round on either side of the table and met while the gentlemen dawdled before going out.

'And do you mean that your friend was literally buried alive?' asked Lyon, in some suspense.

Colonel Capadose looked at him a moment, as if he had already lost the thread of the conversation. Then his face brightened—and when it brightened it was doubly handsome. 'Upon my soul he was chucked into the ground!'

'And he was left there?'

'He was left there till I came and hauled him out.'

'*You* came?'

'I dreamed about him—it's the most extraordinary story: I heard him calling to me in the night. I took upon myself to dig him up.

You know there are people in India—a kind of beastly race, the ghouls—who violate graves. I had a sort of presentiment that they would get at him first. I rode straight, I can tell you; and, by Jove, a couple of them had just broken ground! Crack—crack, from a couple of barrels, and they showed me their heels, as you may believe. Would you credit that I took him out myself? The air brought him to and he was none the worse. He has got his pension—he came home the other day; he would do anything for me.'

'He called to you in the night?' said Lyon, much startled

'That's the interesting point. Now *what was it?* It wasn't his ghost, because he wasn't dead. It wasn't himself, because he couldn't. It was something or other! You see India's a strange country—there's an element of the mysterious: the air is full of things you can't explain.'

They passed out of the dining-room, and Colonel Capadose, who went among the first, was separated from Lyon; but a minute later, before they reached the drawing-room, he joined him again. 'Ashmore tells me who you are. Of course I have often heard of you—I'm very glad to make your acquaintance; my wife used to know you.'

'I'm glad she remembers me. I recognised her at dinner and I was afraid she didn't.'

'Ah, I daresay she was ashamed,' said the Colonel, with indulgent humour.

'Ashamed of me?' Lyon replied, in the same key.

'Wasn't there something about a picture? Yes; you painted her portrait.'

'Many times,' said the artist; 'and she may very well have been ashamed of what I made of her.'

'Well, I wasn't, my dear sir; it was the sight of that picture, which you were so good as to present to her, that made me first fall in love with her.'

'Do you mean that one with the children—cutting bread and butter?'

'Bread and butter? Bless me, no—vine leaves and a leopard skin —a kind of Bacchante.'

'Ah, yes,' said Lyon; 'I remember. It was the first decent portrait I painted. I should be curious to see it to-day.'

'Don't ask her to show it to you—she'll be mortified!' the Colonel exclaimed.

'Mortified?'

'We parted with it—in the most disinterested manner,' he laughed. 'An old friend of my wife's—her family had known him intimately when they lived in Germany—took the most extraordinary fancy to it: The Grand Duke of Silberstadt-Schreckenstein, don't you know? He came out to Bombay while we were there and he spotted your picture (you know he's one of the greatest collectors in Europe), and made such eyes at it that, upon my word—it happened to be his birthday—she told him he might have it, to get rid of him. He was perfectly enchanted—but we miss the picture.'

'It is very good of you,' Lyon said. 'If it's in a great collection—a work of my incompetent youth—I am infinitely honoured.'

'Oh, he has got it in one of his castles; I don't know which—you know he has so many. He sent us, before he left India—to return the compliment—a magnificent old vase.'

'That was more than the thing was worth,' Lyon remarked.

Colonel Capadose gave no heed to this observation; he seemed to be thinking of something. After a moment he said, 'If you'll come and see us in town she'll show you the vase.' And as they passed into the drawing-room he gave the artist a friendly propulsion. 'Go and speak to her; there she is—she'll be delighted.'

Oliver Lyon took but a few steps into the wide saloon; he stood there a moment looking at the bright composition of the lamplit group of fair women, the single figures, the great setting of white and gold, the panels of old damask, in the centre of each of which was a single celebrated picture. There was a subdued lustre in the scene and an air as of the shining trains of dresses tumbled over the carpet. At the furthest end of the room sat Mrs. Capadose, rather isolated; she was on a small sofa, with an empty place beside her. Lyon could not flatter himself she had been keeping it for him; her failure to respond to his recognition at table contradicted that, but he felt an extreme desire to go and occupy it. Moreover he had her husband's sanction; so he crossed the room, stepping over the tails of gowns, and stood before his old friend.

'I hope you don't mean to repudiate me,' he said.

She looked up at him with an expression of unalloyed pleasure. 'I am so glad to see you. I was delighted when I heard you were coming.'

'I tried to get a smile from you at dinner—but I couldn't.'

'I didn't see—I didn't understand. Besides, I hate smirking and telegraphing. Also I'm very shy—you won't have forgotten that. Now we can communicate comfortably.' And she made a better place for him on the little sofa. He sat down and they had a talk that he enjoyed, while the reason for which he used to like her so came back to him, as well as a good deal of the very same old liking. She was still the least spoiled beauty he had ever seen, with an absence of coquetry or any insinuating art that seemed almost like an omitted faculty; there were moments when she struck her interlocutor as some fine creature from an asylum—a surprising deaf-mute or one of the operative blind. Her noble pagan head gave her privileges that she neglected, and when people were admiring her brow she was wondering whether there were a good fire in her bedroom. She was simple, kind and good; inexpressive but not inhuman or stupid. Now and again she dropped something that had a sifted, selected air—the sound of an impression at first hand. She had no imagination, but she had added up her feelings, some of her reflections, about life. Lyon talked of the old days in Munich, reminded her of incidents, pleasures and pains, asked her about her father and the others; and she told him in return that she was so impressed with his own fame, his brilliant position in the world, that she had not felt very sure he would speak to her or that his little sign at table was meant for her. This was plainly a perfectly truthful speech—she was incapable of any other—and he was affected by such humility on the part of a woman whose grand line was unique. Her father was dead; one of her brothers was in the navy and the other on a ranch in America; two of her sisters were married and the youngest was just coming out and very pretty. She didn't mention her stepmother. She asked him about his own personal history and he said that the principal thing that had happened to him was that he had never married.

'Oh, you ought to,' she answered. 'It's the best thing.'

'I like that—from you!' he returned.

'Why not from me? I am very happy.'

'That's just why I can't be. It's cruel of you to praise your state. But I have had the pleasure of making the acquaintance of your husband. We had a good bit of talk in the other room.'

'You must know him better—you must know him really well,' said Mrs. Capadose.

'I am sure that the further you go the more you find. But he makes a fine show, too.'

She rested her good gray eyes on Lyon. 'Don't you think he's handsome?'

'Handsome and clever and entertaining. You see I'm generous.'

'Yes; you must know him well,' Mrs. Capadose repeated.

'He has seen a great deal of life,' said her companion.

'Yes, we have been in so many places. You must see my little girl. She is nine years old—she's too beautiful.'

'You must bring her to my studio some day—I should like to paint her.'

'Ah, don't speak of that,' said Mrs. Capadose. 'It reminds me of something so distressing.'

'I hope you don't mean when *you* used to sit for me—though that may well have bored you.'

'It's not what you did—it's what we have done. It's a confession I must make—it's a weight on my mind! I mean about that beautiful picture you gave me—it used to be so much admired. When you come to see me in London (I count on your doing that very soon) I shall see you looking all round. I can't tell you I keep it in my own room because I love it so, for the simple reason——' And she paused a moment.

'Because you can't tell wicked lies,' said Lyon.

'No, I can't. So before you ask for it——'

'Oh, I know you parted with it—the blow has already fallen,' Lyon interrupted.

'Ah then, you have heard? I was sure you would! But do you know what we got for it? Two hundred pounds.'

'You might have got much more,' said Lyon, smiling.

'That seemed a great deal at the time. We were in want of the money—it was a good while ago, when we first married. Our means were very small then, but fortunately that has changed rather for the better. We had the chance; it really seemed a big sum, and I am afraid we jumped at it. My husband had expectations which have partly come into effect, so that now we do well enough. But meanwhile the picture went.'

'Fortunately the original remained. But do you mean that two hundred was the value of the vase?' Lyon asked.

'Of the vase?'

'The beautiful old Indian vase—the Grand Duke's offering.'

'The Grand Duke?'

'What's his name?—Silberstadt-Schreckenstein. Your husband mentioned the transaction.'

'Oh, my husband,' said Mrs. Capadose; and Lyon saw that she coloured a little.

Not to add to her embarrassment, but to clear up the ambiguity, which he perceived the next moment he had better have left alone, he went on: 'He tells me it's now in his collection.'

'In the Grand Duke's? Ah, you know its reputation? I believe it contains treasures.' She was bewildered, but she recovered herself, and Lyon made the mental reflection that for some reason which would seem good when he knew it the husband and the wife had prepared different versions of the same incident. It was true that he did not exactly see Everina Brant preparing a version; that was not her line of old, and indeed it was not in her eyes to-day. At any rate they both had the matter too much on their conscience. He changed the subject, said Mrs. Capadose must really bring the little girl. He sat with her some time longer and thought—perhaps it was only a fancy—that she was rather absent, as if she were annoyed at their having been even for a moment at cross-purposes. This did not prevent him from saying to her at the last, just as the ladies began to gather themselves together to go to bed: 'You seem much impressed, from what you say, with my renown and my prosperity, and you are so good as greatly to exaggerate them. Would you have married me if you had known that I was destined to success?'

'I did know it.'

'Well, I didn't.'

'You were too modest.'

'You didn't think so when I proposed to you.'

'Well, if I had married you I couldn't have married *him*—and he's so nice,' Mrs. Capadose said. Lyon knew that she thought it—he had learned that at dinner—but it vexed him a little to hear her say it. The gentleman designated by the pronoun came up, amid the prolonged handshaking for good-night, and Mrs. Capadose remarked to her husband as she turned away, 'He wants to paint Amy.'

'Ah, she's a charming child, a most interesting little creature,' the Colonel said to Lyon. "She does the most remarkable things.'

Mrs. Capadose stopped, in the rustling procession that followed the hostess out of the room. 'Don't tell him, please don't,' she said.

'Don't tell him what?'

'Why, what she does. Let him find out for himself.' And she passed on.

'She thinks I swagger about the child—that I bore people,' said the Colonel. 'I hope you smoke.' He appeared ten minutes later in the smoking-room, in a brilliant equipment, a suit of crimson foulard covered with little white spots. He gratified Lyon's eye, made him feel that the modern age has its splendour too and its opportunities for costume. If his wife was an antique he was a fine specimen of the period of colour: he might have passed for a Venetian of the sixteenth century. They were a remarkable couple, Lyon thought, and as he looked at the Colonel standing in bright erectness before the chimney-piece while he emitted great smoke-puffs he did not wonder that Everina could not regret she had not married *him.* All the gentlemen collected at Stayes were not smokers and some of them had gone to bed. Colonel Capadose remarked that there probably would be a smallish muster, they had had such a hard day's work. That was the worst of a hunting-house—the men were so sleepy after dinner; it was devilish stupid for the ladies, even for those who hunted themselves—for women were so extraordinary they never showed it. But most fellows revived under the stimulating influences of the smoking room, and some of them, in this confidence, would turn up yet. Some of the grounds of their confidence—not all of them—might have been seen in a cluster of glasses and bottles on a table near the fire, which made the great salver and its contents twinkle sociably. The others lurked as yet in various improper corners of the minds of the most loquacious. Lyon was alone with Colonel Capadose for some moments before their companions, in varied eccentricities of uniform, straggled in, and he perceived that this wonderful man had but little loss of vital tissue to repair.

They talked about the house, Lyon having noticed an oddity of construction in the smoking-room; and the Colonel explained that it consisted of two distinct parts, one of which was of very great antiquity. They were two complete houses in short, the old one and the new, each of great extent and each very fine in its way. The two formed together an enormous structure—Lyon must make a point of going all over it. The modern portion had been erected by the old man when he bought the property; oh yes, he had bought it, forty years before—it hadn't been in the family: there hadn't been any particular family for it to be in. He had had the good taste not to spoil the original house—he had not touched it beyond what was just necessary for joining it on. It was very curious indeed—a most irregular, rambling, mysterious pile, where they every now and then discovered a walled-up room or a secret staircase. To his mind it was essentially gloomy, however; even the modern additions, splendid as they were, failed to make it cheerful. There was some story about a skeleton having been found years before, during some repairs, under a stone slab of the floor of one of the passages; but the family were rather shy of its being talked about. The place they were in was of course in the old part, which contained after all some of the best rooms: he had an idea it had been the primitive kitchen, half modernised at some intermediate period.

'My room is in the old part too then—I'm very glad,' Lyon said. 'It's very comfortable and contains all the latest conveniences, but I observed the depth of the recess of the door and the evident antiquity of the corridor and staircase—the first short one—after I came out. That panelled corridor is admirable; it looks as if it stretched away, in its brown dimness (the lamps didn't seem to me to make much impression on it), for half a mile.'

'Oh, don't go to the end of it!' exclaimed the Colonel, smiling.

'Does it lead to the haunted room?' Lyon asked.

His companion looked at him a moment. 'Ah, you know about that?'

'No, I don't speak from knowledge, only from hope. I have never had any luck—I have never stayed in a dangerous house. The places I go to are always as safe as Charing Cross. I want to see—whatever there is, the regular thing. *Is* there a ghost here?'

'Of course there is—a rattling good one.'

'And have you seen him?'

'Oh, don't ask me what *I've* seen—I should tax your credulity. I don't like to talk of these things. But there are two or three as bad —that is, as good!—rooms as you'll find anywhere.'

'Do you mean in my corridor?' Lyon asked.

'I believe the worst is at the far end. But you would be ill-advised to sleep there.'

'Ill-advised?'

'Until you've finished your job. You'll get letters of importance the next morning, and you'll take the 10.20.'

'Do you mean I will invent a pretext for running away?'

'Unless you are braver than almost any one has ever been. They don't often put people to sleep there, but sometimes the house is so crowded that they have to. The same thing always happens—ill-concealed agitation at the breakfast-table and letters of the greatest importance. Of course it's a bachelor's room, and my wife and I are at the other end of the house. But we saw the comedy three days ago—the day after we got here. A young fellow had been put there —I forget his name—the house was so full; and the usual conse-quence followed. Letters at breakfast—an awfully queer face—an urgent call to town—so very sorry his visit was cut short. Ashmore and his wife looked at each other, and off the poor devil went.'

'Ah, that wouldn't suit me; I must paint my picture,' said Lyon. 'But do they mind your speaking of it? Some people who have a good ghost are very proud of it, you know.'

What answer Colonel Capadose was on the point of making to this inquiry our hero was not to learn, for at that moment their host had walked into the room accompanied by three or four gentlemen.

Lyon was conscious that he was partly answered by the Colonel's not going on with the subject. This however on the other hand was rendered natural by the fact that one of the gentlemen appealed to him for an opinion on a point under discussion, something to do with the everlasting history of the day's run. To Lyon himself Mr. Ashmore began to talk, expressing his regret at having had so little direct conversation with him as yet. The topic that suggested itself was naturally that most closely connected with the motive of the artist's visit. Lyon remarked that it was a great disadvantage to him not to have had some preliminary acquaintance with Sir David—in most cases he found that so important. But the present sitter was so far advanced in life that there was doubtless no time to lose. 'Oh, I can tell you all about him,' said Mr. Ashmore; and for half an hour he told him a good deal. It was very interesting as well as very eulogistic, and Lyon could see that he was a very nice old man, to have endeared himself so to a son who was evidently not a gusher. At last he got up—he said he must go to bed if he wished to be fresh for his work in the morning. To which his host replied, 'Then you must take your candle; the lights are out; I don't keep my servants up.'

In a moment Lyon had his glimmering taper in hand, and as he was leaving the room (he did not disturb the others with a good-night; they were absorbed in the lemon-squeezer and the soda-water cork) he remembered other occasions on which he had made his way to bed alone through a darkened country-house; such occasions had not been rare, for he was almost always the first to leave the smoking-room. If he had not stayed in houses conspicuously haunted he had, none the less (having the artistic temperament), sometimes found the great black halls and staircases rather 'creepy': there had been often a sinister effect, to his imagination, in the sound of his tread in the long passages or the way the winter moon peeped into tall windows on landings. It occurred to him that if houses without supernatural pretensions could look so wicked at night, the old corridors of Stayes would certainly give him a sensation. He didn't know whether the proprietors were sensitive; very often, as he had said to Colonel Capadose, people enjoyed the impeachment. What determined him to speak, with a certain sense of risk, was the impression that the Colonel told queer stories. As he had his hand on the door he said to Arthur Ashmore, 'I hope I shan't meet any ghosts.'

'Any ghosts?'

'You ought to have some—in this fine old part.'

'We do our best, but *que voulez-vous?*' said Mr. Ashmore. 'I don't think they like the hot-water pipes.'

'They remind them too much of their own climate? But haven't you a haunted room—at the end of my passage?'

'Oh, there are stories—we try to keep them up.'

'I should like very much to sleep there,' Lyon said.

'Well, you can move there to-morrow if you like.'

'Perhaps I had better wait until I have done my work.'

'Very good; but you won't work there, you know. My father will sit to you in his own apartments.'

'Oh, it isn't that; it's the fear of running away, like that gentleman three days ago.'

'Three days ago? What gentleman?' Mr. Ashmore asked.

'The one who got urgent letters at breakfast and fled by the 10.20. Did he stand more than one night?'

'I don't know what you are talking about. There was no such gentleman—three days ago.'

'Ah, so much the better,' said Lyon, nodding good-night and departing. He took his course, as he remembered it, with his wavering candle, and, though he encountered a great many gruesome objects, safely reached the passage out of which his room opened. In the complete darkness it seemed to stretch away still further, but he followed it, for the curiosity of the thing, to the end. He passed several doors with the name of the room painted upon them, but he found nothing else. He was tempted to try the last door—to look into the room of evil fame; but he reflected that this would be indiscreet, since Colonel Capadose handled the brush—as a *raconteur*—with such freedom. There might be a ghost and there might not; but the Colonel himself, he inclined to think, was the most mystifying figure in the house.

Lyon found Sir David Ashmore a capital subject and a very comfortable sitter into the bargain. Moreover he was a very agreeable old man, tremendously puckered but not in the least dim; and he wore exactly the furred dressing-gown that Lyon would have chosen. He was proud of his age but ashamed of his infirmities, which however he greatly exaggerated and which did not prevent him from sitting there as submissive as if portraiture in oils had been a branch of surgery. He demolished the legend of his having feared the operation would be fatal, giving an explanation which pleased our friend much better. He held that a gentleman should be painted but once in his life—that it was eager and fatuous to be hung up all over the place. That was good for women, who made a pretty wall-pattern; but the male face didn't lend itself to decorative repetition. The proper time for the likeness was at the last, when the whole man was there—you got the totality of his experience. Lyon could not reply that that period was not a real compendium—you had to allow so for leakage; for there had been no crack in Sir David's crystallisation. He spoke of his portrait as a plain map of the country, to be consulted by his children in a case of uncertainty. A proper map could be drawn up only when the country had been travelled. He gave Lyon his mornings, till luncheon, and they talked of many things, not neglecting, as a stimulus to gossip, the people in the house. Now that he did not 'go out,' as he said, he saw much less of the visitors at Stayes: people came and went whom he knew nothing about, and he liked to hear Lyon describe them. The artist sketched with a fine point and did not caricature, and it usually befell that when Sir David did not know the sons and daughters he had known the fathers and mothers. He was one of those terrible old gentlemen who are a repository of antecedents. But in the case of the Capadose family, at whom they arrived by an easy stage, his knowledge embraced two, or even three, generations. General Capadose was an old crony, and he remembered his father before him. The general was rather a smart soldier, but in private life of too speculative a turn—

always sneaking into the City to put his money into some rotten thing. He married a girl who brought him something and they had half a dozen children. He scarcely knew what had become of the rest of them, except that one was in the Church and had found preferment—wasn't he Dean of Rockingham? Clement, the fellow who was at Stayes, had some military talent; he had served in the East, he had married a pretty girl. He had been at Eton with his son, and he used to come to Stayes in his holidays. Lately, coming back to England, he had turned up with his wife again; that was before he—the old man—had been put to grass. He was a taking dog, but he had a monstrous foible.

'A monstrous foible?' said Lyon.

'He's a thumping liar.'

Lyon's brush stopped short, while he repeated, for somehow the formula startled him, 'A thumping liar?'

'You are very lucky not to have found it out.'

'Well I confess I have noticed a romantic tinge——'

'Oh, it isn't always romantic. He'll lie about the time of day, about the name of his hatter. It appears there are people like that.'

'Well, they are precious scoundrels,' Lyon declared, his voice trembling a little with the thought of what Everina Brant had done with herself.

'Oh, not always,' said the old man. 'This fellow isn't in the least a scoundrel. There is no harm in him and no bad intention; he doesn't steal nor cheat nor gamble nor drink; he's very kind—he sticks to his wife, is fond of his children. He simply can't give you a straight answer.'

'Then everything he told me last night, I suppose, was mendacious: he delivered himself of a series of the stiffest statements. They stuck, when I tried to swallow them, but I never thought of so simple an explanation.'

'No doubt he was in the vein,' Sir David went on. 'It's a natural peculiarity—as you might limp or stutter or be left-handed. I believe it comes and goes, like intermittent fever. My son tells me that his friends usually understand it and don't haul him up—for the sake of his wife.'

'Oh, his wife—his wife!' Lyon murmured, painting fast.

'I daresay she's used to it.'

'Never in the world, Sir David. How can she be used to it?'

'Why, my dear sir, when a woman's fond!—And don't they mostly handle the long bow themselves? They are connoisseurs—they have a sympathy for a fellow-performer.'

Lyon was silent a moment; he had no ground for denying that Mrs. Capadose was attached to her husband. But after a little he rejoined: 'Oh, not this one! I knew her years ago—before her marriage; knew her well and admired her. She was as clear as a bell.'

'I like her very much,' Sir David said, 'but I have seen her back him up.'

Lyon considered Sir David for a moment, not in the light of a model. 'Are you very sure?'

The old man hesitated; then he answered, smiling, 'You're in love with her.'

'Very likely. God knows I used to be!'

'She must help him out—she can't expose him.'

'She can hold her tongue,' Lyon remarked.

'Well, before you probably she will.'

'That's what I'm curious to see.' And Lyon added, privately, 'Mercy on us, what he must have made of her!' He kept this reflection to himself, for he considered that he had sufficiently betrayed his state of mind with regard to Mrs. Capadose. None the less it occupied him now immensely, the question of how such a woman would arrange herself in such a predicament. He watched her with an interest deeply quickened when he mingled with the company; he had had his own troubles in life, but he had rarely been so anxious about anything as he was now to see what the loyalty of a wife and the infection of an example would have made of an absolutely truthful mind. Oh, he held it as immutably established that whatever other women might be prone to do she, of old, had been perfectly incapable of a deviation. Even if she had not been too simple to deceive she would have been too proud; and if she had not had too much conscience she would have had too little eagerness. It was the last thing she would have endured or condoned—the particular thing she would not have forgiven. Did she sit in torment while her husband turned his somersaults, or was she now too so perverse that she thought it a fine thing to be striking at the expense of one's honour? It would have taken a wondrous alchemy—working backwards, as it were—to produce this latter result. Besides these two alternatives (that she suffered tortures in silence and that she was so much in love that her husband's humiliating idiosyncrasy seemed to her only an added richness—a proof of life and talent), there was still the possibility that she had not found him out, that she took his false pieces at his own valuation. A little reflection rendered this hypothesis untenable; it was too evident that the account he gave of things must repeatedly have contradicted her own knowledge. Within an hour or two of his meeting them Lyon had seen her confronted with that perfectly gratuitous invention about the profit they had made off his early picture. Even then indeed she had not, so far as he could see, smarted, and—but for the present he could only contemplate the case.

Even if it had not been interfused, through his uneradicated tenderness for Mrs. Capadose, with an element of suspense, the question would still have presented itself to him as a very curious problem, for he had not painted portraits during so many years without becoming something of a psychologist. His inquiry was limited for the moment to the opportunity that the following three days might yield, as the Colonel and his wife were going on to another house. It fixed itself largely of course upon the Colonel too— this gentleman was such a rare anomaly. Moreover it had to go on very quickly. Lyon was too scrupulous to ask other people what they thought of the business—he was too afraid of exposing the woman he once had loved. It was probable also that light would come to him from the talk of the rest of the company: the Colonel's queer habit, both as it affected his own situation and as it affected his wife, would be a familiar theme in any house in which he was in the habit of staying. Lyon had not observed in the circles in which he visited any marked abstention from comment on the singularities of their members. It interfered with his progress that the Colonel hunted all day, while he plied his brushes and chatted with Sir David; but a Sunday intervened and that partly made it up. Mrs. Capadose fortunately did not hunt, and when his work was over she was not inaccessible. He took a couple of longish walks with her (she was fond of that), and beguiled her at tea into a friendly nook in the hall. Regard her as he might he could not make out to himself that she was consumed by a hidden shame; the sense of being married to a man whose word had no worth was not, in her spirit, so far as he could guess, the canker within the rose. Her mind appeared to have nothing on it but its own placid frankness, and when he looked into her eyes (deeply, as he occasionally permitted himself to do), they had no uncomfortable consciousness. He talked to her again and still again of the dear old days—reminded her of things that he had not (before this reunion) the least idea that he remembered. Then he spoke to her of her husband, praised his appearance, his talent for conversation, professed to have felt a quick friendship for him and asked (with an inward audacity at which he trembled a little) what manner of man he was. 'What manner?' said Mrs. Capadose. 'Dear me, how can one describe one's husband? I like him very much.'

'Ah, you have told me that already!' Lyon exclaimed, with exaggerated ruefulness.

'Then why do you ask me again?' She added in a moment, as if she were so happy that she could afford to take pity on him, 'He is everything that's good and kind. He's a soldier—and a gentleman —and a dear! He hasn't a fault. And he has great ability.'

'Yes; he strikes one as having great ability. But of course I can't think him a dear.'

'I don't care what you think him!' said Mrs. Capadose, looking, it seemed to him, as she smiled, handsomer than he had ever seen her. She was either deeply cynical or still more deeply impenetrable, and he had little prospect of winning from her the intimation that he longed for—some hint that it had come over her that after all she had better have married a man who was not a by-word for the most contemptible, the least heroic, of vices. Had she not seen—had she not felt—the smile go round when her husband executed some especially characteristic conversational caper? How could a woman of her quality endure that day after day, year after year, except by her quality's altering? But he would believe in the alteration only when he should have heard *her* lie. He was fascinated by his problem and yet half exasperated, and he asked himself all kinds of questions. Did she not lie, after all, when she let his falsehoods pass without a protest? Was not her life a perpetual complicity, and did she not aid and abet him by the simple fact that she was not disgusted with him? Then again perhaps she *was* disgusted and it was the mere desperation of her pride that had given her an inscrutable mask. Perhaps she protested in private, passionately; perhaps every night, in their own apartments, after the day's hideous performance, she made him the most scorching scene. But if such scenes were of no avail and he took no more trouble to cure himself, how could she regard him, and after so many years of marriage too, with the perfectly artless complacency that Lyon had surprised in her in the course of the first day's dinner? If our friend had not been in love with her he could have taken the diverting view of the Colonel's delinquencies; but as it was they turned to the tragical in his mind, even while he had a sense that his solicitude might also have been laughed at.

The observation of these three days showed him that if Capadose was an abundant he was not a malignant liar and that his fine faculty exercised itself mainly on subjects of small direct importance. 'He is the liar platonic,' he said to himself; 'he is disinterested, he doesn't operate with a hope of gain or with a desire to injure. It is art for art and he is prompted by the love of beauty. He has an inner vision of what might have been, of what ought to be, and he helps on the good cause by the simple substitution of a *nuance*. He paints, as it were, and so do I!' His manifestations had a considerable variety, but a family likeness ran through them, which consisted mainly of their singular futility. It was this that made them offensive; they encumbered the field of conversation, took up valuable space, converted it into a sort of brilliant sun-shot fog. For a fib told under pressure a convenient place can usually be found, as for a person who presents himself with an author's order at the first night of a play. But the supererogatory lie is the gentleman without a voucher or a ticket who accommodates himself with a stool in the passage.

In one particular Lyon acquitted his successful rival; it had puzzled him that irrepressible as he was he had not got into a mess in the service. But he perceived that he respected the service—that august institution was sacred from his depredations. Moreover though there was a great deal of swagger in his talk it was, oddly enough, rarely swagger about his military exploits. He had a passion for the chase, he had followed it in far countries and some of his finest flowers were reminiscences of lonely danger and escape. The more solitary the scene the bigger of course the flower. A new acquaintance, with the Colonel, always received the tribute of a bouquet: that generalisation Lyon very promptly made. And this extraordinary man had inconsistencies and unexpected lapses—lapses into flat veracity. Lyon recognised what Sir David had told him, that his aberrations came in fits or periods—that he would sometimes keep the truce of God for a month at a time. The muse breathed upon him at her pleasure; she often left him alone. He would neglect the finest openings and then set sail in the teeth of the breeze. As a general thing he affirmed the false rather than denied the true; yet this proportion was sometimes strikingly reversed. Very often he joined in the laugh against himself—he admitted that he was trying it on and that a good many of his anecdotes had an experimental character. Still he never completely retracted nor retreated—he dived and came up in another place. Lyon divined that he was capable at intervals of defending his position with violence, but only when it was a very bad one. Then he might easily be dangerous—then he would hit out and become calumnious. Such occasions would test his wife's equanimity—Lyon would have liked to see her there. In the smoking-room and elsewhere the company, so far as it was composed of his familiars, had an hilarious protest always at hand; but among the men who had known him long his rich tone was an old story, so old that they had ceased to talk about it, and Lyon did not care, as I have said, to elicit the judgement of those who might have shared his own surprise.

The oddest thing of all was that neither surprise nor familiarity prevented the Colonel's being liked; his largest drafts on a sceptical attention passed for an overflow of life and gaiety—almost of good looks. He was fond of portraying his bravery and used a very big brush, and yet he was unmistakably brave. He was a capital rider and shot, in spite of his fund of anecdote illustrating these accomplishments: in short he was very nearly as clever and his career had been very nearly as wonderful as he pretended. His best quality however remained that indiscriminate sociability which took interest and credulity for granted and about which he bragged least. It made him cheap, it made him even in a manner vulgar; but it was so contagious that his listener was more or less on his side as against the probabilities. It was a private reflection of Oliver Lyon's that he not only lied but made one feel one's self a bit of a liar, even (or especially) if one contradicted him. In the evening, at dinner and afterwards, our friend watched his wife's face to see if some faint shade or spasm never passed over it. But she showed nothing, and the wonder was that when he spoke she almost always listened. That was her pride: she wished not to be even suspected of not facing the music. Lyon had none the less an importunate vision of a veiled figure coming the next day in the dusk to certain places to repair the Colonel's ravages, as the relatives of kleptomaniacs punctually call at the shops that have suffered from their pilferings.

'I must apologise, of course it wasn't true, I hope no harm is done, it is only his incorrigible——' Oh, to hear that woman's voice in that deep abasement! Lyon had no nefarious plan, no conscious wish to practise upon her shame or her loyalty; but he did say to himself that he should like to bring her round to feel that there would have been more dignity in a union with a certain other person. He even dreamed of the hour when, with a burning face, she would ask *him* not to take it up. Then he should be almost consoled—he would be magnanimous.

Lyon finished his picture and took his departure, after having worked in a glow of interest which made him believe in his success, until he found he had pleased every one, especially Mr. and Mrs. Ashmore, when he began to be sceptical. The party at any rate changed: Colonel and Mrs. Capadose went their way. He was able to say to himself however that his separation from the lady was not so much an end as a beginning, and he called on her soon after his return to town. She had told him the hours she was at home—she seemed to like him. If she liked him why had she not married him or at any rate why was she not sorry she had not? If she was sorry she concealed it too well. Lyon's curiosity on this point may strike the reader as fatuous, but something must be allowed to a disappointed man. He did not ask much after all; not that she should love him to-day or that she should allow him to tell her that he loved her, but only that she should give him some sign she was sorry. Instead of this, for the present, she contented herself with exhibiting her little daughter to him. The child was beautiful and had the prettiest eyes of innocence he had ever seen: which did not prevent him from wondering whether she told horrid fibs. This idea gave him much entertainment—the picture of the anxiety with which her mother would watch as she grew older for the symptoms of heredity. That was a nice occupation for Everina Brant! Did she lie to the child herself, about her father—was that necessary, when she pressed her daughter to her bosom, to cover up his tracks? Did he control himself before the little girl—so that she might not hear him say things she knew to be other than he said? Lyon doubted this: his genius would be too strong for him, and the only safety for the child would be in her being too stupid to analyse. One couldn't judge yet—she was too young. If she should grow up clever she would be sure to tread in his steps—a delightful improvement in her mother's situation! Her little face was not shifty, but neither was her father's big one: so that proved nothing.

Lyon reminded his friends more than once of their promise that Amy should sit to him, and it was only a question of his lesiure. The desire grew in him to paint the Colonel also—an operation from which he promised himself a rich private satisfaction. He would draw him out, he would set him up in that totality about which he had talked with Sir David, and none but the initiated would know. They, however, would rank the picture high, and it would be indeed six rows deep—a masterpiece of subtle characterisation, of legitimate treachery. He had dreamed for years of producing something which should bear the stamp of the psychologist as well as of the painter, and here at last was his subject. It was a pity it was not better, but that was not *his* fault. It was his impression that already no one drew the Colonel out more than he, and he did it not only by instinct but on a plan. There were moments when he was almost frightened at the success of his plan—the poor gentleman went so terribly far. He would pull up some day, look at Lyon between the eyes—guess he was being played upon—which would lead to his wife's guessing it also. Not that Lyon cared much for that however, so long as she failed to suppose (as she must) that *she* was a part of his joke. He formed such a habit now of going to see her of a Sunday afternoon that he was angry when she went out of town. This occurred often, as the couple were great visitors and the Colonel was always looking for sport, which he liked best when it could be had at other people's expense. Lyon would have supposed that this sort of life was particularly little to her taste, for he had an idea that it was in country-houses that her husband came out strongest. To let him go off without her, not to see him expose himself—that ought properly to have been a relief and a luxury to her. She told Lyon in fact that she preferred staying at home; but she neglected to say it was because in other people's houses she was on the rack: the reason she gave was that she liked so to be with the child. It was not perhaps criminal to draw such a bow, but it was vulgar: poor Lyon was delighted when he arrived at that formula. Certainly some day too he would cross the line—he would become a noxious animal. Yes, in the meantime he was vulgar, in spite of his talents, his fine person, his impunity. Twice, by exception, toward the end of the winter, when he left town for a few days' hunting, his wife remained at home. Lyon had not yet reached the point of asking himself whether the desire not to miss two of his visits had something to do with her immobility. That inquiry would perhaps have been more in place later, when he began to paint the child and she always came with her. But it was not in her to give the wrong name, to pretend, and Lyon could see that she had the maternal passion, in spite of the bad blood in the little girl's veins.

She came inveterately, though Lyon multiplied the sittings: Amy was never entrusted to the governess or the maid. He had knocked off poor old Sir David in ten days, but the portrait of the simple-faced child bade fair to stretch over into the following year. He asked for sitting after sitting, and it would have struck any one who might have witnessed the affair that he was wearing the little girl out. He knew better however and Mrs. Capadose also knew: they were present together at the long intermissions he gave her, when she left her pose and roamed about the great studio, amusing herself with its curiosities, playing with the old draperies and costumes, having unlimited leave to handle. Then her mother and Mr. Lyon sat and talked; he laid aside his brushes and leaned back in his chair; he always gave her tea. What Mrs. Capadose did not know was the way that during these weeks he neglected other orders: women have no faculty of imagination with regard to a man's work beyond a vague idea that it doesn't matter. In fact Lyon put off everything and made several celebrities wait. There were half-hours of silence, when he plied his brushes, during which he was mainly conscious that Everina was sitting there. She easily fell into that if he did not insist on talking, and she was not embarrassed nor bored by it. Sometimes she took up a book—there were plenty of them about; sometimes, a little way off, in her chair, she watched his progress (though without in the least advising or correcting), as if she cared for every stroke that represented her daughter. These strokes were occasionally a little wild; he was thinking so much more of his heart than of his hand. He was not more embarrassed than she was, but he was agitated: it was as if in the sittings (for the child, too, was beautifully quiet) something was growing between them or had already grown—a tacit confidence, an inexpressible secret. He felt it that way; but after all he could not be sure that she did. What he wanted her to do for him was very little; it was not even to confess that she was unhappy. He would be superabundantly gratified if she should simply let him know, even by a silent sign, that she recognized that with him her life would have been finer. Sometimes he guessed—his presumption went so far—that he might see this sign in her contentedly sitting there.

III

At last he broached the question of painting the Colonel: it was now very late in the season—there would be little time before the general dispersal. He said they must make the most of it; the great thing was to begin; then in the autumn, with the resumption of their London life, they could go forward. Mrs. Capadose objected to this that she really could not consent to accept another present of such value. Lyon had given her the portrait of herself of old, and he had seen what they had had the indelicacy to do with it. Now he had offered her this beautiful memorial of the child—beautiful it would evidently be when it was finished, if he could ever satisfy himself; a precious possession which they would cherish for ever. But his generosity must stop there—they couldn't be so tremendously 'beholden' to him. They couldn' order the picture—of course he would understand that, without · explaining: it was a luxury beyond their reach, for they knew the great prices he received. Besides, what had they ever done—what above all had *she* ever done, that he should overload them with benefits? No, he was too dreadfully good; it was really impossible that Clement should sit. Lyon listened to her without protest, without interruption, while he bent forward at his work, and at last he said: 'Well, if you won't take it why not let him sit for me for my own pleasure and profit? Let it be a favour, a service I ask of him. It will do me a lot of good to paint him and the picture will remain in my hands.'

'How will it do you a lot of good?' Mrs. Capadose asked.

'Why he's such a rare model—such an interesting subject. He has such an expressive face. It will teach me no end of things.'

'Expressive of what?' said Mrs. Capadose.

'Why, of his nature.'

'And do you want to paint his nature?'

'Of course I do. That's what a great portrait gives you, and I shall make the Colonel's a great one. It will put me up high. So you see my request is eminently interested.'

'How can you be higher than you are?'

'Oh, I'm insatiable! Do consent,' said Lyon.

'Well, his nature is very noble,' Mrs. Capadose remarked.

'Ah, trust me, I shall bring it out!' Lyon exclaimed, feeling a little ashamed of himself.

Mrs. Capadose said before she went away that her husband would probably comply with his invitation, but she added, 'Nothing would induce me to let you pry into *me* that way!'

'Oh, you,' Lyon laughed—'I could do you in the dark!'

The Colonel shortly afterwards placed his leisure at the painter's disposal and by the end of July had paid him several visits. Lyon was disappointed neither in the quality of his sitter nor in the degree to which he himself rose to the occasion; he felt really confident that he should produce a fine thing. He was in the humour; he was charmed with his *motif* and deeply interested in his problem. The only point that troubled him was the idea that when he should send his picture to the Academy he should not be able to give the title, for the catalogue, simply as 'The Liar.' However, it little mattered, for he had now determined that this character should be perceptible even to the meanest intelligence—as overtopping as it had become to his own sense in the living man. As he saw nothing else in the Colonel to-day, so he gave himself up to the joy of painting nothing else. How he did it he could not have told you, but it seemed to him that the mystery of how to do it was revealed to him afresh every time he sat down to his work. It was in the eyes and it was in the mouth, it was in every line of the face and every fact of the attitude, in the indentation of the chin, in the way the hair was planted, the moustache was twisted, the smile came and went, the breath rose and fell. It was in the way he looked out at a bamboozled world in short—the way he would look out for ever. There were half a dozen portraits in Europe that Lyon rated as supreme; he regarded them as immortal, for they were as perfectly preserved as they were consummately painted. It was to this exemplary group that he aspired to annex the canvas on which he was now engaged. One of the productions that helped to compose it was the magnificent Moroni of the National Gallery—the young tailor, in the white jacket, at his board with his shears. The Colonel was not a tailor, nor was Moroni's model, unlike many tailors, a liar; but as regards the masterly clearness with which the individual should be rendered his work would be on the same line as that. He had to a degree in which he had rarely had it before the satisfaction of feeling life grow and grow under his brush. The Colonel, as it turned out, liked to sit and he liked to talk while he was sitting: which was very fortunate, as his talk largely constituted Lyon's inspiration. Lyon put into pratctice that idea of drawing him out which he had been nursing for so many weeks: he could not possibly have been in a better relation to him for the purpose. He encouraged, beguiled, excited him, manifested an unfathomable credulity, and his only interruptions were when the Colonel did not respond to it. He had his intermissions, his hours of sterility, and then Lyon felt that the picture also languished. The higher his companion soared, the more gyrations he executed, in the blue, the better he painted; he couldn't make his flights long enough. He lashed him on when he flagged; his apprehension became great at moments that the Colonel would discover his game. But he never did, apparently; he basked and expanded in the fine steady light of the painter's attention. In this way the picture grew very fast; it was astonishing what a short business it was, compared with the little girl's. By the fifth of August it was pretty well finished: that was the date of the last sitting the Colonel was for the present able to give, as he was leaving town the next day with his wife. Lyon was amply content—he saw his way so clear: he should be able to do at his convenience what remained, with or without his friend's attendance. At any rate, as there was no hurry, he would let the thing stand over till his own return to London, in November, when he would come back to it with a fresh eye. On the Colonel's asking him if his wife might come and see it the next day, if she should find a minute—this was so greatly her desire—Lyon begged as a special favour that she would wait: he was so far from satisfied as yet. This was the repetition of a proposal Mrs. Capadose had made on the occasion of his last visit to her, and he had then asked for a delay—declared that he was by no means content. He was really delighted, and he was again a little ashamed of himself.

By the fifth of August the weather was very warm, and on that day, while the Colonel sat straight and gossiped, Lyon opened for the sake of ventilation a little subsidiary door which led directly from his studio into the garden and sometimes served as an entrance and an exit for models and for visitors of the humbler sort, and as a passage for canvases, frames, packing-boxes and other professional gear. The main entrance was through the house and his own apartments, and this approach had the charming effect of admitting you first to a high gallery, from which a crooked picturesque staircase enabled you to descend to the wide, decorated, encumbered room. The view of this room, beneath them, with all its artistic ingenuities and the objects of value that Lyon had collected, never failed to elicit exclamations of delight from persons stepping into the gallery. The way from the garden was plainer and at once more practicable and more private. Lyon's domain, in St. John's Wood, was not vast, but when the door stood open of a summer's day it offered a glimpse of flowers and trees, you smelt something sweet and you heard the birds. On this particular morning the side-door had been found convenient by an unannounced visitor, a youngish woman who stood in the room before the Colonel perceived her and whom he perceived before she was noticed by his friend. She was very quiet, and she looked from one of the men to the other. 'Oh, dear, here's another!' Lyon exclaimed, as soon as his eyes rested on her. She belonged, in fact, to a somewhat importunate class—the model in search of employment, and she explained that she had ventured to come straight in, that way, because very often when she went to call upon gentlemen the servants played her tricks, turned her off and wouldn't take in her name.

'But how did you get into the garden?' Lyon asked.

'The gate was open, sir—the servants' gate. The butcher's cart was there.'

'The butcher ought to have closed it,' said Lyon.

'Then you don't require me, sir?' the lady continued.

Lyon went on with his painting; he had given her a sharp look at first, but now his eyes lighted on her no more. The Colonel, however, examined her with interest. She was a person of whom you could scarcely say whether being young she looked old or old she looked young; she had at any rate evidently rounded several of the corners of life and had a face that was rosy but that somehow failed to suggest freshness. Nevertheless she was pretty and even looked as if at one time she might have sat for the complexion. She wore a hat with many feathers, a dress with many bugles, long black gloves, encircled with silver bracelets, and very bad shoes. There was something about her that was not exactly of the governess out of place nor completely of the actress seeking an engagement, but that savoured of an interrupted profession or even of a blighted career. She was rather soiled and tarnished, and after she had been in the room a few moments the air, or at any rate the nostril, became acquainted with a certain alcoholic waft. She was unpractised in the *h,* and when Lyon at last thanked her and said he didn't want her—he was doing nothing for which she could be useful—she replied with rather a wounded manner, 'Well you know you *'ave* 'ad me!'

'I don't remember you,' Lyon answered.

'Well, I daresay the people that saw your pictures do! I haven't much time, but I thought I would look in.'

'I am much obliged to you.'

'If ever you should require me, if you just send me a postcard——'

'I never send postcards,' said Lyon.

'Oh well, I should value a private letter! Anything to Miss Geraldine, Mortimer Terrace Mews, Notting 'ill——'

'Very good; I'll remember,' said Lyon.

Miss Geraldine lingered. 'I thought I'd just stop, on the chance.'

'I'm afraid I can't hold out hopes, I'm so busy with portraits,' Lyon continued.

'Yes; I see you are. I wish I was in the gentleman's place.'

'I'm afraid in that case it wouldn't look like me,' said the Colonel, laughing.

'Oh, of course it couldn't compare—it wouldn't be so 'andsome! But I do hate them portraits!' Miss Geraldine declared. 'It's so much bread out of our mouths.'

'Well, there are many who can't paint them,' Lyon suggested, comfortingly.

'Oh, I've sat to the very first—and only to the first! There's many that couldn't do anything without me.'

'I'm glad you're in such demand.' Lyon was beginning to be bored and he added that he wouldn't detain her—he would send for her in case of need.

'Very well; remember it's the Mews—more's the pity! You don't sit so well as *us!*' Miss Geraldine pursued, looking at the Colonel. 'If *you* should require me, sir——'

'You put him out; you embarrass him,' said Lyon.

'Embarrass him, oh gracious!' the visitor cried, with a laugh which diffused a fragrance. 'Perhaps *you* send postcards, eh?' she went on to the Colonel; and then she retreated with a wavering step. She passed out into the garden as she had come.

'How very dreadful—she's drunk!' said Lyon. He was painting hard, but he looked up, checking himself: Miss Geraldine, in the open doorway, had thrust back her head.

'Yes, I do hate it—that sort of thing!' she cried with an explosion of mirth which confirmed Lyon's declaration. And then she disappeared.

'What sort of thing—what does she mean?' the Colonel asked.

'Oh, my painting you, when I might be painting her.'

'And have you ever painted her?'

'Never in the world; I have never seen her. She is quite mistaken.'

The Colonel was silent a moment; then he remarked, 'She was very pretty—ten years ago.'

'I daresay, but she's quite ruined. For me the least drop too much spoils them; I shouldn't care for her at all.'

'My dear fellow, she's not a model,' said the Colonel, laughing.

'To-day, no doubt, she's not worthy of the name; but she has been one.'

'*Jamais de la vie!* That's all a pretext.'

'A pretext?' Lyon pricked up his ears—he began to wonder what was coming now.

'She didn't want you—she wanted me.'

'I noticed she paid you some attention. What does she want of you?'

'Oh, to do me an ill turn. She hates me—lots of women do. She's watching me—she follows me.'

Lyon leaned back in his chair—he didn't believe a word of this. He was all the more delighted with it and with the Colonel's bright, candid manner. The story had bloomed, fragrant, on the spot. 'My dear Colonel!' he murmured, with friendly interest and commiseration.

'I was annoyed when she came in—but I wasn't startled,' his sitter continued.

'You concealed it very well, if you were.'

'Ah, when one has been through what I have! To-day however I confess I was half prepared. I have seen her hanging about—she knows my movements. She was near my house this morning—she must have followed me.'

'But who is she then—with such a *toupet?*'

'Yes, she has that,' said the Colonel; 'but as you observe she was primed. Still, there was a cheek, as they say, in her coming in. Oh, she's a bad one! She isn't a model and she never was; no doubt she has known some of those women and picked up their form. She had hold of a friend of mine ten years ago—a stupid young gander who might have been left to be plucked but whom I was obliged to take an interest in for family reasons. It's a long story—I had really forgotten all about it. She's thirty-seven if she's a day. I cut in and made him get rid of her—I sent her about her business. She knew it was me she had to thank. She has never forgiven me—I think she's off her head. Her name isn't Geraldine at all and I doubt very much if that's her address.'

'Ah, what is her name?' Lyon asked, most attentive. The details always began to multiply, to abound, when once his companion was well launched—they flowed forth in battalions.

'It's Pearson—Harriet Pearson; but she used to call herself Grenadine—wasn't that a rum appellation? Grenadine—Geraldine—the jump was easy.' Lyon was charmed with the promptitude of this response, and his interlocutor went on: 'I hadn't thought of her for years—I had quite lost sight of her. I don't know what her idea is, but practically she's harmless. As I came in I thought I saw her a little way up the road. She must have found out I come here and have arrived before me. I daresay—or rather I'm sure—she is waiting for me there now.'

'Hadn't you better have protection?' Lyon asked, laughing.

'The best protection is five shillings—I'm willing to go that length. Unless indeed she has a bottle of vitriol. But they only throw vitriol on the men who have deceived them, and I never deceived her—I told her the first time I saw her that it wouldn't do. Oh, if she's there we'll walk a little way together and talk it over and, as I say, I'll go as far as five shillings.'

'Well,' said Lyon, 'I'll contribute another five.' He felt that this was little to pay for his entertainment.

That entertainment was interrupted however for the time by the Colonel's departure. Lyon hoped for a letter recounting the fictive sequel; but apparently his brilliant sitter did not operate with the pen. At any rate he left town without writing; they had taken a rendezvous for three months later. Oliver Lyon always passed the holidays in the same way; during the first weeks he paid a visit to his elder brother, the happy possesser, in the south of England, of a rambling old house with formal gardens, in which he delighted, and then he went abroad—usually to Italy or Spain. This year he carried out his custom after taking a last look at his all but finished work and feeling as nearly pleased with it as he ever felt with the translation of the idea by the hand—always, as it seemed to him, a pitiful compromise. One yellow afternoon, in the country, as he was smoking his pipe on one of the old terraces he was seized with the desire to see it again and do two or three things more to it: he had thought of it so often while he lounged there. The impulse was too strong to be dismissed, and though he expected to return to town in the course of another week he was unable to face the delay. To look at the picture for five minutes would be enough— it would clear up certain questions which hummed in his brain; so that the next morning, to give himself this luxury, he took the train for London. He sent no word in advance; he would lunch at his club and probably return into Sussex by the 5.45.

In St. John's Wood the tide of human life flows at no time very fast, and in the first days of September Lyon found unmitigated emptiness in the straight sunny roads where the little plastered garden-walls, with their incommunicative doors, looked slightly Oriental. There was definite stillness in his own house, to which he admitted himself by his pass-key, having a theory that it was well sometimes to take servants unprepared. The good woman who was mainly in charge and who cumulated the functions of cook and housekeeper was, however, quickly summoned by his step, and (he cultivated frankness of intercourse with his domestics) received him without the confusion of surprise. He told her that she needn't mind the place being not quite straight, he had only come up for a few hours—he should be busy in the studio. To this she replied that he was just in time to see a lady and a gentleman who were there at the moment—they had arrived five minutes before. She had told them he was away from home but they said it was all right; they only wanted to look at a picture and would be very careful of every- thing. 'I hope it is all right, sir,' the housekeeper concluded. 'The gentleman says he's a sitter and he gave me his name—rather an odd name; I think it's military. The lady's a very fine lady, sir; at any rate there they are.'

'Oh, it's all right,' Lyon said, the identity of his visitors being clear. The good woman couldn't know, for she usually had little to do with the comings and goings; his man, who showed people in and out, had accompanied him to the country. He was a good deal surprised at Mrs. Capadose's having come to see her husband's portrait when she knew that the artist himself wished her to forbear; but it was a familiar truth to him that she was a woman of a high spirit. Besides, perhaps the lady was not Mrs. Capadose; the Colonel might have brought some inquisitive friend, a person who wanted a portrait of *her* husband. What were they doing in town, at any rate, at that moment? Lyon made his way to the studio with a certain curiosity; he wondered vaguely what his friends were 'up to.' He pushed aside the curtain that hung in the door of communication —the door opening upon the gallery which it had been found convenient to construct at the time the studio was added to the house. When I say he pushed it aside I should amend my phrase; he laid his hand upon it, but at the moment he was arrested by a very singular sound. It came from the floor of the room beneath him and it startled him extremely, consisting apparently as it did of a passionate wail—a sort of smothered shriek—accompanied by a violent burst of tears. Oliver Lyon listened intently a moment, and then he passed out upon the balcony, which was covered with an old thick Moorish rug. His step was noiseless, though he had not endeavoured to make it so, and after that first instant he found himself profiting irresistibly by the accident of his not having attracted the attention of the two persons in the studio, who were some twenty feet below him. In truth they were so deeply and so strangely engaged that their unconsciousness of observation was explained. The scene that took place before Lyon's eyes was one of the most extraordinary they had ever rested upon. Delicacy and the failure to comprehend kept him at first from interrupting it—for what he saw was a woman who had thrown herself in a flood of tears on her companion's bosom—and these influences were succeeded after a minute (the minutes were very few and very short) by a definite motive which presently had the force to make him step back behind the curtain. I may add that it also had the force to make him avail himself for further contemplation of a crevice formed by his gathering together the two halves of the *portière*. He was perfectly aware of what he was about—he was for the moment an eavesdropper, a spy; but he was also aware that a very odd business, in which his confidence had been trifled with, was going forward, and that if in a measure it didn't concern him, in a measure it very definitely did. His observation, his reflections, accomplished themselves in a flash.

His visitors were in the middle of the room; Mrs. Capadose clung to her husband, weeping, sobbing as if her heart would break. Her distress was horrible to Oliver Lyon but his astonishment was greater than his horror when he heard the Colonel respond to it by the words, vehemently uttered, 'Damn him, damn him, damn him!' What in the world had happened? why was she sobbing and whom was he damning? What had happened, Lyon saw the next instant, was that the Colonel had finally rummaged out his unfinished portrait (he knew the corner where the artist usually placed it, out of the way, with its face to the wall) and had set it up before his wife on an empty easel. She had looked at it a few moments and then—apparently—what she saw in it had produced an explosion of dismay and resentment. She was too busy sobbing and the Colonel was too busy holding her and reiterating his objurgation, to look round or look up. The scene was so unexpected to Lyon that he could not take it, on the spot, as a proof of the triumph of his hand—of a tremendous hit: he could only wonder what on earth was the matter. The idea of the triumph came a little later. Yet he could see the portrait from where he stood; he was startled with its look of life—he had not thought it so masterly. Mrs. Capadose flung herself away from her husband— she dropped into the nearest chair, buried her face in her arms, leaning on a table. Her weeping suddenly ceased to be audible, but she shuddered there as if she were overwhelmed with anguish and shame. Her husband remained a moment staring at the picture; then he went to her, bent over her, took hold of her again, soothed her. 'What is it, darling, what the devil is it?' he demanded.

Lyon heard her answer. 'It's cruel—oh, it's too cruel!'

'Damn him—damn him—damn him!' the Colonel repeated.

'It's all there—it's all there!' Mrs. Capadose went on.

'Hang it, what's all there?'

'Everything there oughtn't to be—everything he has seen—it's too dreadful!'

'Everything he has seen? Why, ain't I a good-looking fellow? He has made me rather handsome.'

Mrs. Capadose had sprung up again; she had darted another glance at the painted betrayal. 'Handsome? Hideous, hideous! Not that—never, never!'

'Not *what*, in heaven's name?' the Colonel almost shouted. Lyon could see his flushed, bewildered face.

'What he has made of you—what you know! *He* knows—he has seen. Every one will know—every one will see. Fancy that thing in the Academy!'

'You're going wild, darling; but if you hate it so it needn't go.'

'Oh, he'll send it—it's so good! Come away—come away!' Mrs. Capadose wailed, seizing her husband.

'It's so good?' the poor man cried.

'Come away—come away,' she only repeated, and she turned toward the staircase that ascended to the gallery.

'Not that way—not through the house, in the state you're in,' Lyon heard the Colonel object. 'This way—we can pass,' he added; and he drew his wife to the small door that opened into the garden. It was bolted, but he pushed the bolt and opened the door. She passed out quickly, but he stood there looking back into the room. 'Wait for me a moment!' he cried out to her; and with an excited stride he re-entered the studio. He came up to the picture again, and again he stood looking at it. 'Damn him—damn him—damn him!' he broke out once more. It was not clear to Lyon whether this malediction had for its object the original or the painter of the portrait. The Colonel turned away and moved rapidly about the room, as if he were looking for something; Lyon was unable for the instant to guess his intention. Then the artist said to himself, below his breath, 'He's going to do it a harm!' His first impulse was to rush down and stop him; but he paused, with the sound of Everina Brant's sobs still in his ears. The Colonel found what he was looking for—found it among some odds and ends on a small table and rushed back with it to the easel. At one and the same moment Lyon perceived that the object he had seized was a small Eastern dagger and that he had plunged it into the canvas. He seemed animated by a sudden fury, for with extreme vigour of hand he dragged the instrument down (Lyon knew it to have no very fine edge) making a long, abominable gash. Then he plucked it out and dashed it again several times into the face of the likeness, exactly as if he were stabbing a human victim: it had the oddest effect—that of a sort of figurative suicide. In a few seconds more the Colonel had tossed the dagger away—he looked at it as he did so, as if he expected it to reek with blood—and hurried out of the place, closing the door after him.

The strangest part of all was—as will doubtless appear—that Oliver Lyon made no movement to save his picture. But he did not feel as if he were losing it or cared not if he were, so much more did he feel that he was gaining a certitude. His old friend *was* ashamed of her husband, and he had made her so, and he had scored a great success, even though the picture had been reduced to rags. The revelation excited him so—as indeed the whole scene did—that when he came down the steps after the Colonel had gone he trembled with his happy agitation; he was dizzy and had to sit down a moment. The portrait had a dozen jagged wounds— the Colonel literally had hacked it to death. Lyon left it where it was, never touched it, scarcely looked at it; he only walked up and down his studio, still excited, for an hour. At the end of this time his good woman came to recommend that he should have some luncheon; there was a passage under the staircase from the offices.

'Ah, the lady and gentleman have gone, sir? I didn't hear them.'

'Yes; they went by the garden.'

But she had stopped, staring at the picture on the easel. 'Gracious, how you *'ave* served it, sir!'

Lyon imitated the Colonel. 'Yes, I cut it up—in a fit of disgust.'

'Mercy, after all your trouble! Because they weren't pleased, sir?'

'Yes; they weren't pleased.'

'Well, they must be very grand! Blessed if I would!'

'Have it chopped up; it will do to light fires,' Lyon said.

He returned to the country by the 3.30 and a few days later passed over to France. During the two months that he was absent from England he expected something—he could hardly have said what; a manifestation of some sort on the Colonel's part. Wouldn't he write, wouldn't he explain, wouldn't he take for granted Lyon had discovered the way he had, as the cook said, served him and deem it only decent to take pity in some fashion or other on his mystification? Would he plead guilty or would he repudiate suspicion? The latter course would be difficult and make a considerable draft upon his genius, in view of the certain testimony of Lyon's housekeeper, who had admitted the visitors and would establish the connection between their presence and the violence wrought. Would the Colonel proffer some apology or some amends, or would any word from him be only a further expression of that destructive petulance which our friend had seen his wife so suddenly and so potently communicate to him? He would have either to declare that he had not touched the picture or to admit that he had, and in either case he would have to tell a fine story. Lyon was impatient for the story and, as no letter came, disappointed that it was not produced. His impatience however was much greater in respect to Mrs. Capadose's version, if version there was to be; for certainly that would be the real test, would show how far she would go for her husband, on the one side, or for him, Oliver Lyon, on the other. He could scarcely wait to see what line she would take; whether she would simply adopt the Colonel's, whatever it might be. He wanted to draw her out without waiting, to get an idea in advance. He wrote to her, to this end, from Venice, in the tone of their established friendship, asking for news, narrating his wanderings, hoping they should soon meet in town and not saying a word about the picture. Day followed day, after the time, and he received no answer; upon which he reflected that she couldn't trust herself to write—was still too much under the influence of the emotion produced by his 'betrayal.' Her husband had espoused that emotion and she had espoused the action he had taken in consequence of it, and it was a complete rupture and everything was at an end. Lyon considered this prospect rather ruefully, at the same time that he thought it deplorable that such charming people should have put themselves so grossly in the wrong. He was at last cheered, though little further enlightened, by the arrival of a letter, brief but breathing good-humour and hinting neither at a grievance nor at a bad conscience. The most interesting part of it to Lyon was the postscript, which consisted of these words: 'I have a confession to make to you. We were in town for a couple of days, the 1st of September, and I took the occasion to defy your authority—it was very bad of me but I couldn't help it. I made Clement take me to your studio—I wanted so dreadfully to see what you had done with him, your wishes to the contrary notwithstanding. We made your servants let us in and I took a good look at the picture. It is really wonderful!' 'Wonderful' was non-committal, but at least with this letter there was no rupture.

The third day after Lyon's return to London was a Sunday, so that he could go and ask Mrs. Capadose for luncheon. She had given him in the spring a general invitation to do so and he had availed himself of it several times. These had been the occasions (before he sat to him) when he saw the Colonel most familiarly. Directly after the meal his host disappeared (he went out, as he said, to call on *his* women) and the second half-hour was the best, even when there were other people. Now, in the first days of December, Lyon had the luck to find the pair alone, without even Amy, who appeared but little in public. They were in the drawing-room, waiting for the repast to be announced, and as soon as he came in the Colonel broke out, 'My dear fellow, I'm delighted to see you! I'm so keen to begin again.'

'Oh, do go on, it's so beautiful,' Mrs. Capadose said, as she gave him her hand.

Lyon looked from one to the other; he didn't know what he had expected, but he had not expected this. 'Ah, then, you think I've got something?'

'You've got everything,' said Mrs. Capadose, smiling from her golden-brown eyes.

'She wrote you of our little crime?' her husband asked. 'She dragged me there—I had to go.' Lyon wondered for a moment whether he meant by their little crime the assault on the canvas; but the Colonel's next words didn't confirm this interpretation. 'You know I like to sit—it gives such a chance to my *bavardise*. And just now I have time.'

'You must remember I had almost finished,' Lyon remarked.

'So you had. More's the pity. I should like you to begin again.'

'My dear fellow, I shall have to begin again!' said Oliver Lyon with a laugh, looking at Mrs. Capadose. She did not meet his eyes—she had got up to ring for luncheon. 'The picture has been smashed,' Lyon continued.

'Smashed? Ah, what did you do that for?' Mrs. Capadose asked, standing there before him in all her clear, rich beauty. Now that she looked at him she was impenetrable.

'I didn't—I found it so—with a dozen holes punched in it!'

'I say!' cried the Colonel.

Lyon turned his eyes to him, smiling. 'I hope *you* didn't do it?'

'Is it ruined?' the Colonel inquired. He was as brightly true as his wife and he looked simply as if Lyon's question could not be serious. 'For the love of sitting to you? My dear fellow, if I had thought of it I would!'

'Nor you either?' the painter demanded of Mrs. Capadose.

Before she had time to reply her husband had seized her arm, as if a highly suggestive idea had come to him. 'I say, my dear, that woman—that woman!'

'That woman?' Mrs. Capadose repeated; and Lyon too wondered what woman he meant.

'Don't you remember when we came out, she was at the door—or a little way from it? I spoke to you of her—I told you about her. Geraldine—Grenadine—the one who burst in that day,' he explained to Lyon. 'We saw her hanging about—I called Everina's attention to her.'

'Do you mean she got at my picture?'

'Ah yes, I remember,' said Mrs. Capadose, with a sigh.

'She burst in again—she had learned the way—she was waiting for her chance,' the Colonel continued. 'Ah, the little brute!'

Lyon looked down; he felt himself colouring. This was what he had been waiting for—the day the Colonel should wantonly sacrifice some innocent person. And could his wife be a party to that final atrocity? Lyon had reminded himself repeatedly during the previous weeks that when the Colonel perpetrated his misdeed she had already quitted the room; but he had argued none the less—it was a virtual certainty—that he had on rejoining her immediately made his achievement plain to her. He was in the flush of performance; and even if he had not mentioned what he had done she would have guessed it. He did not for an instant believe that poor Miss Geraldine had been hovering about his door, nor had the account given by the Colonel the summer before of his relations with this lady deceived him in the slightest degree. Lyon had never seen her before the day she planted herself in his studio; but he knew her and classified her as if he had made her. He was acquainted with the London female model in all her varieties—in every phase of her development and every step of her decay. When he entered his house that September morning just after the arrival of his two friends there had been no symptoms whatever, up and down the road, of Miss Geraldine's reappearance. That fact had been fixed in his mind by his recollecting the vacancy of the prospect when his cook told him that a lady and a gentleman were in his studio: he had wondered there was not a carriage nor a cab at his door. Then he had reflected that they would have come by the underground railway; he was close to the Marlborough Road station and he knew the Colonel, coming to his sittings, more than once had availed himself of that convenience. 'How in the world did she get in?' He addressed the question to his companions indifferently.

'Let us go down to luncheon,' said Mrs. Capadose, passing out of the room.

'We went by the garden—without troubling your servant—I wanted to show my wife.' Lyon followed his hostess with her husband and the Colonel stopped him at the top of the stairs. 'My dear fellow, I *can't* have been guilty of the folly of not fastening the door?'

'I am sure I don't know, Colonel,' Lyon said as they went down. 'It was a very determined hand—a perfect wild-cat.'

'Well, she *is* a wild-cat—confound her! That's why I wanted to get him away from her.'

'But I don't understand her motive.'

'She's off her head—and she hates me; that was her motive.'

'But she doesn't hate me, my dear fellow!' Lyon said, laughing.

'She hated the picture—don't you remember she said so? The more portraits there are the less employment for such as her.'

'Yes; but if she is not really the model she pretends to be, how can that hurt her?' Lyon asked.

The inquiry baffled the Colonel an instant—but only an instant. 'Ah, she was in a vicious muddle! As I say, she's off her head.'

They went into the dining-room, where Mrs. Capadose was taking her place. 'It's too bad, it's too horrid!' she said. 'You see the fates are against you. Providence won't let you be so disinterested— painting masterpieces for nothing.'

'Did *you* see the woman?' Lyon demanded, with something like a sternness that he could not mitigate.

Mrs. Capadose appeared not to perceive it or not to heed it if she did. 'There was a person, not far from your door, whom Clement called my attention to. He told me something about her but we were going the other way.'

'And do you think she did it?'

'How can I tell? If she did she was mad, poor wretch.'

'I should like very much to get hold of her,' said Lyon. This was a false statement, for he had no desire for any further conversation with Miss Geraldine. He had exposed his friends to himself, but he had no desire to expose them to any one else, least of all to themselves.

'Oh, depend upon it she will never show again. You're safe!' the Colonel exclaimed.

'But I remember her address—Mortimer Terrace Mews, Notting Hill.'

'Oh, that's pure humbug; there isn't any such place.'

'Lord, what a deceiver!' said Lyon.

'Is there any one else you suspect?' the Colonel went on.

'Not a creature.'

'And what do your servants say?'

'They say it wasn't *them,* and I reply that I never said it was. That's about the substance of our conferences.'

'And when did they discover the havoc?'

'They never discovered it at all. I noticed it first—when I came back.'

'Well, she could easily have stepped in,' said the Colonel. 'Don't you remember how she turned up that day, like the clown in the ring?'

'Yes, yes; she could have done the job in three seconds, except that the picture wasn't out.'

'My dear fellow, don't curse me!—but of course I dragged it out.'

'You didn't put it back?' Lyon asked tragically.

'Ah, Clement, Clement, didn't I tell you to?' Mrs. Capadose exclaimed in a tone of exquisite reproach.

The Colonel groaned, dramatically; he covered his face with his hands. His wife's words were for Lyon the finishing touch; they made his whole vision crumble—his theory that she had secretly kept herself true. Even to her old lover she wouldn't be so! He was sick; he couldn't eat; he knew that he looked very strange. He murmured something about it being useless to cry over spilled milk —he tried to turn the conversation to other things. But it was a horrid effort and he wondered whether they felt it as much as he. He wondered all sorts of things: whether they guessed he disbelieved them (that he had seen them of course they would never guess); whether they had arranged their story in advance or it was only an inspiration of the moment; whether she had resisted, protested, when the Colonel proposed it to her, and then had been borne down by him; whether in short she didn't loathe herself as she sat there. The cruelty, the cowardice of fastening their unholy act upon the wretched woman struck him as monstrous—no less monstrous indeed than the levity that could make them run the risk of her giving them, in her righteous indignation, the lie. Of course that risk could only exculpate her and not inculpate them—the probabilities protected them so perfectly; and what the Colonel counted on (what he would have counted upon the day he delivered himself, after first seeing her, at the studio, if he had thought about the matter then at all and not spoken from the pure spontaneity of his genius) was simply that Miss Geraldine had really vanished for ever into her native unknown. Lyon wanted so much to quit the subject that when after a little Mrs. Capadose said to him, 'But can nothing be done, can't the picture be repaired? You know they do such wonders in that way now,' he only replied, 'I don't know, I don't care, it's all over, *n'en parlons plus!*' Her hypocrisy revolted him. And yet, by way of plucking off the last veil of her shame, he broke out to her again, shortly afterward, 'And you *did* like it, really?' To which she returned, looking him straight in his face, without a blush, a pallor, an evasion, 'Oh, I loved it!' Truly her husband had trained her well. After that Lyon said no more and his companions forbore temporarily to insist, like people of tact and sympathy aware that the odious accident had made him sore.

When they quitted the table the Colonel went away without coming upstairs; but Lyon returned to the drawing-room with his hostess, remarking to her however on the way that he could remain but a moment. He spent that moment—it prolonged itself a little—standing with her before the chimney-piece. She neither sat down nor asked him to; her manner denoted that she intended to go out. Yes, her husband had trained her well; yet Lyon dreamed for a moment that now he was alone with her she would perhaps break down, retract, apologise, confide, say to him, 'My dear old friend, forgive this hideous comedy—you understand!' And then how he would have loved her and pitied her, guarded her, helped her always! If she were not ready to do something of that sort why had she treated him as if he were a dear old friend; why had she let him for months suppose certain things—or almost; why had she come to his studio day after day to sit near him on the pretext of her child's portrait, as if she liked to think what might have been? Why had she come so near a tacit confession, in a word, if she was not willing to go an inch further? And she was not willing—she was not; he could see that as he lingered there. She moved about the room a little, rearranging two or three objects on the tables, but she did nothing more. Suddenly he said to her: 'Which way was she going, when you came out?'

'She—the woman we saw?'

'Yes, your husband's strange friend. It's a clew worth following.' He had no desire to frighten her; he only wanted to communicate the impulse which would make her say, 'Ah, spare me—and spare *him!* There was no such person.'

Instead of this Mrs. Capadose replied, 'She was going away from us—she crossed the road. We were coming towards the station.'

'And did she appear to recognise the Colonel—did she look round?'

'Yes; she looked round, but I didn't notice much. A hansom came along and we got into it. It was not till then that Clement told me who she was: I remember he said that she was there for no good. I suppose we ought to have gone back.'

'Yes; you would have saved the picture.'

For a moment she said nothing; then she smiled. 'For you, I am very sorry. But you must remember that I possess the original!'

At this Lyon turned away. 'Well, I must go,' he said; and he left her without any other farewell and made his way out of the house. As he went slowly up the street the sense came back to him of that first glimpse of her he had had at Stayes—the way he had seen her gaze across the table at her husband. Lyon stopped at the corner, looking vaguely up and down. He would never go back—he couldn't. She was still in love with the Colonel—he had trained her too well.

COMMENTARY
by Henry James

In two separate and dissimilar accounts James describes how he came to compose "The Liar." In his *Notebooks* he writes:

June 19th, 1884.   One might write a tale (very short) about a woman married to a man of the most amiable character who is a tremendous, though harmless, liar. She is very intelligent, a fine, quiet, high, pure nature, and she has to sit by and hear him romance—mainly out of vanity, the desire to be interesting, and a peculiar irresistible impulse. He is good, kind, personally very attractive, very handsome, etc.: it is almost his only fault though of course he is increasingly very *light*. What she suffers—what she goes through—generally she tries to rectify, to remove any bad effect by toning down a little, etc. But there comes a day when he tells a very big lie which she has—for reasons to be related—to adopt, to reinforce. To save him from exposure, in a word, she has to lie herself. The struggle, etc.; she lies—but after that she hates him. (Numa Roumestan.)

Numa Roumestan is a tale by Alphonse Daudet published in 1881 and which James had read by 1883 (five years before the appearance of his own story). He probably drew from it a hint for the composition of a short story concerned with a liar and his honest wife. This much the statement in the *Notebooks* seems to indicate. On the other hand, in his "Preface" to *The Aspern Papers* (1908), James details another source for "The Liar."

... I come back, for "The Liar," as for so many of its fellows, to holding my personal experience, poor thing though it may have been, immediately accountable. For by what else in the world but by fatal design had I been placed at dinner one autumn evening of old London days face to face with a gentleman, met for the first time, though favourably known to me by name and fame, in whom I recognised the most unbridled colloquial romancer the "joy of life" had ever found occasion to envy? Under what other conceivable coercion had I been invited to reckon, through the evening, with the type, with the character, with the countenance of this magnificent master's wife, who, veracious, serene and charming, yet not once meeting straight the eyes of one of us, did her duty by each, and by her husband most of all, without so much as, in the vulgar phrase, turning a hair? It was long ago, but I have never, to this hour, forgotten the evening itself—embalmed for me now in an old-time sweetness beyond any aspect of my reproduction. I made but a fifth person, the other couple our host and hostess; between whom and one of the company while we listened to the woven wonders of a summer holiday, the exploits of a salamander, among Mediterranean isles, were exchanged, dimly and discreetly, ever so guardedly, but all expressively, imperceptible lingering looks. It was exquisite, it *could* but become, inevitably, some "short story" or other, which it clearly pre-fitted as the hand the glove.

The disparity between the two accounts is explained plausibly by Matthiessen and Murdock, the editors of James' *Notebooks*. Pointing out that the novella itself did not appear until May and June 1888 in the *Century Magazine*, four years after the entry in the *Notebooks*, they argue "that the original germ for the story came from Daudet, and that James put it down in his notebook prior to the dinner party. Then, later, he met the 'liar' in the flesh, and wrote the tale—perhaps referring to the notebook or perhaps not remembering it or its relation to *Numa Roumestan* at all."

The editors continue with their analysis of the possible sources of the novella. " 'The Liar' opens with a dinner party, which is unparalleled in Daudet. The strength of the tale comes from James' centering, as in the notebook, not on the 'liar' but on the problem of his wife, and from the introduction of an emotional relation between the wife and an artist, through whose observation the story is told. He has wooed her vainly years before. Because he is still deeply interested in her and feels that she has once slighted him, he tries to find out how far she will go to protect her husband, hoping that she will give some sign of a feeling that if she had married the artist, 'her life would have been finer.' In the sketch she protects her husband, but 'after that she hates him'; in the story she is still in love with the 'liar.' This change in the ending increases the effectiveness of the story by making it almost a case of the 'possession' of a pure spirit by an impure one, and by saving it from the relative banality of a presentation simply of a wife loyal to her husband under unpleasant circumstances."*

Growing Up
Joyce Cary

Robert Quick, coming home after a business trip, found a note from his wife. She would be back at four, but the children were in the garden. He tossed down his hat, and still in his dark business suit, which he disliked very much, made at once for the garden.

He had missed his two small girls and looked forward eagerly to

The Notebooks of Henry James, ed. F. O. Matthiessen and Kenneth B. Murdock (New York, 1947), pp. 61–62.

their greeting. He had hoped indeed that they might, as often before, have been waiting at the corner of the road, to flag the car, and drive home with him.

The Quicks' garden was a wilderness. Except for a small vegetable patch near the pond, and one bed where Mrs Quick grew flowers for the house, it had not been touched for years. Old apple trees tottered over seedy laurels, unpruned roses. Tall ruins of dahlias and delphiniums hung from broken sticks.

The original excuse for this neglect was that the garden was for the children. They should do what they liked there. The original truth was that neither of the Quicks cared for gardening. Besides, Mrs Quick was too busy with family, council, and parish affairs, Quick with his office, to give time to a hobby that bored them both.

But the excuse had become true. The garden belonged to the children, and Quick was even proud of it. He would boast of his wild garden, so different from any neighbour's shaved grass and combed beds. It had come to seem, for him, a triumph of imagination; and this afternoon, once more, he found it charming in its wildness, an original masterpiece among gardens.

And, in fact, with the sun just warming up in mid-May, slanting steeply past the trees, and making even old weeds shine red and gold, it had the special beauty of untouched woods, where there is still, even among closely farmed lands, a little piece of free nature left, a suggestion of the frontier, primeval forests.

'A bit of real wild country,' thought Quick, a townsman for whom the country was a place for picnics. And he felt at once released, escaped. He shouted, 'Hullo, hullo, children.'

There was no answer. And he stopped, in surprise. Then he thought. 'They've gone to meet me—I've missed them.' And this gave him both pleasure and dismay. The last time the children had missed him, two years before, having gone a mile down the road and lain in ambush behind a hedge, there had been tears. They had resented being searched for, and brought home; they had hated the humiliating failure of their surprise.

But even as he turned back towards the house, and dodged a tree, he caught sight of Jenny, lying on her stomach by the pond, with a book under her nose. Jenny was twelve and had lately taken furiously to reading.

Quick made for the pond with long steps, calling, 'Hullo, hullo, Jenny, hullo,' waving. But Jenny merely turned her head slightly and peered at him through her hair. Then she dropped her cheek on the book as if to say, 'Excuse me, it's really too hot.'

And now he saw Kate, a year older. She was sitting on the swing, leaning sideways against a rope, with her head down, apparently in deep thought. Her bare legs, blotched with mud, lay along the ground, one foot hooked over the other. Her whole air was one of languor and concentration. To her father's 'Hullo,' she answered only in a faint muffled voice, 'Hullo, Daddy.'

'Hullo, Kate.' But he said no more and did not go near. Quick never asked for affection from his girls. He despised fathers who flirted with their daughters, who encouraged them to love. It would have been especially wrong, he thought, with these two. They were naturally impulsive and affectionate—Jenny had moods of passionate devotion, especially in the last months. She was growing up, he thought, more quickly than Kate and she was going to be an exciting woman, strong in all her feelings, intelligent, reflective. 'Well, Jenny,' he said, 'what are you reading now?' But the child answered only by a slight wriggle of her behind.

Quick was amused at his own disappointment. He said to himself, 'Children have no manners but at least they're honest—they never pretend.' He fetched himself a desk chair and the morning paper, which he had hardly looked at before his early start on the road. He would make the best of things. At fifty-two, having lost most of his illusions, he was good at making the best of things. 'It's a lovely day,' he thought, 'and I'm free till Sunday night.' He looked round him as he opened the paper and felt again the pleasure of the garden. What a joy, at last, to be at peace. And the mere presence of the children was a pleasure. Nothing could deprive him of that. He was home again.

Jenny had got up and wandered away among the trees; her legs too were bare and dirty, and her dress had a large green stain at the side. She had been in the pond. And now Kate allowed herself to collapse slowly out of the swing and lay on her back with her hair tousled in the dirt, her arms thrown apart, her small dirty hands with black nails turned palm upwards to the sky. Her cocker bitch, Snort, came loping and sniffing, uttered one short bark and rooted at her mistress' legs. Kate raised one foot and tickled her stomach, then rolled over and buried her face in her arms. When Snort tried to push her nose under Kate's thigh as if to turn her over, she made a half kick and murmured, 'Go away, Snort.'

'Stop it, Snort,' Jenny echoed in the same meditative tone. The sisters adored each other and one always came to the other's help. But Snort only stopped a moment to gaze at Jenny, then tugged at Kate's dress. Kate made another energetic kick and said, 'Oh, do go away, Snort.'

Jenny stopped in her languid stroll, snatched a bamboo from the border, and hurled it at Snort like a spear.

The bitch, startled, uttered a loud uncertain bark and approached, wagging her behind so vigorously that she curled her body sideways at each wag. She was not sure if this was a new game, or if she had committed some grave crime. Jenny gave a yell and rushed at her. She fled yelping. At once Kate jumped up, seized another bamboo and threw it, shouting, 'Tiger, tiger.'

The two children dashed after the bitch, laughing, bumping together, falling over each other and snatching up anything they could find to throw at the fugitive, pebbles, dead daffodils, bits of flower-pots, lumps of earth. Snort, horrified, overwhelmed, dodged to and fro, barked hysterically, crazily, wagged her tail in desperate submission; finally put it between her legs and crept whining between a broken shed and the wall.

Robert was shocked. He was fond of the sentimental foolish Snort, and he saw her acute misery. He called to the children urgently, 'Hi, Jenny—don't do that. Don't do that, Kate. She's frightened—you might put her eye out. Hi, stop—stop.'

This last cry expressed real indignation. Jenny had got hold of a rake and was trying to hook Snort by the collar. Robert began to struggle out of his chair. But suddenly Kate turned round, aimed a pea-stick at him and shouted at the top of her voice, 'Yield, Paleface.' Jenny at once turned and cried, 'Yes, yes—Paleface, yield.' She burst into a shout of laughter and could not speak, but rushed at the man with the rake carried like a lance.

The two girls, staggering with laughter, threw themselves upon their father. 'Paleface—Paleface Robbie. Kill him—scalp him. Torture him.'

They tore at the man and suddenly he was frightened. It seemed to him that both the children, usually so gentle, so affectionate, had gone completely mad, vindictive. They were hurting him, and he did not know how to defend himself without hurting them, without breaking their skinny bones, which seemed as fragile as a bird's legs. He dared not even push too hard against the thin ribs which seemed to bend under his hand. Snort, suddenly recovering confidence, rushed barking from cover and seized this new victim by the sleeve, grunting and tugging.

'Hi,' he shouted, trying to catch at the bitch. 'Call her off, Kate. Don't, don't children.' But they battered at him, Kate was jumping on his stomach, Jenny had seized him by the collar as if to strangle him. Her face, close to his own, was that of a homicidal maniac; her eyes were wide and glaring, her lips were curled back to show all her teeth. And he was really strangling. He made a violent effort to throw the child off, but her hands were firmly twined in his collar. He felt his ears sing. Then suddenly the chair gave way—all three fell with a crash. Snort, startled, and perhaps pinched, gave a yelp, and snapped at the man's face.

Kate was lying across his legs, Jenny on his chest; she still held his collar in both hands. But now, gazing down at him, her expression changed. She cried, 'Oh, she's bitten you. Look Kate.' Kate, rolling off his legs, came to her knees. 'So she has, bad Snort.'

The girls were still panting, flushed, struggling with laughter. But Jenny reproached her sister, 'It's not a joke. It might be poisoned.'

'I know,' Kate was indignant. But burst out again into helpless giggles.

Robert picked himself up and dusted his coat. He did not utter any reproaches. He avoided even looking at the girls in case they should see his anger and surprise. He was deeply shocked. He could not forget Jenny's face, crazy, murderous; he thought, 'Not much affection there—she wanted to hurt. It was as if she hated me.'

It seemed to him that something new had broken into his old simple and happy relation with his daughters; that they had suddenly receded from him into a world of their own in which he had no standing, a primitive, brutal world.

He straightened his tie. Kate had disappeared; Jenny was gazing at his forehead and trying to suppress her own giggles. But when he turned away, she caught his arm, 'Oh, Daddy, where are you going?'

'To meet your mother—she must be on her way.'

'Oh, but you can't go like that—we've got to wash your bite.'

'That's all right, Jenny. It doesn't matter.'

'But Kate is getting the water—and it might be quite bad.'

And now, Kate, coming from the kitchen with a bowl of water, called out indignantly, 'Sit down, Daddy—sit down—how dare you get up.'

She was playing the stern nurse. And in fact, Robert, though still in a mood of disgust, found himself obliged to submit to this new game. At least it was more like a game. It was not murderous. And a man so plump and bald could not allow himself even to appear upset by the roughness of children. Even though the children would not understand why he was upset, why he was shocked.

'Sit down at once, man,' Jenny said. 'Kate, put up the chair.'

Kate put up the chair, the two girls made him sit down, washed the cut, painted it with iodine, stuck a piece of plaster on it. Mrs Quick, handsome, rosy, good-natured, practical, arrived in the middle of this ceremony, with her friend Jane Martin, Chairman of the Welfare Committee. Both were much amused by the scene, and the history of the afternoon. Their air said plainly to Robert, 'All you children—amusing yourselves while we run the world.'

Kate and Jenny were sent to wash and change their dirty frocks. The committee was coming to tea. And at tea, the two girls, dressed in smart clean frocks, handed round cake and bread and butter with demure and reserved looks. They knew how to behave at tea, at a party. They were enjoying the dignity of their own performance. Their eyes passed over their father as if he did not exist, or rather as if he existed only as another guest, to be waited on.

And now, seeking as it were a new if lower level of security, of resignation, he said to himself, 'Heavens, but what did I expect? In a year or two more I shan't count at all. Young men will come prowling, like the dogs after Snort—I shall be an old buffer, useful only to pay bills.'

The ladies were talking together about a case—the case of a boy of fourteen, a nice respectable boy, most regular at Sunday school, who had suddenly robbed his mother's till and gone off in a stolen car. Jenny, seated at her mother's feet, was listening intently, Kate was feeding chocolate roll to Snort, and tickling her chin.

Quick felt all at once a sense of stuffiness. He wanted urgently to get away, to escape. Yes, he needed some male society. He would go to the club. Probably no one would be there but the card-room crowd, and he could not bear cards. But he might find old Wilkins in the billiard room. Wilkins at seventy was a crashing, a dreary bore, who spent half his life at the club; who was always telling you how he had foreseen the slump, and how clever he was at investing his money. What good was money to old Wilkins? But, Quick thought, he could get up a game with Wilkins, pass an hour or two with him, till dinner-time, even dine with him. He could phone his wife. She would not mind. She rather liked a free evening for her various accounts. And he need not go home till the children were in bed.

And when, after tea, the committee members pulled out their agenda, he stole away. Suddenly, as he turned by the corner house, skirting its front garden wall, he heard running steps and a breathless call. He turned, it was Jenny. She arrived, panting, holding herself by the chest. 'Oh, I couldn't catch you.'

'What is it now, Jenny?'

'I wanted to look—at the cut.'

Robert began to stoop. But she cried, 'No, I'll get on the wall. Put me up.'

He lifted her on the garden wall which made her about a foot taller than himself. Having reached this superior position, she poked the plaster.

'I just wanted to make sure it was sticking. Yes, it's all right.'

She looked down at him with an expression he did not recognise.

What was the game, medical, maternal? Was she going to laugh? But the child frowned. She was also struck by something new and unexpected.

Then she tossed back her hair. 'Good-bye.' She jumped down and ran off. The man walked slowly towards the club. 'No,' he thought, 'not quite a game—not for half a second. She's growing up—and so am I.'

COMMENTARY
by Joyce Cary

In his fiction Joyce Cary had long been sympathetic to children. He was interested in their ability to live as such in an adult world without becoming part of it. He was particularly fascinated by the process of their growing up, by their efforts to achieve a reconciliation—tentative and groping as it had to be—with maturity. In a collection of essays called *Art and Reality*, he spoke of the child as the latter approached knowledge and hence an awareness of reality.

Of course, the child also shows individual character from a very early age. But only, I suggest, a strictly independent character when it begins to reflect, to judge. Before that it simply reacts to its emotional make-up. It is a piece of common reality of which the differentiation is simply that of one creature from another, with different potentiality and strength, different quality, as its seed belonged to a good or bad strain, but made of the same ingredients. As soon, however, as it begins to acquire knowledge, to reflect on it, to form ideas, it becomes a true individual soul. It can value the reality it knows, of emotions. It can form moral ideas, it can face a moral situation, which is always unique, and decide upon its response. It is not only independent, but obliged to be so, not only a moral being, but a solitary person in a dangerous world of vicissitude.*

Cary wrote several novels about children; *Charley is my Darling* is perhaps the best known. In a "Preface" to the Carfax edition of

Art and Reality (New York, 1958), pp. 12–13.

this novel, he attempts to explain the personality of the adolescent mind more fully and explicitly than he was later to suggest in the above passage. In the "Preface" he said:

I was once asked by an official of the Board which looks after young offenders, how I had come to know so much about them. It had not struck me before that I had any special knowledge, but when I reflected I thought that if I did have knowledge, it came chiefly from a good memory of my own childhood. And it has always seemed to me that every ordinary child is by nature a delinquent, that the only difference between us as children was the extent of our delinquency, whether we were found out in it and how we were punished for it.

. . . . .

[There are] complex motives at work already in a child's mind; forces that are not different in kind from those that move a grown-up. The suddenness of temptation or, rather, inspiration, which (like many that come to an artist) is so quick that he doesn't even notice it, it leaves no moment for reflection. The imagination sees its opportunity, its prey, and instantly leaps upon it. You can watch this happen with any good talker, and you can see such inspired talkers carried suddenly away into brutalities. They drop bricks. That is to say, they are whirled into delinquency before they know it.

Such people, it is said, have given way to a sudden temptation. It has been too attractive for their self-control. For children, with their powerful imaginations and weak control, the wonder is not that they do some wrong, but that they don't do much more.

I was a lucky child, surrounded not only by affection but a lively family of cousins, aunts and uncles, full of energy and imagination, and also of a very ready instruction in what was right and wrong. I had always new vistas of discovery and interest opening before me; I was encouraged to talk, to tell stories, to write and draw; I had freedom to range for miles over the little beaches of Donegal; and yet I knew very clearly (according to family ideas, which were old-fashioned perhaps but all the more definite) what was wicked, what was merely mischief, what was neither but, all the same, not done. I was neither bored nor confused. And boredom and confusion are surely the two prime sources of childish wickedness. . . . The child is a born creator. He has to be, for though in sympathy he is one with those he loves, in mind he is alone. He has to do his own learning and thinking. And Nature, for his very necessary good, sets him to enjoy it. Anyone can see how children enjoy discovery and reflection. But also how soon they are bored with what is known. It is as if Nature says to them, 'Go on, go on, there's plenty more that you must know'; and has made the joy of discovery evanescent; the imagination, like the appetite, perpetually greedy. So that being shut out from its need on one side it dashes after it on another.

Just as the grown-up world is for ever seeking new arts, new ideas, so children want change; and just as grown-ups who are bored take to drink or gambling or mere destructiveness, for the kick, so bored children get up a fight, or a dare, or steal, or smash. These too are novelties, adventures, and also explorations.

But the world that stands to be explored is also a moral structure which, simply because it is one of related ideas, is much harder for him to grasp. He perceives that it is there, he feels its importance to his comfort and security every moment of the day, but it is not present to his eyes and ears; he cannot see and touch it. He is not equipped with the experience and judgment necessary to put it together for himself. For this purpose nature has provided him (and many other small mammals which grow slowly in understanding) with parents. And if they refuse the duty of making the situation clear to him he will suffer. I am ready to bet that a good deal of what is called neurosis and frustration among young children is due to nothing but the failure of parents and teachers (often from the most conscientious) to do so, that is, to give a clear picture without uncertainties. Without such a picture, children don't know where they are, and they do all kinds of evil (because it is just this sphere of good and evil that is puzzling them) to find out. A child will torture a cat or some other smaller child, in order to see what will happen, both to himself and the victim, and what he feels like in the new circumstances. The 'crime' is a moral experiment.

But beyond this experimental effort, a child, being still confused and frustrated, still unable to know, once and for all, what is right and wrong, will commit a real crime, a spiteful cruelty, out of rage and spite; he will choose some valued thing to dirty or to smash because he identifies it with a world which obstinately closes itself to his imagination. For of course the imagination is always looking for significance; both in the physical and moral world, that is its job, to put together coherent wholes, a situation with meaning, a place where the child does know, all the time, where he is.

. . . . .

Knowledge, in short, the experience of the mind, is just as important to a child's happiness and 'goodness' as affection, adventure; above all, the knowledge of his own moral position. And the last is often more difficult for him to come by, not because he could not grasp a complex situation ('this is a grand deed but a bad one'), but because grown-ups do not trust the power of his imagination to form a picture in more than one dimension.*

Coming Home
Elizabeth Bowen

All the way home from school Rosalind's cheeks burnt, she felt something throbbing in her ears. It was sometimes terrible to live so far away. Before her body had turned the first corner her mind had many times wrenched open their gate, many times rushed up their path through the damp smells of the garden, waving the essay-book, and seen Darlingest coming to the window. Nothing like this had ever happened before to either her or Darlingest; it was the supreme moment that all these years they had been approaching, of which those dim, improbable future years would be spent in retrospect.

Rosalind's essay had been read aloud and everybody had praised it. Everybody had been there, the big girls sitting along the sides of the room had turned and looked at her, raising their eyebrows and smiling. For an infinity of time the room had held nothing but the rising and falling of Miss Wilfred's beautiful voice doing the service of Rosalind's brain. When the voice dropped to silence and the room was once more unbearably crowded, Rosalind had looked at the clock and seen that her essay had taken four and a half minutes to read. She found that her mouth was dry and her eyes ached from staring at a small fixed spot in the heart of whirling circles, and her

Charley Is My Darling ([Carfax edition], London, 1951), pp. 5, 7–10.

knotted hands were damp and trembling. Somebody behind her gently poked the small of her back. Everybody in the room was thinking about Rosalind; she felt their admiration and attention lapping up against her in small waves. A long way off somebody spoke her name repeatedly, she stood up stupidly and everybody laughed. Miss Wilfred was trying to pass her back the red exercise-book. Rosalind sat down again thinking to herself how dazed she was, dazed with glory. She was beginning already to feel about for words for Darlingest.

She had understood some time ago that nothing became real for her until she had had time to live it over again. An actual occurrence was nothing but the blankness of a shock, then the knowledge that something had happened; afterwards one could creep back and look into one's mind and find new things in it, clear and solid. It was like waiting outside the hen-house till the hen came off the nest and then going in to look for the egg. She would not touch this egg until she was with Darlingest, then they would go and look for it together. Suddenly and vividly this afternoon would be real for her. "I won't think about it yet," she said, "for fear I'd spoil it."

The houses grew scarcer and the roads greener, and Rosalind relaxed a little; she was nearly home. She looked at the syringa-bushes by the gate, and it was as if a cold wing had brushed against her. Supposing Darlingest were out . . . ?

She slowed down her running steps to a walk. From here she would be able to call to Darlingest. But if she didn't answer there would be still a tortuous hope; she might be at the back of the house. She decided to pretend it didn't matter, one way or the other; she had done this before, and it rather took the wind out of Somebody's sails, she felt. She hitched up her essay-book under her arm, approached the gate, turned carefully to shut it, and walked slowly up the path looking carefully down at her feet, not up at all at the drawing-room window. Darlingest would think she was playing a game. Why didn't she hear her tapping on the glass with her thimble?

As soon as she entered the hall she knew that the house was empty. Clocks ticked very loudly; upstairs and downstairs the doors were a little open, letting through pale strips of light. Only the kitchen door was shut, down the end of the passage, and she could hear Emma moving about behind it. There was a spectral shimmer of light in the white panelling. On the table was a bowl of primroses; Darlingest must have put them there that morning. The hall was chilly; she could not think why the primroses gave her such a feeling of horror, then she remembered the wreath of primroses, and the scent of it, lying on the raw new earth of that grave. . . . The pair of grey gloves were gone from the bowl of visiting-cards. Darlingest had spent the morning doing those deathly primroses, and then taken up her grey gloves and gone out, at the end of the afternoon, just when she knew her little girl would be coming in. A quarter-past four. It was unforgivable of Darlingest: she had been a mother for more than twelve years, the mother exclusively of Rosalind, and still, it seemed, she knew no better than to do a thing like that. Other people's mothers had terrible little babies: they ran quickly in and out to go to them, or they had smoky husbands who came in and sat, with big feet. There was something distracted about other people's mothers. But Darlingest, so exclusively one's own. . . .

Darlingest could never have really believed in her. She could never have really believed that Rosalind would do anything wonderful at school, or she would have been more careful to be in to hear about it. Rosalind flung herself into the drawing-room; it was honey-coloured and lovely in the pale spring light, another little clock was ticking in the corner, there were more bowls of primroses and black-eyed, lowering anemones. The tarnished mirror on the wall distorted and reproved her angry face in its mild mauveness. Tea was spread on the table by the window, tea for two that the two might never . . . Her work and an open book lay on the tumbled cushions of the window-seat. All the afternoon she had sat there waiting and working, and now—poor little Darlingest, perhaps she had gone out because she was lonely.

People who went out sometimes never came back again. Here she was, being angry with Darlingest, and all the time . . . Well, she had drawn on those grey gloves and gone out wandering along the roads, vague and beautiful, because she was lonely, and then?

Ask Emma? No, she wouldn't; fancy having to ask *her!*

"Yes, your mother'll be in soon, Miss Rosie. Now run and get your things off, there's a good girl—" Oh no, intolerable.

The whole house was full of the scent and horror of the primroses. Rosalind dropped the exercise-book on the floor, looked at it, hesitated, and putting her hands over her mouth, went upstairs, choking back her sobs. She heard the handle of the kitchen door turn; Emma was coming out. O God! Now she was on the floor by Darlingest's bed, with the branches swaying and brushing outside the window, smothering her face in the eiderdown, smelling and tasting the wet satin. Down in the hall she heard Emma call her, mutter something, and slam back into the kitchen.

How could she ever have left Darlingest? She might have known, she might have known. The sense of insecurity had been growing on her year by year. A person might be part of you, almost part of your body, and yet once you went away from them they might utterly cease to be. The sea of horror ebbing and flowing round the edges of the world, whose tides were charted in the newspapers, might sweep out a long wave over them and they would be gone. There was no security. Safety and happiness were a game that grown-up people played with children to keep them from understanding, possibly to keep themselves from thinking. But they did think, that was what made grown-up people—queer. Anything might happen, there was no security. And now Darlingest—

This was her dressing-table, with the long beads straggling over it, the little coloured glass barrels and bottles had bright flames in the centre. In front of the looking-glass, filmed faintly over with a cloud of powder, Darlingest had put her hat on—for the last time. Supposing all that had ever been reflected in it were imprisoned somewhere in the back of a looking-glass. The blue hat with the drooping brim was hanging over the corner of a chair. Rosalind had never been kind about that blue hat, she didn't think it was becoming. And Darlingest had loved it so. She must have gone wearing the brown one; Rosalind went over to the wardrobe and stood on tip-toe to look on the top shelf. Yes, the brown hat was gone. She would never see Darlingest again, in the brown hat, coming down the road to meet her and not seeing her because she was thinking about something else. Peau d'Espagne crept faintly from among the folds of the dresses; the blue, the gold, the soft furred edges of the tea-gown dripping out of the wardrobe. She heard herself making a high, whining noise at the back of her throat, like a puppy, felt her swollen face distorted by another paroxysm.

"I can't bear it, I can't bear it. What have I done? I did love her, I did so awfully love her.

"Perhaps she was all right when I came in; coming home smiling. Then I stopped loving her, I hated her and was angry. And it happened. She was crossing a road and something happened to her. I was angry and she died. I killed her.

"I don't know that she's dead. I'd better get used to believing it, it will hurt less afterwards. Supposing she does come back this time; it's only for a little. I shall never be able to keep her; now I've found out about this I shall never be happy. Life's nothing but waiting for awfulness to happen and trying to think about something else.

"If she could come back just this once—Darlingest."

Emma came half-way upstairs; Rosalind flattened herself behind the door.

"Will you begin your tea, Miss Rosie?"

"No. Where's mother?"

"I didn't hear her go out. I have the kettle boiling—will I make your tea?"

"No. *No.*"

Rosalind slammed the door on the angry mutterings, and heard with a sense of desolation Emma go downstairs. The silver clock by Darlingest's bed ticked; it was five o'clock. They had tea at a quarter-past four; Darlingest was never, never late. When they came to tell her about *It,* men would come, and they would tell Emma, and Emma would come up with a frightened, triumphant face and tell her.

She saw the grey-gloved hands spread out in the dust.

A sound at the gate. "I can't bear it, I can't bear it. Oh, save me, God!"

Steps on the gravel.

Darlingest.

She was at the window, pressing her speechless lips together.

Darlingest came slowly up the path with the long ends of her veil, untied, hanging over her shoulders. A paper parcel was pressed between her arm and her side. She paused, stood smiling down at the daffodils. Then she looked up with a start at the windows, as though she heard somebody calling. Rosalind drew back into the room.

She heard her mother's footsteps cross the stone floor of the hall, hesitate at the door of the drawing-room, and come over to the foot of the stairs. The voice was calling "Lindie! Lindie, duckie!" She was coming upstairs.

Rosalind leaned the weight of her body against the dressing-table and dabbed her face with the big powder-puff; the powder clung in paste to her wet lashes and in patches over her nose and cheeks. She was not happy, she was not relieved, she felt no particular feeling about Darlingest, did not even want to see her. Something had slackened down inside her, leaving her a little sick.

"Oh, you're *there*," said Darlingest from outside, hearing her movements. "Where did, where were—?"

She was standing in the doorway. Nothing had been for the last time, after all. She had come back. One could never explain to her how wrong she had been. She was holding out her arms; something drew one towards them.

"But, my little *Clown*," said Darlingest, wiping off the powder. "But, oh—" She scanned the glazed, blurred face. "Tell me why," she said.

"You were late."

"Yes, it was horrid of me; did you mind? . . . But that was silly, Rosalind, I can't be always in."

"But you're my mother."

Darlingest was amused; little trickles of laughter and gratification ran out of her. "You weren't *frightened*, Silly Billy." Her tone changed to distress. "Oh, Rosalind, don't be cross."

"I'm not," said Rosalind coldly.

"Then come—"

"I was wanting my tea."

"Rosalind, *don't* be—"

Rosalind walked past her to the door. She was hurting Darlingest, beautifully hurting her. She would never tell her about that essay.

Everybody would be talking about it, and when Darlingest heard and asked her about it she would say: "Oh, that? I didn't think you'd be interested." That would hurt. She went down into the drawing-room, past the primroses. The grey gloves were back on the table. This was the mauve and golden room that Darlingest had come back to, from under the Shadow of Death, expecting to find her little daughter. . . . They would have sat together on the window-seat while Rosalind read the essay aloud, leaning their heads closer together as the room grew darker.

That was all spoilt.

Poor Darlingest, up there alone in the bedroom, puzzled, hurt, disappointed, taking off her hat. She hadn't known she was going to be hurt like this when she stood out there on the gravel, smiling at the daffodils. The red essay-book lay spread open on the carpet. There was the paper bag she had been carrying, lying on a table by the door; macaroons, all squashy from being carried the wrong way, disgorging, through a tear in the paper, a little trickle of crumbs.

The pathos of the forgotten macaroons, the silent pain! Rosalind ran upstairs to the bedroom.

Darlingest did not hear her; she had forgotten. She was standing in the middle of the room with her face turned towards the window, looking at something a long way away, smiling and singing to herself and rolling up her veil.

Plot

We might well start our discussion of plot with the central element of Aristotle's definition. This he took to be "the imitation of the action;—for by plot I here mean the arrangement of incidents." In working out his terms, Aristotle had in mind the tragedies of ancient Greece. Yet in several significant details, his formula is relevant to fiction. The action of a short story or a novel, thus, is not a literal copy of a real action. Rather—as in tragedy—it is "the imitation" of real action, a symbolic representation of probable or believable events. The action is that event or series of events which we might expect to take place under a given set of circumstances proposed by the author. And it lends itself to interpretations consistent with the author's view of experience.

Although character in the Aristotelian definition (contrary to the usual assumptions of modern storytelling) is subordinated to plot, the one cannot be separated from the other: plot cannot be meaningful apart from agents of movement, or characters. As Mark Schorer says, "Plot is a form of organized actions; but actions require actors and these are the 'people' of fiction, its characters. Plot cannot exist without people; we cannot see the people without plots.... Actions and characters are therefore inseparable, and we cannot tell them apart any more than, according to W. B. Yeats' poem, we can the dance from the dancer."*

Indeed, someone like Turgenev thought of plot largely in terms of character. He once told Henry James, who was himself influenced by the Russian's method of characterization and plot arrangement, that "if I watch [my characters] long enough I see them come together, I see them *placed,* I see them engaged in this or that act and in this or that difficulty. How they look and move and speak and behave, always in the setting I have found for them is my account of them."

The essence of fiction, then, is its organized concern with some part of the life experience. Whatever pleasure and illumination it affords derive first of all from its resemblance to the actions—mental as well as physical—of human beings recognizably located in time and space. Plot is the narrative means by which characters advance certain problems that are meant to warrant our attention and involvement. Or, as Miss Bowen said in her *Notes on Writing a Novel,* "plot must not cease to move forward." Because it is generally consequential as well as sequential, we expect fiction to include both values and causal process.

For E. M. Forster, in this connection, "a plot is ... a narrative of events, the emphasis falling on causality. 'The king died and then the queen died.'" That statement, he said, represents merely a story, "the lowest and simplest of literary organisms." Then by way of further illustration, he amplified his initial story. "'The king died, and then the queen died of grief,' is a plot. The time-sequence is preserved, but the sense of causality overshadows it. Or again: 'The queen died, no one knew why, until it was discovered that it was through grief at

*O body swayed to music, O brightening glance,
  How can we know the dancer from the dance?
            —from *Among School Children*

the death of the king.' This is plot with a mystery in it, a form capable of high development. It suspends the time sequence, it moves as far away from the story as its limitations will allow. Consider the death of the queen. If it is in a story we say 'and then?' If it is in a plot we ask 'why?' ... A plot cannot be told to a gaping audience of cave men or to a tyrannical sultan or to their modern descendant the movie public. They can only be kept awake by 'and then—and then'—They can only supply curiosity. But a plot demands intelligence and memory also."* A plot either explicitly or through implication must supply answers to questions it has raised. And it can do this only if its details emerge from causes, only if both convey meanings which have acquired symbolic support from action and character.

Another element which is necessary to all plots is *conflict,* the strain of opposition which animates the characters and impels the movement of the plot. Conflict may exist within a single character as he is forced to meet a crisis or make a decision. It may be externalized, between a character and his society or environment, or between two characters—the protagonist and antagonist. Conflict always predicates an antagonistic meeting of forces, characters, or wills—intellectually, physically, emotionally. It initiates and heightens tension; it creates *suspense* until the *resolution* is inevitably reached.

There are various kinds of plot which we need not discuss here; indeed we cannot. But they range from the simple linear to the complex contrapuntal, from externalized, strict chronology to the indirection of time-shifts and stream-of-consciousness. Each type has its own value in terms of its own relevance. We need to ask only a few basic but all-important questions about plot. What has the author tried to do in his "imitation of an action"? Has he been successful in relating form to intention? Has he said what he had to say in the only way it could be said? Does his plot, in short, give a sense of its own inevitability.

Of this last point Elizabeth Bowen has strong opinions. "Plot," she said, "might seem to be a matter of choice. It is not. The partic-

---

Aspects of the Novel ([1927], New York, 1954), p. 86.

ular plot is something the novelist is driven to. It is what is left after the whittling away of alternatives. The novelist is confronted, at a moment . . . by the impossibility of saying what is to be said in any other way.

"He is forced towards his plot. By what? By the 'what is to be said.' What is 'what is to be said?' A mass of subjective matter that has accumulated—impressions received, feelings about experience, distorted results of ordinary observation, and something else—X. This matter is *extra* matter. It is superfluous to the non-writing life of the writer. It is luggage left in the hall between two journeys, as opposed to the perpetual furniture of rooms. It is destined to be elsewhere. It cannot move till the destination is known. Plot is the knowing of destination."

That *knowing,* as R. V. Cassill poignantly describes it in his personal reflections on "The Biggest Band," is more than a simple collection of recalled experiences. It is imagination superimposed on the evidence of reality. It is, to quote his own metaphor, a gathering "of transparent film slides stacked one on top of the other, so that each single picture modifies as it writes with each of the other pictures beneath to become a new image." The plot toward which the storyteller is "forced" may be a gently nostalgic one like Cassill's, the evocation of memory many times relived. Or it may be one of tragic futility, the product of a creative necessity—as in the stories by Flannery O'Connor and William Faulkner—that finds symbolic equivalents for frustration, faded vanity, and sadistic prejudice in violence. Again, as for Galsworthy, it may take shape in an ironic sequence of events in which the imagination itself is thrust against the wastefulness of self-delusion. The possibilities are virtually endless. Whatever course is followed, however, each author represented in this anthology fulfills the basic truth that plot "is what is left after the whittling-away of alternatives." Each writer must have been "confronted, at a moment . . . by the impossibility of saying what is to be said in any other way." Each knows his destination, hence the kind of plot he had to contrive.

The Consummation
John Galsworthy

About 1889 there lived in London a man named Harrison, of an amiable and perverse disposition. One morning, at Charing Cross Station, a lady in whom he was interested said to him:

"But Mr. Harrison, why don't you *write?* You are just the person!"

Harrison saw that he was, and at the end of two years had produced eleven short stories, with two of which he was not particularly pleased, but as he naturally did not like to waste them, he put them with the others and sent them all to a publisher. In the course of time he received from the publisher a letter saying that for a certain consideration or commission he would be prepared to undertake the risk of publishing these stories upon Harrison's incurring all the expenses. This pleased Harrison, who, feeling that no time should be wasted in making his "work" public, wrote desiring the publisher to put the matter in hand. The publisher replied to this with an estimate and an agreement, to which Harrison responded with a cheque. The publisher answered at once with a polite letter, suggesting that for Harrison's advantage a certain additional sum should be spent on advertisements. Harrison saw the point of this directly, and replied with another cheque—knowing that between gentlemen there could be no question of money.

In due time the book appeared. It was called "In the Track of the Stars," by Cuthbert Harrison; and within a fortnight Harrison began to receive reviews. He read them with an extraordinary pleasure, for they were full of discriminating flattery. One asked if he were a "Lancelot in disguise." Two Liberal papers described the stories as masterpieces; one compared them to the best things in Poe and de Maupassant; and another called him a second Rudyard Kipling. He was greatly encouraged, but, being by nature modest, he merely wrote to the publisher inquiring what he thought of a second edition. His publisher replied with an estimate, mentioning casually that he had already sold about four hundred copies. Harrison referred to his cheque-book and saw that the first edition had been a thousand copies. He replied, therefore, that he would wait. He waited, and at the end of six months wrote again. The publisher replied that he had now sold four hundred and three copies, but that, as Mr. Harrison had at present an unknown name, he did not advise a second edition: there was no market for short stories. These had, however, been so well received that he recommended Mr. Harrison to write a long story. The book was without doubt a success, so far as a book of short stories could ever be a success. . . . He sent Harrison a small cheque, and a large number of reviews which Harrison had already received.

Harrison decided not to have a second edition, but to rest upon his *succés d'estime.* All his relations were extremely pleased, and almost immediately he started writing his long story. Now it happened that among Harrison's friends was a man of genius, who sent Harrison a letter.

"I had no idea," he said, "that you could write like this; of course, my dear fellow, the stories are not 'done'; there is no doubt about it, they are *not* 'done.' But you have plenty of time; you are young, and I see that you can do things. Come down here and let us have a talk about what you are at now."

On receiving this Harrison wasted no time, but went down. The man of genius, over a jug of claret-cup, on a summer's afternoon, pointed out how the stories were not "done."

"They show a feeling for outside drama," said he, "but there is none of the real drama of psychology."

Harrison showed him his reviews. He left the man of genius on the following day with a certain sensation of soreness. In the course of a few weeks, however, the soreness wore off, and the words of the man of genius began to bear fruit, and at the end of two months Harrison wrote:

"You are quite right—the stories were not 'done.' I think, however, that I am now on the right path."

At the end of another year, after submitting it once or twice to the man of genius, he finished his second book, and called it "John Endacott." About this time he left off alluding to his "work" and began to call his writings "stuff."

He sent it to the publisher with the request that he would consider its publication on a royalty. In rather more than the ordinary course of time the publisher replied, that in his opinion (a lay one) "John Endacott" didn't quite fulfil the remarkable promise of Mr. Harrison's first book; and, to show Harrison his perfect honesty, he enclosed an extract from the "reader's" opinion, which stated that Mr. Harrison had "fallen between the stools of art and the British public." Much against the publisher's personal feelings, therefore, the publisher considered that he could only undertake the risk in the then bad condition of trade—if Mr. Harrison would guarantee the expenses.

Harrison hardened his heart, and replied that he was not prepared to guarantee the expenses. Upon which the publisher returned his manuscript, saying that in his opinion (a lay one) Mr. Harrison was taking the wrong turning, which he (the publisher) greatly regretted, for he had much appreciated the pleasant relations which had always existed between them.

Harrison sent the book to a younger publisher, who accepted it on a postponed royalty. It appeared.

At the end of three weeks Harrison began to receive reviews. They were mixed. One complained that there was not enough plot; another, fortunately by the same post, that there was too much plot.

The general tendency was to regret that the author of "In the Track of the Stars" had not fulfilled the hopes raised by his first book, in which he had shown such promise of completely hitting the public taste. This might have depressed Harrison had he not received a letter from the man of genius couched in these terms:

"My dear fellow, I am more pleased than I can say. I am now more than ever convinced that you can do things."

Harrison at once began a third book.

Owing to the unfortunate postponement of his royalty he did not receive anything from his second book. The publisher sold three hundred copies. During the period (eighteen months) that he was writing his third book the man of genius introduced Harrison to a critic, with the words: "You may rely on his judgment; the beggar is infallible."

While to the critic he said: "I tell you, this fellow can do things."

The critic was good to Harrison, who, as before said, was of an amiable disposition.

When he had finished his third book he dedicated it to the man of genius and called it "Summer."

"My dear fellow," wrote the man of genius, when he received his copy, "It is *good!* There is no more to be said about it; it *is* good! I read it with indescribable pleasure."

On the same day Harrison received a letter from the critic which contained the following: "Yes, it's undoubtedly an advance. It's not quite Art, but it's a great advance!"

Harrison was considerably encouraged. The same publisher brought out the book, and sold quite two hundred copies; but he wrote rather dolefully to Harrison, saying that the public demand seemed "almost exhausted." Recognising the fact that comparisons are odious, Harrison refrained from comparing the sale of the book with that of "In the Track of the Stars," in which he had shown such promise of "completely hitting the public taste." Indeed, about this time he began to have dreams of abandoning the sources of his private income and living the true literary life. He had not many reviews, and began his fourth book.

He was two years writing this "work," which he called "A Lost Man," and dedicated to the critic. He sent a presentation copy to the man of genius, from whom he received an almost immediate reply:

"My dear fellow, it is amazing, really amazing how you progress! Who would ever imagine you were the same man that wrote 'In the Track of the Stars'! Yet I pique myself on the fact that even in your first book I spotted that you could do things. Oh!—I wish I could write like you! 'A Lost Man' is wonderfully good."

The man of genius was quite sincere in these remarks, which he wrote after perusing the first six chapters. He never, indeed, actually finished reading the book—he felt so tired, as if Harrison had exhausted him—but he always alluded to it as "wonderfully good," just as if he really had finished it.

Harrison sent another copy to the critic, who wrote a genuinely warm letter, saying that he, Harrison, had "achieved" it at last. "This," he said, "is *art*. I doubt if you will ever do anything better than this. . . . I crown you."

Harrison at once commenced his fifth book.

He was more than three years upon this new "work," and called it "A Pilgrimage." There was a good deal of difficulty in getting it published. Two days after it appeared, however, the critic wrote to Harrison: "I cannot tell you," he said, "how very good I think your new book. It is perhaps stronger than 'A Lost Man,' perhaps more original. If anything it is too—I have not finished it yet, but I've written off at once to let you know."

As a matter of fact, he never finished the book. He could not—it was too——! "It's wonderfully good," he said, however, to his wife, and he made *her* read it.

Meanwhile, the man of genius wired saying: "Am going to write to you about your book. Positively am, but have lumbago and cannot hold pen."

Harrison never received any letter, but the critic received one saying: "Can you read it? I *can't*. Altogether over 'done.' "

Harrison was elated. His new publisher was not. He wrote in a peevish strain, saying there was *absolutely no sale*. Mr. Harrison must take care what he was doing or he would exhaust his public, and enclosing a solitary review, which said amongst other things: "This book may be very fine art, too fine altogether. *We* found it dull."

Harrison went abroad, and began his sixth book. He named it "The Consummation," and worked at it in hermit-like solitude; in it, for the first time, he satisfied himself. He wrote, as it were, with his heart's blood, with an almost bitter delight. And he often smiled to himself as he thought how with his first book he had so nearly hit the public taste; and how of his fourth the critic had said: "This is *art*. I doubt if you will ever do anything better than this." How far away they seemed! Ah! *this* book was indeed the "consummation" devoutly to be wished.

In the course of time he returned to England and took a cottage at Hampstead, and there he finished the book. The day after it was finished he took the manuscript and, going to a secluded spot on the top of the Heath, lay down on the grass to read it quietly through. He read three chapters, and, putting the remainder down sat with his head buried in his hands.

"Yes," he thought, "I *have* done it at last. *It is good,* wonderfully good!" and for two hours he sat like that, with his head in his hands. He had indeed exhausted his public. It was *too* good—*he could not read it himself!*

Returning to his cottage, he placed the manuscript in a drawer. He never wrote another word.

Dry September
William Faulkner

Through the bloody September twilight, aftermath of sixty-two rainless days, it had gone like fire in a dry grass—the rumor, the story, whatever it was. Something about Miss Minnie Cooper and a Negro. Attacked, insulted, frightened: none of them, gathered in the barbershop on that Saturday evening where the ceiling fan stirred, without freshening it, the vitiated air, sending back upon them, in recurrent surges of stale pomade and lotion, their own stale breath and odors, knew exactly what had happened.

"Except it wasn't Will Mayes," a barber said. He was a man of middle age; a thin, sand-colored man with a mild face, who was shaving a client. "I know Will Mayes. He's a good nigger. And I know Miss Minnie Cooper, too."

"What do you know about her?" a second barber said.

"Who is she?" the client said. "A girl?"

"No," the barber said. "She's about forty, I reckon. She ain't married. That's why I don't believe—"

"Believe hell!" a hulking youth in a sweat-stained silk shirt said. "Won't you take a white woman's word before a nigger's?"

"I don't believe Will Mayes did it," the barber said. "I know Will Mayes."

"Maybe you know who did it, then. Maybe you already got him out of town, you damn nigger-lover."

"I don't believe anybody did anything. I don't believe anything happened. I leave it to you fellows if them ladies that gets old without getting married don't have notions that a man can't—"

"Then you're a hell of a white man," the client said. He moved under the cloth. The youth had sprung to his feet.

"You don't?" he said. "Do you accuse a white woman of telling a lie?"

The barber held the razor poised above the half-risen client. He did not look around.

"It's this durn weather," another said. "It's enough to make any man do anything. Even to her."

Nobody laughed. The barber said in his mild, stubborn tone: "I ain't accusing nobody of nothing. I just know and you fellows know how a woman that never——"

"You damn nigger-lover!" the youth said.

"Shut up, Butch," another said. "We'll get the facts in plenty of time to act."

"Who is? Who's getting them?" the youth said. "Facts, hell! I—"

"You're a fine white man," the client said. "Ain't you?" In his frothy beard he looked like a desert-rat in the moving pictures. "You tell them, Jack," he said to the youth. "If they ain't any white men in this town, you can count on me, even if I ain't only a drummer and a stranger."

"That's right, boys," the barber said. "Find out the truth first. I know Will Mayes."

"Well, by God!" the youth shouted. "To think that a white man in this town—"

"Shut up, Butch," the second speaker said. "We got plenty of time."

The client sat up. He looked at the speaker. "Do you claim that anything excuses a nigger attacking a white woman? Do you mean to tell me that you're a white man and you'll stand for it? You better go back North where you come from. The South don't want your kind here."

"North what?" the second said. "I was born and raised in this town."

"Well, by God!" the youth said. He looked about with a strained, baffled gaze, as if he was trying to remember what it was he wanted to say or to do. He drew his sleeve across his sweating face. "Damn if I'm going to let a white woman—"

"You tell them, Jack," the drummer said. "By God, if they—"

The screen-door crashed open. A man stood in the floor, his feet apart and his heavy-set body poised easily. His white shirt was open at the throat; he wore a felt hat. His hot, bold glance swept the group. His name was Plunkett. He had commanded troops at the front in France and had been decorated for valor.

"Well," he said, "are you going to sit there and let a black son rape a white woman on the streets of Jefferson?"

Butch sprang up again. The silk of his shirt clung flat to his heavy shoulders. At each armpit was a dark half-moon. "That's what I been telling them! That's what I—"

"Did it really happen?" a third said. "This ain't the first man-scare she ever had, like Hawkshaw says. Wasn't there something about a man on the kitchen roof, watching her undress, about a year ago?"

"What?" the client said. "What's that?" The barber had been slowly forcing him back into the chair; he arrested himself reclining, his head lifted, the barber still pressing him down.

Plunkett whirled on the third speaker. "Happen? What the hell difference does it make? Are you going to let the black sons get away with it until one really does it?"

"That's what I'm telling them!" Butch shouted. He cursed, long and steady, pointless.

"Here, here," a fourth said. "Not so loud. Don't talk so loud."

"Sure," Plunkett said; "no talking necessary at all. I've done my talking. Who's with me?" He poised on the balls of his feet, roving his gaze.

The barber held the client's face down, the razor poised. "Find out the facts first, boys. I know Willy Mayes. It wasn't him. Let's get the sheriff and do this thing right."

Plunkett whirled upon him his furious, rigid face. The barber did not look away. They looked like men of different races. The other barbers had ceased also above their prone clients. "You mean to tell me," Plunkett said, "that you'd take a nigger's word before a white woman's? Why, you damn nigger-loving—"

The third rose and grasped Plunkett's arm; he too had been a soldier. "Now, now! Let's figure this thing out. Who knows anything about what really happened?"

"Figure out hell!" Plunkett jerked his arm free. "All that're with me get up from there. The ones that ain't—" He roved his gaze, dragging his sleeve across his face.

Three men rose. The client in the chair sat up. "Here," he said, jerking at the cloth around his neck; "get this rag off me. I'm with him. I don't live here, but, by God, if our mothers and wives and sisters—" He smeared the cloth over his face and flung it to the floor. Plunkett stood in the floor and cursed the others. Another rose and moved toward him. The remainder sat uncomfortably, not looking at one another, then one by one they rose and joined him.

The barber picked the cloth from the floor. He began to fold it neatly. "Boys, don't do that. Will Mayes never done it. I know."

"Come on," Plunkett said. He whirled. From his hip pocket protruded the butt of a heavy automatic pistol. They went out. The screen-door crashed behind them reverberant in the dead air.

The barber wiped the razor carefully and swiftly, and put it away, and ran to the rear, and took his hat from the wall. "I'll be back soon as I can," he said to the other barbers. "I can't let—" He went out, running. The two other barbers followed him to the door and caught it on the rebound, leaning out and looking up the street after him. The air was flat and dead. It had a metallic taste at the base of the tongue.

"What can he do?" the first said. The second one was saying "Jees Christ, Jees Christ" under his breath. "I'd just as lief be Will Mayes as Hawk, if he gets Plunkett riled."

"Jees Christ, Jees Christ," the second whispered.

"You reckon he really done it to her?" the first said.

II

She was thirty-eight or thirty-nine. She lived in a small frame house with her invalid mother and a thin, sallow, unflagging aunt, where each morning, between ten and eleven, she would appear on the porch in a lace-trimmed boudoir cap, to sit swinging in the porch swing until noon. After dinner she lay down for a while, until the afternoon began to cool. Then, in one of the three or four new voile dresses which she had each summer, she would go down-town to spend the afternoon in the stores with the other ladies, where they would handle the goods and haggle over prices in cold, immediate voices, without any intention of buying.

She was of comfortable people—not the best in Jefferson, but good people enough—and she was still on the slender side of ordinary-looking, with a bright, faintly haggard manner and dress. When she was young she had had a slender, nervous body and a sort of hard vivacity which had enabled her to ride for the time upon the crest of the town's social life as exemplified by the high-school party and church-social period of her contemporaries while still children enough to be un-class-conscious.

She was the last to realize that she was losing ground; that those among whom she had been a little brighter and louder flame than any other were beginning to learn the pleasure of snobbery—male—and retaliation—female. That was when her face began to wear that bright, haggard look. She still carried it to parties on shadowy porticos and summer lawns, like a mask or a flag, with that bafflement and furious repudiation of truth in her eyes. One evening at a party she heard a boy and two girls, all schoolmates, talking. She never accepted another invitation.

She watched the girls with whom she had grown up as they married and got houses and children, but no man ever called on her steadily until the children of the other girls had been calling her "aunty" for several years, the while their mothers told them in bright voices about how popular Minnie had been as a girl. Then the town began to see her driving on Sunday afternoons with the cashier in the bank. He was a widower of about forty—a high-colored man, smelling always faintly of the barbershop or of whiskey. He owned the first automobile in town, a red runabout; Minnie had the first motoring bonnet and veil the town ever saw. Then the town began to say: "Poor Minnie!" "But she is old enough to take care of herself," others said. That was when she first asked her schoolmates that the children call her "cousin" instead of "aunty."

It was twelve years now since she had been relegated into adultery by public opinion, and eight years since the cashier had gone to a Memphis bank, returning for one day each Christmas, which he spent at an annual bachelors' party in a hunting-club on the river. From behind their curtains the neighbors would see him pass, and during the across-the-street Christmas-day visiting they would tell her about him, about how well he looked, and how they heard that he was prospering in the city, watching with bright, secret eyes her haggard, bright face. Usually by that hour there would be the scent of whiskey on her breath. It was supplied her by a youth, a clerk at the soda-fountain: "Sure; I buy it for the old gal. I reckon she's entitled to a little fun."

Her mother kept to her room altogether now; the gaunt aunt ran the house. Against that background Minnie's bright dresses, her idle and empty days, had a quality of furious unreality. She went out in the evenings only with women now, neighbors, to the moving pictures. Each afternoon she dressed in one of the new dresses and went down-town alone, where her young cousins were already strolling in the late afternoons with their delicate, silken heads and thin, awkward arms and conscious hips, clinging to one another or shrieking and giggling with paired boys in the soda-fountain when she passed and went on along the serried stores, in the doors of which sitting and lounging men did not even follow her with their eyes any more.

III

The barber went swiftly up the street where the sparse lights, insect-swirled, glared in rigid and violent suspension in the lifeless air. The day had died in a pall of dust; above the darkened square, shrouded by the spent dust, the sky was clear as the inside of a brass bell. Below the east was a rumor of the twice-waxed moon.

When he overtook them Plunkett and three others were getting into a car parked in an alley. Plunkett stooped his thick head, peering out beneath the top. "Changed your mind, did you?" he said. "Damn good thing; by God, tomorrow when this town hears about how you talked tonight—"

"Now, now," the other ex-soldier said. "Hawkshaw's all right. Come on, Hawk; jump in!"

"Will Mayes never done it, boys," the barber said. "If anybody done it. Why, you all know well as I do there ain't any town where they got better niggers than us. And you know how a lady will kind of think things about men where there ain't any reason to, and Miss Minnie anyway—"

"Sure, sure," the soldier said. "We're just going to talk to him a little; that's all."

"Talk hell!" Butch said. "When we're done with the—"

"Shut up, for God's sake!" the soldier said. "Do you want everybody in town—"

"Tell them, by God!" Plunkett said. "Tell every one of the sons that'll let a white woman—"

"Let's go; let's go: here's the other car." The second car slid squealing out of a cloud of dust at the alley-mouth. Plunkett started his car and backed out and took the lead. Dust lay like fog in the street. The street lights hung nimbused as in water. They drove on out of town.

A rutted lane turned at right angles. Dust hung above it too, and above all the land. The dark bulk of the ice-plant, where the Negro Mayes was night-watchman, rose against the sky. "Better stop here, hadn't we?" the soldier said. Plunkett did not reply. He hurled the car up and slammed to a stop, the headlights glaring on the blank wall.

"Listen here, boys," the barber said; "if he's here, don't that prove he never done it? Don't it? If it was him, he would run. Don't you see he would?" The second car came up and stopped. Plunkett got down; Butch sprang down beside him. "Listen, boys," the barber said.

"Cut the lights off!" Plunkett said. The breathless darkness rushed down. There was no sound in it save their lungs as they sought air in the parched dust in which for two months they had lived; then the diminishing crunch of Plunkett's and Butch's feet, and a moment later, Plunkett's voice:

"Will! . . . Will!"

Below the east the wan hemorrhage of the moon increased. It heaved above the ridge, silvering the air, the dust, so that they seemed to breathe, live, in a bowl of molten lead. There was no sound of night-bird nor insect, no sound save their breathing and a faint ticking of contracting metal about the cars. Where their bodies touched one another they seemed to sweat dryly, for no more moisture came. "Christ!" a voice said; "let's get out of here."

But they didn't move until vague noises began to grow out of the darkness ahead; then they got out and waited tensely in the breathless dark. There was another sound: a blow, a hissing expulsion of breath and Plunkett cursing in undertone. They stood a moment longer, then they ran forward. They ran in a stumbling clump, as though they were fleeing something. "Kill him, kill the son!" a voice whispered. Plunkett flung them back.

"Not here," he said. "Get him into the car." They hauled the Negro up. "Kill him, kill the black son!" the voice murmured. They dragged the Negro to the car. The barber had waited beside the car. He could feel himself sweating and he knew he was going to be sick at the stomach.

"What is it, captains?" the Negro said. "I ain't done nothing. 'Fore God, Mr. John." Someone produced handcuffs. They worked busily about him as though he were a post, quiet, intent, getting in one another's way. He submitted to the handcuffs, looking swiftly and constantly from dim face to dim face. "Who's here, captains?" he said, leaning to peer into the faces until they could feel his breath and smell his sweaty reek. He spoke a name or two. "What you-all say I done, Mr. John?"

Plunkett jerked the car-door open. "Get in!" he said.

The Negro did not move. "What you-all going to do with me, Mr. John? I ain't done nothing. White folks, captains, I ain't done nothing: I swear 'fore God." He called another name.

"Get in!" Plunkett said. He struck the Negro. The others expelled their breath in a dry hissing and struck him with random blows, and he whirled and cursed them, and swept his manacled hands across their faces and slashed the barber upon the mouth, and the barber struck him also. "Get him in there," Plunkett said. They pushed at him. He ceased struggling and got in, and sat quietly as the others took their places. He sat between the barber and the soldier, drawing his limbs in so as not to touch them, his eyes going swiftly and constantly from face to face. Butch clung to the running-board. The car moved on. The barber nursed his mouth in his handkerchief.

"What's the matter, Hawk?" the soldier said.

"Nothing," the barber said. They regained the high road and turned away from town. The second car dropped back out of the dust. They went on, gaining speed; the final fringe of houses dropped behind.

"Goddam, he stinks!" the soldier said.

"We'll fix that," the man in front beside Plunkett said. On the running-board Butch cursed into the hot rush of air. The barber leaned suddenly forward and touched Plunkett's shoulder.

"Let me out, John."

"Jump out, nigger-lover," Plunkett said without turning his head. He drove swiftly. Behind them the sourceless lights of the second car glared in the dust. Presently Plunkett turned into a narrow road. It too was rutted in disuse. It led back to an old brick-kiln—a series of reddish mounds and weed-and-vine-choked vats without bottom. It had been used for pasture once, until one day the owner missed one of his mules. Although he prodded carefully in the vats with a long pole, he could not even find the bottom of them.

"John," the barber said.

"Jump out, then," Plunkett said, hurling the car along the ruts.

Beside the barber the Negro spoke:

"Mr. Henry."

The barber sat forward. The narrow tunnel of the road rushed up and past. Their motion was like an extinct furnace blast: cooler, but utterly dead. The car bounded from rut to rut.

"Mr. Henry," the Negro said.

The barber began to tug furiously at the door. "Look out, there!" the soldier said, but he had already kicked the door open and swung onto the running-board. The soldier leaned across the Negro and grasped at him, but he had already jumped. The car went on without checking speed.

The impetus hurled him crashing, through dust-sheathed weeds, into the ditch. Dust puffed about him, and in a thin, vicious crackling of sapless stems he lay choking and retching until the second car passed and died away. Then he rose and limped on until he reached the high road and turned toward town, brushing at his clothes with his hands. The moon was higher, riding high and clear of the dust at last, and after a while the town began to glare beneath the dust. He went on, limping. Presently he heard the cars and the glow of them grew in the dust behind him and he left the road and crouched again in the weeds until they passed. Plunkett's car came last now. There were four people in it and Butch was not on the running-board.

They went on; the dust swallowed them; the glare and the sound died away. The dust of them hung for a while, but soon the eternal dust absorbed it again. The barber climbed back onto the road and limped on toward town.

IV

As she dressed after supper, on that Saturday evening, her own flesh felt like fever. Her hands trembled among the hooks and eyes, and her eyes had a feverish look, and her hair swirled crisp and crackling under the comb. While she was still dressing, the friends called for her and sat while she donned her sheerest underthings and stockings and a new voile dress. "Do you feel strong enough to go out?" they said, their eyes bright too, with a dark glitter. "When you have had time to get over the shock, you must tell us what happened. What he said and did; everything."

In the leafed darkness, as they walked toward the square, she began to breathe deeply, something like a swimmer preparing to dive, until she ceased trembling, the four of them walking slowly because of the terrible heat and out of solicitude for her. But as they neared the square she began to tremble again, walking with her head up, her hands clinched at her sides, their voices about her murmurous, also with that feverish, glittering quality of their eyes.

They entered the square, she in the center of the group, fragile in her fresh dress. She was trembling worse. She walked slower and slower, as children eat ice-cream, her head up and her eyes bright in the haggard banner of her face, passing the hotel and the coatless drummers in chairs along the curb looking around at her: "That's the one: see? The one in pink in the middle." "Is that her? What did they do with the nigger? Did they—?" "Sure. He's all right." "All right, is he?" "Sure. He went on a little trip." Then the drug-store, where even the young men lounging in the doorway tipped their hats and followed with their eyes the motion of her hips and legs when she passed.

They went on, passing the lifted hats of the gentlemen, the suddenly ceased voices, protective, deferent. "Do you see?" the friends said. Their voices sounded like long hovering sighs of hissing exultation. "There's not a Negro on the square. Not one."

They reached the picture-show. It was like a miniature fairyland with its lighted lobby and colored lithographs of life caught in its terrible and beautiful mutations. Her lips began to tingle. In the dark, when the picture began, it would be all right; she could hold back the laughing so it would not waste away so fast and so soon. So she hurried on before the turning faces, the undertones of low astonishment, and they took their accustomed places where she could see the aisle against the silver glare and the young men and girls coming in two and two against it.

The lights flicked away; the screen glowed silver, and soon life began to unfold, beautiful and passionate and sad, while still the young men and girls entered, scented and sibilant in the half-dark, their paired backs in silhouette delicate and sleek, their slim, quick bodies awkward, divinely young, while beyond them the silver dream accumulated, inevitably on and on. She began to laugh. In trying to suppress it, it made more noise than ever; heads began to turn. Still laughing, her friends raised her and led her out, and she stood at the curb, laughing on a high, sustained note, until the taxi came up and they helped her in.

They removed the pink voile and the sheer underthings, and the stockings, and put her to bed, and cracked ice for her temples, and sent for the doctor. He was hard to locate, so they ministered to her with hushed ejaculations, renewing the ice and fanning her. While the ice was fresh and cold she stopped laughing and lay still for a time, moaning only a little. But soon the laughing welled again and her voice rose screaming.

"Shhhhhhhhhhh! Shhhhhhhhhhh!" they said, freshening the ice-pack, smoothing her hair, examining it for gray; "poor girl!" Then to one another: "Do you suppose anything really happened?" their eyes darkly aglitter, secret and passionate. "Shhhhhhhhhhh! Poor girl! Poor Minnie!"

V

It was midnight when Plunkett drove up to his neat new house. It was trim and fresh as a bird-cage and almost as small, with its clean green-and-white paint. He locked the car and mounted the porch and entered. His wife rose from a chair beside the reading-lamp. Plunkett stopped in the floor and stared at her until she looked down.

"Look at that clock!" he said, lifting his arm, pointing. She stood before him, her face lowered, a magazine in her hands. Her face was pale, strained, and weary-looking. "Haven't I told you about sitting up like this, waiting to see when I come in?"

"John!" she said. She laid the magazine down. Poised on the balls of his feet, he glared at her with his hot eyes, his sweating face.

"Didn't I tell you?" He went toward her. She looked up then. He caught her shoulder. She stood passive, looking at him.

"Don't, John. I couldn't sleep.... The heat; something. Please, John. You're hurting me."

"Didn't I tell you?" He released her and half struck, half flung her across the chair, and she lay there and watched him quietly as he left the room.

He went on through the house, ripping off his shirt, and on the dark, screen porch at the rear he stood and mopped his head and shoulders with the shirt and flung it away. He took the pistol from his hip and laid it on the table beside the bed, and sat on the bed and removed his shoes, and rose and slipped his trousers off. He was sweating again already, and he stooped and hunted furiously for the shirt. At last he found it and wiped his body again, and, with his body pressed against the dusty screen, he stood panting. There was no movement, no sound, not even an insect. The dark world seemed to lie stricken beneath the cold moon and the lidless stars.

COMMENTARY

by William Faulkner and Others

The incident upon which "Dry September" is built is probably derived from an actual lynching which occurred during Faulkner's boyhood and then was talked about so often that it became a virtual folktale. What follows is an account of the event told by an eyewitness who grew up in the Faulkner country.

At noon one day late in August, when I was a boy fourteen or fifteen, my father Linburn Cullen, who was then a deputy sheriff, was called by telephone and told that a Negro had just killed a woman out north of Oxford and that he should come to join a posse at once. Before leaving, my father instructed me and my older brother to stay at home and keep out of trouble. But as soon as he had gone, we picked up our shotguns and headed to the place where we thought the killer would travel as he fled to the nearest big thicket from the location of his crime.

As we drew near this place, we heard gunfire and saw a big Negro run across the railroad at Saddler's Crossing about two hundred yards ahead of us. At that time I could run like a foxhound and I never lost sight of him until he jumped into a vine-covered ditch leading into Toby Tubby Bottom. He was running along a valley between two hills, and my brother ran down one of them and I the other. In the valley there was one clear place which the criminal would have to cross before he reached the big thicket in Toby Tubby Bottom. I kept my eyes on this opening, and when I reached it, I knew that he was hiding somewhere back up the valley. The posse was coming on, so I knew that soon we would have him. When the Negro, Nelse Patton, saw that I knew he was hiding in the thicket, he attempted to come by me. I yelled for him to halt and when he kept on running, I shot at him with the squirrel shot from both barrels of my shot gun. This stopped him. . . .

I reloaded and ran up close to him and told him to put up his hands. He said to my brother, "Mr. Jenks, you knows I'se a good nigger."

"I know you're a good nigger," my brother said, "but get your hands up." . . .

After turning Nelse over to the sheriff, I went to the scene of the crime. Mrs. Mattie McMillan way lying in the dusty road about seventy-five yards from her home. . . . Her head had been severed from her body, all but the neck bone. . . .

The news spread over the county like wildfire, and that night at least two thousand people gathered around the jail. Judge Roan came out on the porch and made a plea to the crowd that they let the law take its course. Then Senator W. V. Sullivan made a fiery speech, telling the mob that they would be weaklings and cowards to let such a vicious beast live until morning. . . . After Senator Sullivan's speech, the mob began pitching us boys through the jail windows, and no guard in that jail would have dared shoot one of us. Soon a mob was inside. My brother and I held my father, and the sons of the other guards held theirs. They weren't hard to hold anyway. In this way we took over the lower floor of the jail.

From eight o'clock that night until two in the morning the mob worked to cut through the jail walls into the cells with sledge hammers and crowbars. . . . When the mob finally got through and broke the lock off the murderer's cell, Nelse had armed himself with a heavy iron coal-shovel handle. From a corner near the door, he fought like a tiger, seriously wounding three men. He was then shot to death and thrown out of the jail. Someone (I don't know who) cut his ears off, scalped him, cut his testicles out, tied a rope around his neck, tied him to a car, and dragged his body around the streets. Then they hanged him to a walnut-tree limb just outside the south entrance to the courthouse. They had torn his clothes off dragging him around, and my father bought a new pair of overalls and put them on him before the next morning.

Nelse Patton's crime and the lynching of Nelse are more widely known than anything else of this kind that ever happened in Lafayette County. William Faulkner was eleven years old at the time, and since he has spent most of his life in this community, he must have heard numerous stories about the Patton case. Faulkner has written about many lynchings in his books, and I believe that several of them are generally based on the story of Nelse Patton. . . .

The papers gave special attention to Senator Sullivan's role in the lynching. This is a quotation from the Jackson *Daily Clarion-Ledger*, of Thursday morning, September 10, 1908. Errors are again reproduced from the original. . . .

(Associated Press Report)

Memphis, Tenn. Sept. 9.—A special from Oxford, Miss., quotes former U. S. Senator W. V. Sullivan as follows, with reference to the lynching of last night:

"I led the mob which lynched Nelse Patton and I am proud of it."

"I directed every movement of the mob, and I did everything I could to see that he was lynched."

"Cut a white woman's throat? and a negro? Of course I wanted him lynched."

"I saw his body dangling from a tree this morning and I am glad of it."

"When I heard of the horrible crime, I started to work immediately to get a mob. I did all I could to raise one. I was at the jail last night and I heard Judge Roane advise against lynching. I got up immediately after and urged the mob to lynch Patton."

"I aroused the mob and directed them to storm the jail."

"I had my revolver, but did not use it. I gave it to a deputy sheriff and told him: Shoot Patton and shoot to kill."

"He used the revolver and shot. I suppose the bullets from my gun were some of those that killed the negro."

"I don't care what investigation is made, or what are the consequences. I am willing to stand them."

"I wouldn't mind standing the consequences any time for lynching a man who cut a white woman's throat. I will lead a mob in such a case any time."*

*John B. Cullen, in collaboration with Floyd C. Watkins, *Old Times in the Faulkner Country* (Chapel Hill, 1961), pp. 89–92, 97–98.

There are many differences of detail and conception between the actual event and the account in "Dry September." We must remember that the short story is a work of the imagination, that while the author is bound to certain realistic fact he is also free to manipulate it as is necessary for both the vision and design of his fiction. Faulkner himself speaks of the relationship between his work and the world—its people and facts—that helped produce his art. He makes clear that in his stories of southern violence he is not writing of specific people who live in a specific place. He is not writing of individuals who live in the deep south. On the contrary, he is trying to understand the nature of so-called civilized personalities who may live anywhere and who thirst after the blood of other human beings.

Once while visiting at the University of Virginia, Faulkner was asked a series of questions to which he answered. Both questions and answers are general; yet they have relevance to the understanding and interpretation of "Dry September." For that reason the dialogue is reproduced here.

Q. I'd like to ask if your people are derived principally from an area or region of Mississippi. . . .

A. I don't think that people are that different. I think there is not a great deal of difference between Southerners and Northerners, and Americans and Russians and Chinese. That I'm simply using the background, the color, the smells, the sounds that I am familiar with, but the people in my opinion are not that different. They could be anywhere. Of course they would wear different clothes, and their behavior might be a little awry from what it is in North Mississippi, but the behavior would be the same, they would have the same anguishes, the same hopes, and they—Russians or Chinese—would still want to be better than they are afraid they might be, and they would try to be better. . . .

Q. There are so many parallels of violence in your writings which suggest the actions of the Ku Klux Klan that I am curious to know why you have never mentioned it directly that I know of.

A. The spirit that moves a man to put on a sheet and burn sticks in your yard is pretty prevalent in Mississippi, but not all Mississippians wear the sheet and burn the sticks. That they scorn and hate and look with contempt on the people that do, but the same spirit, the same impulse is in them too, but they are going to use a different method from wearing a night-shirt and burning sticks. The Ku Klux Klan is the dull dreary minority. There's nothing dramatic enough in the Ku Klux Klan for me to have needed to use that in a story, though I can't say that some day I won't need to use it. . . .

Q. Sir, a few minutes ago you mentioned that people in your home town were looking into your books for familiar characters. Realizing that you've got a rich legacy in your experiences, but it seems to me that nowadays the modern novelist is writing merely thinly disguised autobiography. Which do you think is really more valuable from the sense of the arts, the disguised autobiography, or making it up from the whole cloth, as it were?

A. I would say that the writer has three sources, imagination, observation, and experience. He himself doesn't know how much of which he uses at any given moment because each of the sources themselves are not too important to him. That he is writing about people, and he uses his material from the three sources as the carpenter reaches into his lumber room and finds a board that fits the particular corner he's building. Of course, any writer, to begin with, is writing his own biography because he has discovered the world and then suddenly discovered that the world is important enough or moving enough or tragic enough to put down on paper or in music or on canvas, and at that time all he knows is what has happened to him because he has not developed his capacity to perceive, to draw conclusions, to have an insight into people. His only insight in it is into himself, and it's a biography because that's the only gauge he has to measure—is what he has experienced himself. As he gets older and works more, imagination is like any muscle, it improves with use. Imagination develops, his observations get shrewder as he gets older, as he writes, so that when he reaches his peak, his best years, when his work is best, he himself doesn't know and doesn't have time to bother and doesn't really care how much of what comes from each of these sources, that then he is writing about people, writing about the aspirations, the troubles, the anguishes, the courage, and the cowardice, the baseness and the splendor of man, of the human heart. . . .

Q. I was just wondering, if you have this—have a story, then your purpose is more producing something that's enjoyable to be read, but if it has a theme in it, in order to focus on the theme, in order to make the theme as fully developed—I should think you'd have to keep that in mind, keep what the—

A.   If I understand you right, in that case the message would be one of the craftsman's tools, that—well, that's perfectly valid. A message is one of his tools, just like the rhetoric, just like the punctuation. That's quite valid, but you don't write a story just to show your versatility with your tools. You write a story to tell about people, man in his constant struggle with his own heart, with the hearts of others, or with his environment. It's man in the ageless eternal struggles which we inherit and we go through as though they'd never happened before, shown for a moment in a dramatic instant of the furious motion of being alive, that's all any story is. You catch this fluidity which is human life and you focus a light on it and you stop it long enough for people to be able to see it.*

The Comforts of Home
Flannery O'Connor

Thomas withdrew to the side of the window and with his head between the wall and the curtain he looked down on the driveway where the car had stopped. His mother and the little slut were getting out of it. His mother emerged slowly, stolid and awkward, and then the little slut's long slightly bowed legs slid out, the dress pulled above the knees. With a shriek of laughter she ran to meet the dog, who bounded, overjoyed, shaking with pleasure, to welcome her. Rage gathered throughout Thomas's large frame with a silent ominous intensity, like a mob assembling.

It was now up to him to pack a suitcase, go to the hotel, and stay there until the house should be cleared.

*Faulkner in the University, ed. Frederick L. Gwynn and Joseph L. Blotner (Charlottesville, Virginia, 1959), pp. 87, 94, 102–3, 239.

He did not know where a suitcase was, he disliked to pack, he needed his books, his typewriter was not portable, he was used to an electric blanket, he could not bear to eat in restaurants. His mother, with her daredevil charity, was about to wreck the peace of the house.

The back door slammed and the girl's laugh shot up from the kitchen, through the back hall, up the stairwell and into his room, making for him like a bolt of electricity. He jumped to the side and stood glaring about him. His words of the morning had been unequivocal: "If you bring that girl back into this house, I leave. You can choose—her or me."

She had made her choice. An intense pain gripped his throat. It was the first time in his thirty-five years. . . . He felt a sudden burning moisture behind his eyes. Then he steadied himself, overcome by rage. On the contrary: she had not made any choice. She was counting on his attachment to his electric blanket. She would have to be shown.

The girl's laughter rang upward a second time and Thomas winced. He saw again her look of the night before. She had invaded his room. He had waked to find his door open and her in it. There was enough light from the hall to make her visible as she turned toward him. The face was like a comedienne's in a musical comedy—a pointed chin, wide apple cheeks and feline empty eyes. He had sprung out of his bed and snatched a straight chair and then he had backed her out the door, holding the chair in front of him like an animal trainer driving out a dangerous cat. He had driven her silently down the hall, pausing when he reached it to beat on his mother's door. The girl, with a gasp, turned and fled into the guest room.

In a moment his mother had opened her door and peered out apprehensively. Her face, greasy with whatever she put on it at night, was framed in pink rubber curlers. She looked down the hall where the girl had disappeared. Thomas stood before her, the chair still lifted in front of him as if he were about to quell another beast. "She tried to get in my room," he hissed, pushing in. "I woke up and she was trying to get in my room." He closed the door behind him and his voice rose in outrage. "I won't put up with this! I won't put up with it another day!"

His mother, backed by him to her bed, sat down on the edge of it. She had a heavy body on which sat a thin, mysteriously gaunt and incongruous head.

"I'm telling you for the last time," Thomas said, "I won't put up with this another day." There was an observable tendency in all of her actions. This was, with the best intentions in the world, to make a mockery of virtue, to pursue it with such a mindless intensity that everyone involved was made a fool of and virtue itself became ridiculous. "Not another day," he repeated.

His mother shook her head emphatically, her eyes still on the door.

Thomas put the chair on the floor in front of her and sat down on it. He leaned forward as if he were about to explain something to a defective child.

"That's just another way she's unfortunate," his mother said. "So awful, so awful. She told me the name of it but I forget what it is but it's something she can't help. Something she was born with. Thomas," she said and put her hand to her jaw, "suppose it were you?"

Exasperation blocked his windpipe. "Can't I make you see," he croaked, "that if she can't help herself you can't help her?"

His mother's eyes, intimate but untouchable, were the blue of great distances after sunset. "Nimpermaniac," she murmured.

"Nymphomaniac," he said fiercely. "She doesn't need to supply you with any fancy names. She's a moral moron. That's all you need to know. Born without the moral faculty—like somebody else would be born without a kidney or a leg. Do you understand?"

"I keep thinking it might be you," she said, her hand still on her jaw. "If it were you, how do you think I'd feel if nobody took you in? What if you were a nimpermaniac and not a brilliant smart person and you did what you couldn't help and . . . ."

Thomas felt a deep unbearable loathing for himself as if he were turning slowly into the girl.

"What did she have on?" she asked abruptly, her eyes narrowing.

"Nothing!" he roared. "Now will you get her out of here!"

"How can I turn her out in the cold?" she said. "This morning she was threatening to kill herself again."

"Send her back to jail," Thomas said.

"I would not send *you* back to jail, Thomas," she said.

He got up and snatched the chair and fled the room while he was still able to control himself.

Thomas loved his mother. He loved her because it was his nature to do so, but there were times when he could not endure her love for him. There were times when it became nothing but pure idiot mystery and he sensed about him forces, invisible currents entirely out of his control. She proceeded always from the tritest of considerations—it was the *nice thing to do*—into the most foolhardy engagements with the devil, whom, of course, she never recognized.

The devil for Thomas was only a manner of speaking, but it was a manner appropriate to the situations his mother got into. Had she been in any degree intellectual, he could have proved to her from early Christian history that no excess of virtue is justified, that a moderation of good produces likewise a moderation in evil, that if Antony of Egypt had stayed at home and attended to his sister, no devils would have plagued him.

Thomas was not cynical and so far from being opposed to virtue, he saw it as the principle of order and the only thing that makes life bearable. His own life was made bearable by the fruits of his mother's saner virtues—by the well-regulated house she kept and the excellent meals she served. But when virtue got out of hand with her, as now, a sense of devils grew upon him, and these were not mental quirks in himself or the old lady, they were denizens with personalities, present though not visible, who might any moment be expected to shriek or rattle a pot.

The girl had landed in the county jail a month ago on a bad check charge and his mother had seen her picture in the paper. At the breakfast table she had gazed at it for a long time and then passed it over the coffee pot to him. "Imagine," she said, "only nineteen years old and in that filthy jail. And she doesn't look like a bad girl."

Thomas glanced at the picture. It showed the face of a shrewd ragamuffin. He observed that the average age for criminality was steadily lowering.

"She looks like a wholesome girl," his mother said.

"Wholesome people don't pass bad checks," Thomas said.

"You don't know what you'd do in a pinch."

"I wouldn't pass a bad check," Thomas said.

"I think," his mother said, "I'll take her a little box of candy."

If then and there he had put his foot down, nothing else would have happened. His father, had he been living, would have put his foot down at that point. Taking a box of candy was her favorite nice thing to do. When anyone within her social station moved to town, she called and took a box of candy; when any of her friend's children had babies or won a scholarship, she called and took a box of candy; when an old person broke his hip, she was at his bedside with a box of candy. He had been amused at the idea of her taking a box of candy to the jail.

He stood now in his room with the girl's laugh rocketing away in his head and cursed his amusement.

When his mother returned from the visit to the jail, she had burst into his study without knocking and had collapsed full-length on his couch, lifting her small swollen feet up on the arm of it. After a moment, she recovered herself enough to sit up and put a newspaper under them. Then she fell back again. "We don't know how the other half lives," she said.

Thomas knew that though her conversation moved from cliché to cliché there were real experiences behind them. He was less sorry for the girl's being in jail than for his mother having to see her there. He would have spared her all unpleasant sights. "Well," he said and put away his journal, "you had better forget it now. The girl has ample reason to be in jail."

"You can't imagine what all she's been through," she said, sitting up again, "listen." The poor girl, Star, had been brought up by a stepmother with three children of her own, one an almost grown boy who had taken advantage of her in such dreadful ways that she had been forced to run away and find her real mother. Once found, her real mother had sent her to various boarding schools to get rid of her. At each of these she had been forced to run away by the presence of perverts and sadists so monstrous that their acts defied description. Thomas could tell that his mother had not been spared the details that she was sparing him. Now and again when she spoke vaguely, her voice shook and he could tell that she was remembering some horror that had been put to her graphically. He had hoped that in a few days the memory of all this would wear off, but it did not. The next day she returned to the jail with Kleenex and cold-cream and a few day later, she announced that she had consulted a lawyer.

It was at these times that Thomas truly mourned the death of his father though he had not been able to endure him in life. The old man would have had none of this foolishness. Untouched by useless compassion, he would (behind her back) have pulled the necessary strings with his crony, the sheriff, and the girl would have been packed off to the state penitentiary to serve her time. He had always been engaged in some enraged action until one morning when (with an angry glance at his wife as if she alone were responsible) he had dropped dead at the breakfast table. Thomas had inherited his father's reason without ruthlessness and his mother's love of good without her tendency to pursue it. His plan for all practical action was to wait and see what developed.

The lawyer found that the story of the repeated atrocities was for the most part untrue, but when he explained to her that the girl was a psychopathic personality, not insane enough for the asylum, not criminal enough for the jail, not stable enough for society, Thomas's mother was more deeply affected than ever. The girl readily admitted that her story was untrue on account of her being a congenital liar; she lied, she said, because she was insecure. She had passed through the hands of several psychiatrists who had put the finishing touches to her education. She knew there was no hope for her. In the presence of such an affliction as this, his mother seemed bowed down by some painful mystery that nothing would make endurable but a redoubling of effort. To his annoyance, she appeared to look on *him* with compassion, as if her hazy charity no longer made distinctions.

A few days later she burst in and said that the lawyer had got the girl paroled—to her.

Thomas rose from his Morris chair, dropping the review he had been reading. His large bland face contracted in anticipated pain. "You are not," he said, "going to bring that girl here!"

"No, no," she said, "calm yourself, Thomas." She had managed with difficulty to get the girl a job in a pet shop in town and a place to board with a crotchety old lady of her acquaintance. People were not kind. They did not put themselves in the place of someone like Star who had everything against her.

Thomas sat down again and retrieved his review. He seemed just to have escaped some danger which he did not care to make clear to himself. "Nobody can tell you anything," he said, "but in a few days that girl will have left town, having got what she could out of you. You'll never hear from her again."

Two nights later he came home and opened the parlor door and was speared by a shrill depthless laugh. His mother and the girl sat close to the fireplace where the gas logs were lit. The girl gave the immediate impression of being physically crooked. Her hair was cut like a dog's or an elf's and she was dressed in the latest fashion. She was training on him a long familiar sparkling stare that turned after a second into an intimate grin.

"Thomas!" his mother said, her voice firm with the injunction not to bolt, "this is Star you've heard so much about. Star is going to have supper with us."

The girl called herself Star Drake. The lawyer had found that her real name was Sarah Ham.

Thomas neither moved nor spoke but hung in the door in what seemed a savage perplexity. Finally he said, "How do you do, Sarah," in a tone of such loathing that he was shocked at the sound of it. He reddened, feeling it beneath him to show contempt for any creature so pathetic. He advanced into the room, determined at least on a decent politeness and sat down heavily in a straight chair.

"Thomas writes history," his mother said with a threatening look at him. "He's president of the local Historical Society this year."

The girl leaned forward and gave Thomas an even more pointed attention. "Fabulous!" she said in a throaty voice.

"Right now Thomas is writing about the first settlers in this county," his mother said.

"Fabulous!" the girl repeated.

Thomas by an effort of will managed to look as if he were alone in the room.

"Say, you know who he looks like?" Star asked, her head on one side, taking him in at an angle.

"Oh some one very distinguished!" his mother said archly.

"This cop I saw in the movie I went to last night," Star said.

"Star," his mother said, "I think you ought to be careful about the kind of movies you go to. I think you ought to see only the best ones. I don't think crime stories would be good for you."

"Oh this was a crime-does-not-pay," Star said, "and I swear this cop looked exactly like him. They were always putting something over on the guy. He would look like he couldn't stand it a minute longer or he would blow up. He was a riot. And not bad looking," she added with an appreciative leer at Thomas.

"Star," his mother said, "I think it would be grand if you developed a taste for music."

Thomas sighed. His mother rattled on and the girl, paying no attention to her, let her eyes play over him. The quality of her look was such that it might have been her hands, resting now on his knees, now on his neck. Her eyes had a mocking glitter and he knew that she was well aware he could not stand the sight of her. He needed nothing to tell him he was in the presence of the very stuff of corruption, but blameless corruption because there was no responsible faculty behind it. He was looking at the most unendurable form of innocence. Absently he asked himself what the attitude of God was to this, meaning if possible to adopt it.

His mother's behavior throughout the meal was so idiotic that he could barely stand back to look at her and since he could less stand to look at Sarah Ham, he fixed on the sideboard across the room a continuous gaze of disapproval and disgust. Every remark of the girl's his mother met as if it deserved serious attention. She advanced several plans for the wholesome use of Star's spare time. Sarah Ham paid no more attention to this advice than if it came from a parrot. Once when Thomas inadvertently looked in her direction, she winked. As soon as he had swallowed the last spoonful of dessert, he rose and muttered, "I have to go, I have a meeting."

"Thomas," his mother said, "I want you to take Star home on your way. I don't want her riding in taxis by herself at night."

For a moment Thomas remained furiously silent. Then he turned and left the room. Presently he came back with a look of obscure determination on his face. The girl was ready, meekly waiting at the parlor door. She cast up at him a great look of admiration and confidence. Thomas did not offer his arm but she took it anyway and moved out of the house and down the steps, attached to what might have been a miraculously moving monument.

"Be good!" his mother called.

Sarah Ham snickered and poked him in the ribs.

While getting his coat he had decided that this would be his opportunity to tell the girl that unless she ceased to be a parasite on his mother, he would see to it, personally, that she was returned to jail. He would let her know that he understood what she was up to, that he was not an innocent and that there were certain things he would not put up with. At his desk, pen in hand, none was more articulate than Thomas. As soon as he found himself shut into the car with Sarah Ham, terror seized his tongue.

She curled her feet up under her and said, "Alone at last," and giggled.

Thomas swerved the car away from the house and drove fast toward the gate. Once on the highway, he shot forward as if he were being pursued.

"Jesus!" Sarah Ham said, swinging her feet off the seat, "where's the fire?"

Thomas did not answer. In a few seconds he could feel her edging closer. She stretched, eased nearer, and finally hung her hand limply over his shoulder. "Tomsee doesn't like me," she said, "but I think he's fabulously cute."

Thomas covered the three and a half miles into town in a little over four minutes. The light at the first intersection was red but he ignored it. The old woman lived three blocks beyond. When the car screeched to a halt at the place, he jumped out and ran around to the girl's door and opened it. She did not move from the car and Thomas was obliged to wait. After a moment one leg emerged, then her small white crooked face appeared and stared up at him. There was something about the look of it that suggested blindness but it was the blindness of those who don't know that they cannot see. Thomas was curiously sickened. The empty eyes moved over him. "Nobody likes me," she said in a sullen tone. "What if you were me and I couldn't stand to ride you three miles?"

"My mother likes you," he muttered.

"Her!" the girl said. "She's just about seventy-five years behind the times!"

Breathlessly Thomas said, "If I find you bothering her again, I'll have you put back in jail." There was a dull force behind his voice though it came out barely above a whisper.

"You and who else?" she said and drew back in the car as if now she did not intend to get out at all. Thomas reached into it, blindly grasped the front of her coat, pulled her out by it and released her. Then he lunged back to the car and sped off. The other door was still hanging open and her laugh, bodiless but real, bounded up the street as if it were about to jump in the open side of the car and ride away with him. He reached over and slammed the door and then drove toward home, too angry to attend his meeting. He intended to make his mother well aware of his displeasure. He intended to leave no doubt in her mind. The voice of his father rasped in his head.

Numbskull, the old man said, put your foot down now. Show her who's boss before she shows you.

But when Thomas reached home, his mother, wisely, had gone to bed.

The next morning he appeared at the breakfast table, his brow lowered and the thrust of his jaw indicating that he was in a dangerous humor. When he intended to be determined, Thomas began like a bull that, before charging, backs with his head lowered and paws the ground. "All right now listen," he began, yanking out his chair and sitting down, "I have something to say to you about that girl and I don't intend to say it but once." He drew his breath. "She's nothing but a little slut. She makes fun of you behind your back. She means to get everything she can out of you and you are nothing to her."

His mother looked as if she too had spent a restless night. She did not dress in the morning but wore her bathrobe and a grey turban around her head, which gave her face a disconcerting omniscient look. He might have been breakfasting with a sibyl.

"You'll have to use canned cream this morning," she said, pouring his coffee. "I forgot the other."

"All right, did you hear me?" Thomas growled.

"I'm not deaf," his mother said and put the pot back on the trivet. "I know I'm nothing but an old bag of wind to her."

"Then why do you persist in this foolhardy . . . ."

"Thomas," she said, and put her hand to the side of her face, "it might be . . . ."

"It's not me!" Thomas said, grasping the table leg at his knee.

She continued to hold her face, shaking her head slightly. "Think of all you have," she began. "All the comforts of home. And morals, Thomas. No bad inclinations, nothing bad you were born with."

Thomas began to breathe like some one who feels the onset of asthma. "You are not logical," he said in a limp voice. "*He* would have put his foot down."

The old lady stiffened. "You," she said, "are not like him."

Thomas opened his mouth silently.

"However," his mother said, in a tone of such subtle accusation that she might have been taking back the compliment, "I won't invite her back again since you're so dead set against her."

"I am not set against her," Thomas said. "I am set against your making a fool of yourself."

As soon as he left the table and closed the door of his study on himself, his father took up a squatting position in his mind. The old man had had the countryman's ability to converse squatting, though he was no countryman but had been born and brought up in the city and only moved to a smaller place later to exploit his talents. With steady skill he had made them think him one of them. In the midst of a conversation on the courthouse lawn, he would squat and his two or three companions would squat with him with no break in the surface of the talk. By gesture he had lived his lie; he had never deigned to tell one.

Let her run over you, he said. You ain't like me. Not enough to be a man.

Thomas began vigorously to read and presently the image faded. The girl had caused a disturbance in the depths of his being, somewhere out of the reach of his power of analysis. He felt as if he had seen a tornado pass a hundred yards away and had an intimation that it would turn again and head directly for him. He did not get his mind firmly on his work until mid-morning.

Two nights later, his mother and he were sitting in the den after their supper, each reading a section of the evening paper, when the telephone began to ring with the brassy intensity of a fire alarm. Thomas reached for it. As soon as the receiver was in his hand, a shrill female voice screamed into the room, "Come get this girl! Come get her! Drunk! Drunk in my parlor and I won't have it! Lost her job and come back here drunk! I won't have it!"

His mother leapt up and snatched the receiver.

The ghost of Thomas's father rose before him. Call the sheriff, the old man prompted. "Call the sheriff," Thomas said in a loud voice. "Call the sheriff to go there and pick her up."

"We'll be right there," his mother was saying. "We'll come and get her right away. Tell her to get her things together."

"She ain't in no condition to get nothing together," the voice screamed. "You shouldn't have put something like her off on me! My house is respectable!"

"Tell her to call the sheriff," Thomas shouted.

His mother put the receiver down and looked at him. "I wouldn't turn a dog over to that man," she said.

Thomas sat in the chair with his arms folded and looked fixedly at the wall.

"Think of the poor girl, Thomas," his mother said, "with nothing. Nothing. And we have everything."

When they arrived, Sarah Ham was slumped spraddle-legged against the banister on the boarding house front-steps. Her tam was down on her forehead where the old woman had slammed it and her clothes were bulging out of her suitcase where the old woman had thrown them in. She was carrying on a drunken conversation with herself in a low personal tone. A streak of lipstick ran up one side of her face. She allowed herself to be guided by his mother to the car and put in the back seat without seeming to know who the rescuer was. "Nothing to talk to all day but a pack of goddamned parakeets," she said in a furious whisper.

Thomas, who had not got out of the car at all, or looked at her after the first revolted glance, said, "I'm telling you, once and for all, the place to take her is the jail."

His mother, sitting on the back seat, holding the girl's hand, did not answer.

"All right, take her to the hotel," he said.

"I cannot take a drunk girl to a hotel, Thomas," she said. "You know that."

"Then take her to a hospital."

"She doesn't need a jail or a hotel or a hospital," his mother said, "she needs a home."

"She does not need mine," Thomas said.

"Only for tonight, Thomas," the old lady sighed. "Only for tonight."

Since then eight days had passed. The little slut was established in the guest room. Every day his mother set out to find her a job and a place to board, and failed, for the old woman had broadcast a warning. Thomas kept to his room or the den. His home was to him home, workshop, church, as personal as the shell of a turtle and as necessary. He could not believe that it could be violated in this way. His flushed face had a constant look of stunned outrage.

As soon as the girl was up in the morning, her voice throbbed out in a blues song that would rise and waver, then plunge low with insinuations of passion about to be satisfied and Thomas, at his desk, would lunge up and begin frantically stuffing his ears with Kleenex. Each time he started from one room to another, one floor to another, she would be certain to appear. Each time he was half way up or down the stairs, she would either meet him and pass, cringing coyly, or go up or down behind him, breathing small tragic spearmint-flavored sighs. She appeared to adore Thomas's repugnance to her and to draw it out of him every chance she got as if it added delectably to her martyrdom.

The old man—small, wasp-like, in his yellowed panama hat, his seersucker suit, his pink carefully-soiled shirt, his small string tie—appeared to have taken up his station in Thomas's mind and from there, usually squatting, he shot out the same rasping suggestion every time the boy paused from his forced studies. Put your foot down. Go to see the sheriff.

The sheriff was another edition of Thomas's father except that he wore a checkered shirt and a Texas type hat and was ten years younger. He was as easily dishonest, and he had genuinely admired the old man. Thomas, like his mother, would have gone far out of his way to avoid his glassy pale blue gaze. He kept hoping for another solution, for a miracle.

With Sarah Ham in the house, meals were unbearable.

"Tomsee doesn't like me," she said the third or fourth night at the supper table and cast her pouting gaze across at the large rigid figure of Thomas, whose face was set with the look of a man trapped by insufferable odors. "He doesn't want me here. Nobody wants me anywhere."

"Thomas's name is Thomas," his mother interrupted. "Not Tomsee."

"I made Tomsee up," she said. "I think it's cute. He hates me."

"Thomas does not hate you," his mother said. "We are not the kind of people who hate," she added, as if this were an imperfection that had been bred out of them generations ago.

"Oh, I know when I'm not wanted," Sarah Ham continued. "They didn't even want me in jail. If I killed myself I wonder would God want me?"

"Try it and see," Thomas muttered.

The girl screamed with laughter. Then she stopped abruptly, her face puckered and she began to shake. "The best thing to do," she said, her teeth clattering, "is to kill myself. Then I'll be out of everybody's way. I'll go to hell and be out of God's way. And even the devil won't want me. He'll kick me out of hell, not even in hell . . . ." she wailed.

Thomas rose, picked up his plate and knife and fork and carried them to the den to finish his supper. After that, he had not eaten another meal at the table but had had his mother serve him at his desk. At these meals, the old man was intensely present to him. He appeared to be tipping backwards in his chair, his thumbs beneath his galluses, while he said such things as, She never ran me away from my own table.

A few night later, Sarah Ham slashed her wrists with a paring knife and had hysterics. From the den where he was closeted after supper, Thomas heard a shriek, then a series of screams, then his mother's scurrying footsteps through the house. He did not move. His first instant of hope that the girl had cut her throat faded as he realized she could not have done it and continue to scream the way she was doing. He returned to his journal and presently the screams subsided. In a moment his mother burst in with his coat and hat. "We have to take her to the hospital," she said. "She tried to do away with herself. I have a tourniquet on her arm. Oh Lord, Thomas," she said, "imagine being so low you'd do a thing like that!"

Thomas rose woodenly and put on his hat and coat. "We will take her to the hospital," he said, "and we will leave her there."

"And drive her to despair again?" the old lady cried. "Thomas!"

Standing in the center of his room now, realizing that he had reached the point where action was inevitable, that he must pack, that he must leave, that he must go, Thomas remained immovable.

His fury was directed not at the little slut but at his mother. Even though the doctor had found that she had barely damaged herself and had raised the girl's wrath by laughing at the tourniquet and putting only a streak of iodine on the cut, his mother could not get over the incident. Some new weight of sorrow seemed to have been thrown across her shoulders, and not only Thomas, but Sarah Ham was infuriated by this, for it appeared to be a general sorrow that would have found another object no matter what good fortune came to either of them. The experience of Sarah Ham had plunged the old lady into mourning for the world.

The morning after the attempted suicide, she had gone through the house and collected all the knives and scissors and locked them in a drawer. She emptied a bottle of rat poison down the toilet and took up the roach tablets from the kitchen floor. Then she came to Thomas's study and said in a whisper, "Where is that gun of his? I want to lock it up."

"The gun is in my drawer," Thomas roared, "and I will not lock it up. If she shoots herself, so much the better!"

"Thomas," his mother said, "she'll hear you!"

"Let her hear me!" Thomas yelled. "Don't you know she has no intention of killing herself? Don't you know her kind never kill themselves? Don't you...."

His mother slipped out the door and closed it to silence him and

Sarah Ham's laugh, quite close in the hall, came rattling into his room. "Tomsee'll find out. I'll kill myself and then he'll be sorry he wasn't nice to me. I'll use his own lil gun, his own lil ol' pearl-handled revol-lervuh!" she shouted and let out a long tormented-sounding laugh in imitation of a movie monster.

Thomas ground his teeth. He pulled out his desk drawer and felt for the pistol. It was an inheritance from the old man, whose opinion it had been that every house should contain a loaded gun. He had discharged two bullets one night into the side of a prowler, but Thomas had never shot anything. He had no fear that the girl would use the gun on herself and he closed the drawer. Her kind clung tenaciously to life and were able to wrest some histrionic advantage from every moment.

Several ideas for getting rid of her had entered his head but each of these had been suggestions whose moral tone indicated that they had come from a mind akin to his father's, and Thomas had rejected them. He could not get the girl locked up again until she did something illegal. The old man would have been able with no qualms at all to get her drunk and send her out on the highway in his car, meanwhile notifying the highway patrol of her presence on the road, but Thomas considered this below his moral stature. Suggestions continued to come to him, each more outrageous than the last.

He had not the vaguest hope that the girl would get the gun and shoot herself, but that afternoon when he looked in the drawer, the gun was gone. His study locked from the inside, not the out. He cared nothing about the gun, but the thought of Sarah Ham's hands sliding among his papers infuriated him. Now even his study was contaminated. The only place left untouched by her was his bedoom.

That night she entered it.

In the morning at breakfast, he did not eat and did not sit down. He stood beside his chair and delivered his ultimatum while his mother sipped her coffee as if she were both alone in the room and in great pain. "I have stood this," he said, "for as long as I am able. Since I see plainly that you care nothing about me, about my peace or comfort or working conditions, I am about to take the only step open to me. I will give you one more day. If you bring the girl back into this house this afternoon, I leave. You can choose—her or me."

He had more to say but at that point his voice cracked and he left.

At ten o'clock his mother and Sarah Ham left the house.

At four he heard the car wheels on the gravel and rushed to the window. As the car stopped, the dog stood up, alert, shaking.

He seemed unable to take the first step that would set him walking to the closet in the hall to look for the suitcase. He was like a man handed a knife and told to operate on himself if he wished to live. His huge hands clenched helplessly. His expression was a turmoil of indecision and outrage. His pale blue eyes seemed to sweat in his broiling face. He closed them for a moment and on the back of his lids, his father's image leered at him. Idiot! the old man hissed, idiot! The criminal slut stole your gun! See the sheriff! See the sheriff!

It was a moment before Thomas opened his eyes. He seemed newly stunned. He stood where he was for at least three minutes, then he turned slowly like a large vessel reversing its direction and faced the door. He stood there a moment longer, then he left, his face set to see the ordeal through.

He did not know where he would find the sheriff. The man made his own rules and kept his own hours. Thomas stopped first at the jail where his office was, but he was not in it. He went to the courthouse and was told by a clerk that the sheriff had gone to barbershop across the street. "Yonder's the deppity," the clerk said and pointed out the window to the large figure of a man in a checkered shirt, who was leaning against the side of a police car, looking into space.

"It has to be the sheriff," Thomas said and left for the barbershop. As little as he wanted anything to do with the sheriff, he realized that the man was at least intelligent and not simply a mound of sweating flesh.

The barber said the sheriff had just left. Thomas started back to the courthouse and as he stepped on to the sidewalk from the street, he saw a lean, slightly stooped figure gesticulating angrily at the deputy.

Thomas approached with an aggressiveness brought on by nervous agitation. He stopped abruptly three feet away and said in an over-loud voice, "Can I have a word with you?" without adding the sheriff's name, which was Farebrother.

Farebrother turned his sharp creased face just enough to take Thomas in, and the deputy did likewise, but neither spoke. The sheriff removed a very small piece of cigaret from his lip and dropped it at his feet. "I told you what to do," he said to the deputy. Then he moved off with a slight nod that indicated Thomas could follow him if he wanted to see him. The deputy slunk around the front of the police car and got inside.

Farebrother, with Thomas following, headed across the court-house square and stopped beneath a tree that shaded a quarter of the front lawn. He waited, leaning slightly forward, and lit another cigaret.

Thomas began to blurt out his business. As he had not had time to prepare his words, he was barely coherent. By repeating the same thing over several times, he managed at length to get out what he wanted to say. When he finished, the sheriff was still leaning slightly forward, at an angle to him, his eyes on nothing in particular. He remained that way without speaking.

Thomas began again, slower and in a lamer voice, and Farebrother let him continue for some time before he said, "We had her oncet." He then allowed himself a slow, creased, all-knowing, quarter smile.

"I had nothing to do with that," Thomas said. "That was my mother."

Farebrother squatted.

"She was trying to help the girl," Thomas said. "She didn't know she couldn't be helped."

"Bit off more than she could chew, I reckon," the voice below him mused.

"She has nothing to do with this," Thomas said. "She doesn't know I'm here. The girl is dangerous with that gun."

"He," the sheriff said, "never let anything grow under his feet. Particularly nothing a woman planted."

"She might kill somebody with that gun," Thomas said weakly, looking down at the round top of the Texas type hat.

There was a long time of silence.

"Where's she got it?" Farebrother asked.

"I don't know. She sleeps in the guest room. It must be in there, in her suitcase probably," Thomas said.

Farebrother lapsed into silence again.

"You could come search the guest room," Thomas said in a strained voice. "I can go home and leave the latch off the front door and you can come in quietly and go upstairs and search her room."

Farebrother turned his head so that his eyes looked boldly at Thomas's knees. "You seem to know how it ought to be done," he said. "Want to swap jobs?"

Thomas said nothing because he could not think of anything to say, but he waited doggedly. Farebrother removed the cigaret butt from his lips and dropped it on the grass. Beyond him on the court-house porch a group of loiterers who had been leaning at the left of the door moved over to the right where a patch of sunlight had settled. From one of the upper windows a crumpled piece of paper blew out and drifted down.

"I'll come along about six," Farebrother said. "Leave the latch off the door and keep out of my way—yourself and them two women too."

Thomas let out a rasping sound of relief meant to be "Thanks," and struck off across the grass like some one released. The phrase, "them two women," stuck like a burr in his brain—the subtlety of the insult to his mother hurting him more than any of Farebrother's references to his own incompetence. As he got into his car, his face suddenly flushed. Had he delivered his mother over to the sheriff— to be a butt for the man's tongue? Was he betraying her to get rid of the little slut? He saw at once that this was not the case. He was doing what he was doing for her own good, to rid her of a parasite that would ruin their peace. He started his car and drove quickly home but once he had turned in the driveway, he decided it would be better to park some distance from the house and go quietly in by the back door. He parked on the grass and on the grass walked in a circle toward the rear of the house. The sky was lined with mustard-colored streaks. The dog was asleep on the back doormat. At the approach of his master's step, he opened one yellow eye, took him in, and closed it again.

Thomas let himself into the kitchen. It was empty and the house was quiet enough for him to be aware of the loud ticking of the kitchen clock. It was a quarter to six. He tiptoed hurriedly through the hall to the front door and took the latch off it. Then he stood for a moment listening. From behind the closed parlor door, he heard his mother snoring softly and presumed that she had gone to sleep while reading. On the other side of the hall, not three feet from his study, the little slut's black coat and red pocketbook were slung on a chair. He heard water running upstairs and decided she was taking a bath.

He went into his study and sat down at his desk to wait, noting with distaste that every few moments a tremor ran through him. He sat for a minute or two doing nothing. Then he picked up a pen and began to draw squares on the back of an envelope that lay before him. He looked at his watch. It was eleven minutes to six. After a moment he idly drew the center drawer of the desk out over his lap. For a moment he stared at the gun without recognition. Then he gave a yelp and leaped up. She had put it back!

Idiot! his father hissed, idiot! Go plant it in her pocketbook. Don't just stand there. Go plant it in her pocketbook!

Thomas stood staring at the drawer.

Moron! the old man fumed. Quick while there's time! Go plant it in her pocketbook.

Thomas did not move.

Imbecile! his father cried.

Thomas picked up the gun.

Make haste, the old man ordered.

Thomas started forward, holding the gun away from him. He opened the door and looked at the chair. The black coat and red pocketbook were lying on it almost within reach.

Hurry up, you fool, his father said.

From behind the parlor door the almost audible snores of his mother rose and fell. They seemed to mark an order of time that had nothing to do with the instants left to Thomas. There was no other sound.

Quick, you imbecile, before she wakes up, the old man said.

The snores stopped and Thomas heard the sofa springs groan. He grabbed the red pocketbook. It had a skin-like feel to his touch and as it opened, he caught an unmistakable odor of the girl. Wincing, he thrust in the gun and then drew back. His face burned an ugly dull red.

"What is Tomsee putting in my purse?" she called and her pleased laugh bounced down the staircase. Thomas whirled.

She was at the top of the stair, coming down in the manner of a fashion model, one bare leg and then the other thrusting out the front of her kimona in a definite rhythm. "Tomsee is being naughty," she said in a throaty voice. She reached the bottom and cast a possessive leer at Thomas whose face was now more grey than red. She reached out, pulled the bag open with her finger and peered at the gun.

His mother opened the parlor door and looked out.

"Tomsee put his pistol in my bag!" the girl shrieked.

"Ridiculous," his mother said, yawning. "What would Thomas want to put his pistol in your bag for?"

Thomas stood slightly hunched, his hands hanging helplessly at the wrists as if he had just pulled them up out of a pool of blood.

"I don't know what for," the girl said, "but he sure did it," and she proceeded to walk around Thomas, her hands on her hips, her neck thrust forward and her intimate grin fixed on him fiercely. All at once her expression seemed to open as the purse had opened when Thomas touched it. She stood with her head cocked on one side in an attitude of disbelief. "Oh, boy," she said slowly, "is he a case."

At that instant Thomas damned not only the girl but the entire order of the universe that made her possible.

"Thomas wouldn't put a gun in your bag," his mother said. "Thomas is a gentleman."

The girl made a chortling noise. "You can see it in there," she said and pointed to the open purse.

You *found* it in her bag, you dimwit! the old man hissed.

"I found it in her bag!" Thomas shouted. "The dirty criminal slut stole my gun!"

His mother gasped at the sound of the other presence in his voice. The old lady's sybil-like face turned pale.

"Found it my eye!" Sarah Ham shrieked and started for the pocketbook, but Thomas, as if his arm were guided by his father, caught it first and snatched the gun. The girl in a frenzy lunged at Thomas's throat and would actually have caught him around the neck had not his mother thrown herself forward to protect her.

Fire! the old man yelled.

Thomas fired. The blast was like a sound meant to bring an end to evil in the world. Thomas heard it as a sound that would shatter the laughter of sluts until all shrieks were stilled and nothing was left to disturb the peace of perfect order.

The echo died away in waves. Before the last one had faded, Farebrother opened the door and put his head inside the hall. His nose wrinkled. His expression for some few seconds was that of a man unwilling to admit surprise. His eyes were clear as glass, reflecting the scene. The old lady lay on the floor between the girl and Thomas.

The sheriff's brain worked instantly like a calculating machine. He saw the facts as if they were already in print: the fellow had intended all along to kill his mother and pin it on the girl. But Farebrother had been too quick for him. They were not yet aware of his head in the door. As he scrutinized the scene, further insights were flashed to him. Over her body, the killer and the slut were about to collapse into each other's arms. The sheriff knew a nasty bit when he saw it. He was accustomed to enter upon scenes that were not as bad as he had hoped to find them, but this one met his expectations.

The Biggest Band
R. V. Cass

The Corn State Southern Band was a forlorn hope from the beginning, and, like other forlorn hopes, it moved within an aura of enthusiastic propaganda. Perhaps because it had hardly any distinction except size, we had it drummed into our minds that it was "the biggest band in the world." At full strength it numbered about twenty-four hundred souls, and, if we were not literally the most numerous assembly of horn-blowers and drummers ever massed in a single field, no one who ever heard us at close range bothered to contest this primary claim. All during the winter I was thirteen, I drank this propaganda of size—and of our destiny—reorganizing it all into the form of personal wishes that I would go with the other members to the Chicago World's Fair.

A dreamer named Lothar Swift had organized the band by combining the available personnel from high school, municipal, club, college, church, and lodge bands from the southern part of our state. The principle of organization was simple. Swift included everyone who had a suitable instrument—there were no kazoos or household implements used, as some of our detractors said later—and who was willing to attend rehearsals of the band's divisions, as they were called. (These divisions rehearsed separately in various county seat towns across the state. The band never rehearsed as a whole before it played in Chicago.)

Later, Swift enlarged the band even further by selling instruments to a great many people who had never played before, and by including them too. He was a partner in an instrument store in the state capital, and by dangling the bait of the band's proposed excursion he greatly expanded their sales in spite of Depression conditions.

Still, since I had shown no musical aptitude whatever up to that year, I might not have been swept into his deal if he had not known my mother from the days when she taught his younger sisters at Germany school. Though he was a big frog in a big puddle that year, he had grown up on a clay farm just as my parents had.

When he came to Davisburg to sell horns and enlist band members he called at our house for old times' sake. Before he left he had sold us the trombone. He had given us a fine reduction on price, since the bell of the horn was dented, and had promised my mother, "If the band goes—and we're going—this lad of yours will go to Chicago with us. Why, by next summer he'll be playing 'Flight of the Bumblebee.' The trombone isn't a hard instrument." He threw in with the horn an instruction book, which my mother and Uncle Lou were to use in teaching me. They both knew a little music, though neither of them knew any more about the trombone than I did. My mother suggested that once I'd advanced a little I could probably practice with the Davisburg High School band as a stepping stone to the CSS band. Swift generously countered with an invitation for me to come to a division rehearsal "just as soon as he feels ready."

By May, I had learned a few numbers. Miss Sheldahl, who directed the high school band, let me sit in regularly on their rehearsals, though she would not permit me to appear with them in public. And I had been a few times to division rehearsals in our county seat.

But though my mother and I felt that I was fulfilling my part of the bargain all right, Lothar Swift's promise that I would go to Chicago with the band seemed far less reliable. There were rumors going around that he was having plenty of trouble raising money to move his horde so far, let alone to shelter them once he got them to the city.

Presently a form letter came for me. It said that band members had been put on either an *A* list or a *B* list, according to merit. While it was still the band's intention to pay travel and lodging expenses for all its members, it appeared necessary to ask that all *B* members sell two excursion tickets to "band supporters" who might wish to go along to Chicago. The tickets cost $47.50 apiece. Naturally, of course, I was on the *B* list.

I particularly resented the fact that while I had to sell these tickets in order to go, Lard Williams, who was only a couple of years older than I, had been exempted from this condition and put on the *A* list. I would admit that he could play the trumpet a lot better than I could play my trombone, but I still suspected strongly that this discrimination between us had resulted from some kind of malevolence. I thought I might be getting my deserts for the wrong reason.

There had been a brief, bitter time when I thought it might have been Lard who fingered me to Lothar Swift's stooges for playing through a seven-measure rest during a division rehearsal. It had happened in the "Semper Fidelis Overture" when the ninety or more clarinets of this division were supposed to be having things all to themselves. After I'd blasted right along with them through the rest, Swift had rapped for silence, climbed onto his chair at the far end of the gymnasium in which we were practicing, and shouted in my general direction, "One of you trombones—some of you trombones —has lost your place." I sat there with my head down, making business with the spit valve of my horn, thinking he couldn't locate me in that crowd—even after I'd glanced at the nearby stands and discovered that it *was* the "Semper Fidelis" thing the others had been playing, while I'd been tootling along on the "Mission of the Rose Waltz."

"We can't have that happen in Chicago," Swift bellowed. "The big city critics would be on us like wolves. Now, watch it. Once again . . . ."

Riding back to Davisburg later in my parents' car, Lard had whispered to me, so my mother wouldn't hear, "Why don't you just sit there and *pretend* to blow? Hee, hee, hee." So I understood that he knew who had flubbed.

He needled me about it for days afterward, while I tried to defend myself on the grounds that I had been too far from Swift to see his baton or his signal for the rest. But Lard answered me with giggles —like some one who has acted treacherously and wants to make out there was justification for his act.

So after the letter from the band came, I made some plans for ambushing Lard and fixing his lip so he wouldn't get it into a trumpet mouthpiece for a while. I might have done it, too, if my mother hadn't come through with a timely explanation that she'd seen Lothar's "spies" snooping around in various quarters of the band, "cocking their heads and just listening for any little thing a person might happen to do wrong." I had to admit that one of those monitors might have got me on the *B* list instead of Lard.

Whoever was at fault, I was no longer willing to consider staying home while the band went. Through the winter I'd used the approach of the trip as the vehicle for too many wishes to conceive of giving it up. There were plenty of things I had to see in Chicago —photoelectric cells that opened doors, Bob Ripley's *Believe It or Not,* the Skyride and the Skyride Pylons, and the dirigible *Akron,* which was scheduled to visit the city in the same week as the Band.

I meant to see them, come hell or high water. I was going to ride all night on that excursion train and stay in a big hotel (both for the first time in my life), if I had to rob a filling station to do it.

Most of all, for just this period in the spring, I meant to see Sally Rand. Our Scout leader, who was also the high school coach, had confirmed the necessity of my seeing her. I'd been saving photos of her secretly since about Christmas, but I hadn't mentioned my feeling about her to anyone until one May afternoon at the Scout cabin when the troop came in all pooped from a hike.

Coach Douglas was sprawled out in a downy growth of ferns and Dutchman's-breeches, while I sat against a nearby tree feeling my pulse and wondering if I'd injured my heart from too much exercise in this heat.

"I hear you're going to the Fair next month," he called.

"I hope to." My pulse was over ninety, and I didn't know if that was a danger sign or not.

"Wish I could make it," Coach Douglas said. "I'd really like to see that Sally Rand romp again."

Again! Here was someone who'd seen her with his own eyes. I jumped up and began walking around him in circles, trompling May apples, thyme, and wild fern. "What's she look like?" I asked offhandedly.

"Pretty." Coach Douglas bit through the stem of a flower and spat the fragment toward the blue sky.

"What's she do with the fans?"

"Moves them around."

"Bare?"

"Bare."

Good God. A person could live in Davisburg a hundred years, it seemed to me then, without having the opportunity of seeing a naked woman.

I practiced on my trombone for hours that night. I played all the C sharps that I'd been leaving out because the seventh position was hard for me to reach, and I smoothed out the high passages in "Barcarolle." I was driven by some sort of irrational, superstitious hope that if I suddenly improved enough I might get a letter the next day telling me that it had been a mistake to put me on that *B* list. All the time I knew that it was too late to expect that.

The next day I propositioned my father to buy the two excursion tickets I had to sell. I told him straight out what a crumby life my mother had and how often she'd come close to crying when I talked to her about all the things I expected to see at the Fair. And anyway it would have been pretty funny if they didn't want to come see me playing in the Midwest Concert, given by the biggest band in the world.

"You think I can turn up ninety-five dollars for us to go on?" he said with more solemn concern than my approach deserved. We weren't as awfully poor as we'd been two years ago, but he was just getting back on his feet then from a rough stretch. "Come on, Buddy. I'd have to sell the car. Do you want me to do that? I want you to think about that."

"Couldn't you borrow the money from Uncle Lou?"

"Uncle Lou's helped us too often when we really needed it. No use talking any more. Why don't you go hit up the Packers? That hard old jaybird is the only one in town that I know of who might have that kind of money to throw around."

Wishes gather weight through one's childhood until, mysteriously, they become necessities. I *thought* it was necessary for me to get to Chicago and see Sally Rand. That belief nerved me up to go to the Packers and try to sell them the tickets. It is easy to think now how frivolous was what seemed necessary then. And yet, of course it must have been on the hot afternoon when I went to their house that I began to learn why—really—it was necessary that I make the trip with the Band.

My first call had been pleasant and a lot easier than I had expected, but the trouble was that only Mrs. Packer had been at home. Mr. Packer was a railroad official who spent most of his time at the state capital or in Omaha, seldom coming closer to Davisburg than his big farmhouse just beyond the edge of town. I'd have to look for his car in the drive, his wife told me, if I wanted to catch him, because she really never knew just when his duties would let him come home. And she wasn't going to be the one to decide whether or not they'd buy my tickets.

She'd been so awfully nice to me, though, that I was all keyed up for success. She was a dumpy woman in her sixties, with a fresh-looking pink and white skin and very nice brown eyes. She'd ohed and ahed when I told her about the splendors of science and the glamorous entertainment she was going to see in Chicago. I could tell she wasn't just pretending her interest to be polite. She wanted to go, and I figured that was the point that really counted.

When I came back to clinch my sale I knew that Mr. Packer was home because I'd seen his big black car under the elms of their yard when I went uptown for the mail in the morning, and it was still there. I went up on the shady, wide porch and knocked at their screen door. Their collie came around the corner of the porch, prancing and panting from the heat. He nuzzled bossily at the legs of my overalls.

"Good dog. Good old dog," I said to him in the most salesman-like way I could manage. I knocked again and the collie whined to be patted.

"Not so loud, boy." It was Mr. Packer who had come to answer the door. I had rather hoped it would be Mrs. Packer, so she could lead me to him and help explain the deal we were working out. "You'll wake Mrs. Packer," he said. "Come on around to the swing and keep your voice down."

It seemed to me that he was hardly more than aware of me as we went to the section of the porch that faced the highway and took seats in the swing. His blue eyes searched among the elms and catal-pas of the lawn as though he were looking for some sly, important guest and merely tolerating me until that one arrived. In the midst of my attempt to get my sales talk started he said, "Is that your bike down by the gate? I suppose now that school is out you kids are playing, like kids will. Bikes and all." He yawned in my face and scratched the fishbelly white fat on his arms.

"No, sir," I said. "I spend nearly all my time practicing music. I'm a member of the biggest band in the world."

If this announcement touched him he failed to show it. It occurred to me that he was looking across the highway at the purebred short-horns in his feed lot and gloating on what they were worth, even at Depression prices. I thought that if he had any sense of justice he ought to consider how much I needed a little bit of that wealth.

"Lothar Swift, the well-known conductor and music teacher, organized it," I said. "We call it the Corn State Southern Band, and it has musicians in it from clear across the state. I play the trombone."

He looked me over then as though I were offering myself for sale. His pale lips showed that he was a little bit amused.

"Can you reach seventh position on that horn? Not quite, I'll bet."

That encouraged me, because at least it showed he knew something about musical instruments. "I can usually reach it," I bragged. Then I struck for the heart of the matter with more language from Swift's circular letters. "You may have heard that the biggest band in the world is going to the World's Fair in Chicago to play its Midwest Concert and make other appearances. Do you know that this band has twenty-four hundred musicians?"

"My God," he said absently. "That's a lot, isn't it?"

"Along with this vast assembly of musicians, music lovers of the state can buy excursion tickets to go along with it to the Fair."

"It must sound like hell," he said.

"Your wife wants to go," I told him. "She asked me to come back and talk to you about buying the tickets."

Now for the first time since we had sat in the swing he looked square into my face. There was something so savage and cold in his eyes—a gaze in which I was not a little boy but an equally responsible human—that I considered running for my bike then and there.

I went on recklessly, "I was here a few days ago and she practically promised to buy *one* ticket at least. She said she'd find out if you would go with her."

He kept staring steadily at me while he pulled the collie's head against his knee and began scratching its ears. "She told you that she meant to go to the Fair? That she'd go by herself if I wouldn't go? You're lying, boy." He was so calm in his accusation that it seemed he had spent all his life being lied to and had learned finally that all you can do about lies is to sit steady among the trees on your own farm, maybe waiting for the liars to get tired of their business.

I was scared to say anything more to him just then. We sat rocking in the swing for half an hour without a word. I saw Lard Williams and Percy Black ride past on their bikes, headed for the swimming hole in Mitten Creek, and I resented Lard all over again for his freedom from all this trouble I was having.

Mr. Packer said, "I don't think she could have said that to you, boy. Mrs. Packer isn't going anywhere. She's rotten with cancer."

I don't think I quite understood what this meant. Again he had spoken with total calm, and I took the word "rotten" as merely an impolite way of speaking about his wife rather than as a description that might be accurate. "I was sure when I talked to her that she wanted to go," I insisted, perhaps intending to persuade him not to let his meanness interfere with her pleasure.

Of course that appeal meant nothing to him. I had only one line that was not yet exhausted. "Maybe the band can't go at all unless people like me sell enough tickets. And the Midwest Concert will be something no one ever heard before. Since Mrs. Packer was so interested in it, maybe you could buy a couple of tickets and not use them. To help."

"Why should I?" he asked. His big, cracker-white hands trembled in the dog's mane. He stopped rocking the swing. The hot afternoon seemed unbearably still. I listened for the cooing of pigeons or the sound of a car and heard only Mr. Packer's slow, hissing breath.

"Why?" he asked.

"All right, then," I said. I trotted down across the big lawn to pick up my bike. I supposed that this was the end of my chances to go.

．　．　．　．　．

My mother arranged for me to go by beating down Lothar Swift, beating him with the flail of righteous anger. I came home one evening soon after my failure with the Packers to find her glaring and muttering to herself. "I don't care how high up in the music business Lothar Swift has gone," she burst out, "nor how many horns he's sold with all his slippery promises. He needn't think he can get away with this with me. Don't you think I remember the time he came mousing around to Germany school in the afternoon, pretending to look for his sisters, though he knew they'd gone with the other pupils, him whimpering and simpering around with his Miss Thurman this and Miss Thurman that, and it all so plain on his face what he'd come for that I finally had to take pity on him for being so dumb and say, 'Yes, if you want me to go to Hopewell box supper with you, can't you just say so?'"

While her fury lasted she called him at his store in the state capital. I stood beside the telephone, watching her face get harder and angrier than I could recall having seen it, ever. "You—told—us —last—fall. What? Why, when we bought that horn you promised he'd go if— What? Well, I suspect he can do about as well as lots of the others that you've put on that old *A* list. What? Lothar, I—don't—care. You—told—us—last—fall . . ."

In this way she beat him out of my fare to Chicago, sent me there as a musical liability, and as one who had not sold his quota either. But it cost her something to make such an arrangement. Her conscience hurt her. Later that evening she was preoccupied and nervous. She made a big effort to explain to me the kind of person Lothar Swift was. She said he was a fundamentally decent man, though he tried to squeeze too much out of life and this made him careless with the truth. "I don't want to take the bread out of his mouth," she said. "But he promised us. You and Daddy both heard him promise you'd go." Then more of her concern with the band began to come out. "Lothar's ambitious. I've never had a lot of faith he could do all he's undertaken. Your daddy and I have heard that he's borrowed a lot of money and signed a lot of notes he can't hope to pay off unless he has a lot of luck in Chicago. I just don't know how I'd feel now if he had to default his notes and they put him in jail or something."

I was afraid even now that she might weaken under so much worry—that she might pick up the phone again and cancel my trip after all. I clenched my eyes tight shut and thought of Sally Rand. I saw her only as she was in the photographs, with her fans immovably fixed where they shouldn't have been. Somehow I knew I had to see behind them, and if deception was the price, I was willing to pay it.

"But don't you think this excursion is a great opportunity for young people?" I asked her in my oiliest voice. "I mean, to learn music and to see a great American city that they'd never see otherwise?"

That took her in. "Yes. Sure it is. We've got to try things at least, don't we, Buddy?" She hugged me hard against her side. "Lothar's a clever man and maybe he can swing this project better than people think. He's bitten it off. Let's hope he can chew it."

I hoped he would have the courage to go on writing note after note to banks and backers, as careless of what came after Chicago as I was.

He had the courage. By some miracle of paper financing, artful dodging with the railroads, hotels, Fair committees, and terribly inflated promises to the gullible who went as part of the excursion, he took us.

On a rainy, muggy night in June, four hundred of us, constituting the "east-central" division of the band, boarded a special train at the county seat. We knew that some of the western divisions, with whom we had never yet rehearsed and whom we were not even to see for many hours yet, had loaded at dawn—while ahead of us, to the east, other hundreds were boarding a train that would get them to the LaSalle Street Station before us.

My father had bought me a new Brownie "to get some pictures of that Zeppelin," and my mother had packed my clothes with the abstract, enraptured sorrow that you might expect of a Kamikaze's parent dispatching her only son to the Emperor's service.

At the last minute before boarding, quite carried away by the purifying excitement of the moment, I announced to my mother, "I *won't* go to see Sally Rand." I meant it. I had not understood before how holy a thing it was that all this mob was embarking for.

"Well, I should hope not," she said. "Don't forget to get a new bottle of oil for your horn." She had not even seriously considered the possibility that I might court such a depravity. And that, I thought as I swung up, was probably just as well.

"We'll knock them dead," I screeched as the train began to move.

Once the train was really rolling—the one dependable evidence that Lothar Swift would make his promises good, I had felt—I yielded myself to the excitement of departure with a completely simple loyalty. There was a rumor running through our train that

Swift had put our movement and the problems of housing us in Chicago under the direction of an Army captain who had moved troops in Flanders during the war. I overheard some smart-alec college boy giggle over this, "Swift might just do better if he'd let the captain conduct the band, too." I thought it would serve such a guy right if he were pushed into the Mississippi River for his ingratitude.

I had never seen that river before this trip, and I kept pinching myself awake until we had crossed it. Lard Williams was as impressed by it as I was. "Did you ever see anything as black as that water?" he shouted in my ear. Then he whipped his trumpet from the case and blew a few notes of "When It's Darkness on the Delta." "Do you realize that river is bigger than the Amazon?" he crowed. "It's the biggest damn river on the planet. I don't suppose you realize it, Buddy, but you ought to be plenty grateful to your parents and Lothar Swift for making this trip possible."

All these things were exactly what I had been thinking, but it spoiled them a little to hear him saying them. I grunted disagreeably and went to sleep.

I was wakened a good deal later by the passage of the sandwich butcher through the car. Careful not to wake up Lard, I bought some coffee and a jelly sandwich and leaned out the window to get the wind on my face while I ate.

We had left the rain behind us. The stars were out, but the roll of the prairie around us was as black as the river had been. I watched us zip through the night with a balancing of joys—glad that the land was so black while our train was so flashing, glad that it was silent so that the chatter of our wheels could print itself on it, like the first footstep you take in new snow.

Lard was snoring beside me. I enjoyed a lot of superior thoughts at his expense. Maybe he's with us for no better purpose than to go see some immoral Chicago woman waggle her stomach, I thought, but I'm going for something else. It seemed to me that in the hour of my success I had promised not only my mother that I would shun Sally Rand—the promise was to all those who had wanted to go where we were going and couldn't. People like Mrs. Packer. I felt terribly sorry for her, all over again, and wanted to tell her that even if her husband misunderstood her and said unpleasant things about her physical condition, I, at least, knew better than he what she had wanted. And in a way, I suppose, I felt that I was going to get it for her. Finally, I felt I knew why I'd absolutely had to make this trip. In that sweet night I imagined all my selfishness to be a kind of altruism.

We woke in a green morning before the train had passed through Joliet. A tired conductor came through and said, "You kids better keep your feet out of the windows. You'll be walking on your stumps."

I looked across the aisle at the French-horn player who sat beside his instrument case. His chin was black with beard stubble, and his skin showed that he'd been seeing some hard work in the fields. This is not a bunch of kids, I thought, telling off the conductor. You know who's in this band? *Everybody.*

Those who watched us pour into the city through the LaSalle Street Station would surely have agreed. There were old German farmers with short cornet cases, housewives with clarinets and tubas, girls with bagpipes, the whole Legion Auxiliary fife and drum corps from Osmatoc, the marching band from a Methodist college, a sect of Amish with beards and black bonnets, high school bands in a flashing variety of uniforms, and among them all the misencouraged young like me who belonged only to the totality. Counting the excursionists, there were more than four thousand people in this horde that Lothar Swift had raised up to follow him east.

All of us rallied for the first time in one of the ballrooms at the Marathon Hotel. It was a wild gathering full of noise, anarchy, and administrative ineptitude that delayed our assignment to hotel rooms for many hours. I remember an old lady—she was one of the excursionists, she said, who had paid her own good money for the trip —who whimpered ceaselessly after the first few hours, "I'm tired. I'm hungry. I want to go back." In midafternoon I heard a fat tuba player offer to whip Lothar Swift for "getting us into all this mess."

But evidently, the logjam was already broken, for a very few minutes later, the last of us bandsmen were being whisked up to our rooms briefly before we loaded to move in buses to our first concert. I had only time enough in the room to look out at the blue lake, so intimate and so strange that it was like something that might have grown inside my eye, suddenly striping its color across my field of vision—and to exult that I hadn't come all this way to face it in petty company.

There was trouble on the first day in getting us to our designated area in the middle of the Fairgrounds. Finally, a platoon of special police had to hold back the normally strolling crowds until we could all pass through into the snow-fenced enclosure that had been prepared for us.

In the push to the enclosure, I lost the other trombone players I'd been tagging and found myself in the midst of more bassoon players than you'd think lived in our state. I had to sit down there with them when the band started to play. It seemed to make them uneasy to have me in their midst.

So when the first number was over, I got up with my horn under my arm and went in search of the trombones. Presently, as I was wandering, an old man with a flugelhorn grabbed me and hissed, "Don't you know how bad that looks, romping around that way during a *performance?*" He took a terrific grip on my wrist and forced me to the ground. He tried to hold me down out of sight with one hand and his feet while he played the next number, but in an allegro passage I twisted free and crawled along toward a sound like that of trombones.

I got lost again and crawled out of the band to one of the snow-fence borders. I had no idea what the band was playing—neither what Lothar Swift was conducting in his faroff center nor what any of the divisions *thought* he meant for them to play. I was terribly ashamed of myself for getting lost. I sat there playing "Barcarolle" softly, because at least I could do that better than anything else.

A kid smaller than I came up outside of the fence and jabbed me with a toy whip.

"Who're all those?" he said.

"Corn State Southern Band."

"Boy," he whistled. "There's sure a lot of them."

"They're the biggest band in the world."

He turned his head in an arc wide enough to take in the nearer and farther edges of the multitude, spat, and admitted, "Could be."

"What's that they're playing?" he asked.

"The 'Corn Song.'"

He began to look slyly skeptical. "Why ain't you in there playing with them? You got a horn."

"I can't find where I belong. I ought to be with the rest of the trombones."

"I saw them ten minutes ago," he said, "when I was around on the other end of you all by the Skyride. *They* was playing the 'Corn Song' then."

If Lothar Swift had been as ambitious as my mother thought, or if he'd counted on the band's creating a sensation that would lead to the redemption of his debts, he was sadly corrected. The Chicago newspapers didn't even bother to comment on our size. There had been some talk that a beer company or a farm implement manufacturer was going to sponsor us, but after our poor showing on that first afternoon no one believed it any more. The crowds on the Fairgrounds walked *around* us, because they had to. That was about the limit of the attention we got.

Our second concert, on the following day, was scheduled for the dinner hour, when the grounds were mostly empty. They put us out behind Machinery Hall, where the ground tapered visibly into the garbage fill on which the Fair had been built. There weren't even enough folding chairs provided us for all the band members to sit down, let alone anyone who might have come to hear us. I wondered where the critics were that Lothar Swift had worried so much about the day I had played through the seven-measure rest.

Most of the band members I was acquainted with were talking cynically. Lard got a letter from his parents with the rumor that the band had barely managed to get out of the state before the sheriff pulled in Swift for his bad debts.

I tried to ignore this general gloom as much as I could. I'd taken some pictures of the *Akron* coming in over the lake. I'd seen the Ripley show, the marionettes, and a lot of other educational things. But I'd let myself be so excited by the idea of the band's triumph that this gloom scared me, like the fog I'd seen edging in over the lake when we played behind Machinery Hall.

There was still the Midwest Concert to play. It was scheduled to be in the Court of Nations. I sent off to my parents a picture post-card of the clean and modern pylons that surrounded this court. The picture was full of flags in bright, primary colors against a sky the color of laundry bluing. "We're going to play HERE," I wrote on the card.

In my stupidity, I had been slow to catch on that the Midwest Concert would only be part of the joke of our coming. We were scheduled to play it at six-fifteen in the morning. No one would be out at that hour to hear us.

When I finally caught the insult implied by this scheduling, I knew I'd taken more than enough. I canceled my promises to be good in Chicago.

That night I let Lard Williams and his older buddies ditch me, as they'd tried to do on the previous night. Sneaking through the Fairgrounds by the less crowded walks, I marched—dry of mouth and trembling—to the Streets of Paris where Sally Rand would turn me into a swine with those adroit fans. I even meant to stand at the side of the pavilion, from which vantage Coach Douglas had said you get a choicer view.

They wouldn't let me in. I ran at the entrance stairs with my quarter steaming in my hand, and the barker dropped his cane across my chest to block the way.

"You came to the wrong place, didn't you, sonny?" he said. He raised quite a laugh from the crowd in turning me back. "I expect you thought this was the puppet show, didn't you? A-dults only. A-dults only," he bellowed. "Why boy, you couldn't stand the breeze them fans make when they go into action."

To top off this humiliation, when Lard came back to the hotel room we shared with twelve other Bandsmen, he claimed he had seen her. Spiritlessly I asked him what she was like, and he shuddered in a pretense of disgust. "I don't think it's right to permit that kind of indecent show," he said. "Personally, I wish I had my quarter back. I'd rather have a ham sandwich and a bottle of coke."

Most of our roommates were in bed or asleep on the floor. Fortunately the room was too dim for him to see my face plainly, though enough light refracted in from the metropolitan beacons, traffic, and the street lights for me to see him yawn as he started to take off his shirt.

"You fat idiot," I said. I swung with all my strength at his chest and felt the blow glance from one of his moving elbows.

"Here," he said good-naturedly. "Don't run amok just because you've ruined your mind with dirty thoughts. Relax. Sally Rand is probably like any other woman, though not so decent."

"I've never seen any woman," I said.

"You will," Lard comforted me. "Everybody will. There's just as many of them around as there are men. Be logical."

"Sure," I said bitterly. "I'll see one *sometime*. Like when I'm too old to care." But the worst of it all was that I had discovered you couldn't even count on a profit from being bad in a world like this one. I went to sleep on the hotel room floor feeling the misery of those who have tried to sell their souls and have found no taker.

Naturally no audience came to hear the band at six-fifteen the next morning. For our climactic Midwest Concert only about half of the band members showed up at the Court of Nations. And perhaps it is merely a sad irony that we played better that morning than ever before.

In that morning's program was the "Semper Fidelis Overture," and this time even I knew which number we were playing. I was close enough to Lothar Swift to see the sun flash on his swinging baton. During the seven-measure rest, I looked at the nearly empty balconies above us where the crowd might have been and thought how pitiful it was that only a handful of early-rising janitors should hear what we had made such an effort to bring. But when the rest was over I hit the first following note as hard as I could, feeling oddly free to do my best now that it didn't seem to count for anything.

This unattended concert was the end of the band. Naturally, it dissolved without leaving permanent traces when we went back home. Lothar Swift was never publicly charged with any of the frauds he was said to have perpetrated to get us there, but he lost his share in the instrument store in his efforts to appease the band's creditors, and he disappeared from the state not long afterward. My parents were contented to think that I had profited somehow from the excursion, but after I quit practicing on my trombone they were very hard put to explain just what the profit was. Mrs. Packer died in the Mayo Clinic toward the end of that summer, and I might not then have had the courage to discuss the trip with her even if there had been an opportunity.

In all the years since the Fair, I have told the story of our band a number of times, for laughs. This monster that Swift created has come to seem like one of those kindly, vegetarian dinosaurs that once roamed but never ruled the earth—an altogether preposterous blunder committed against nature and a fine art.

But, if in some imaginary circumstance I should tell the story for Mrs. Packer, I would want to emphasize that last dandy morning in the Court of Nations. I would want her to believe that the lake behind us looked broad as any ocean; that the clear sky looked a million times as big as the patch of ground we sat on. The flags of every country were up in the early morning breeze, and on their rippling fields twinkled the mysterious symbols of authority and fidelity—stars, crescents, crests, hammers, sickles, heraldic beasts, and the proud gold lilies of the forgotten wars. From their staffs over the national pavilions the ultramarine and lemon and scarlet pennants streamed out like dyes leaking into an oceanic current. It was only the empty sky that watched us—but my God, my God, how the drums thundered, how we blew!

COMMENTARY
by R. V. Cassill

The most I will ever know of the imagination is what I experience in its employment. And since I have no primary interest in anything but the imagination, I delight in any chance to review or re-examine the way it has seemed to work in fiction I have written or in anything else I have made. It is perhaps obscene—in the strictest sense of the word—to admit this while doing it, as I am here. But I have always inclined more to obscenity than to pornography, as D. H. Lawrence advised writers to do.

To review, indeed, seems to be a necessary ingredient in the imaginative apprehension of my self. I am an amateur painter. Over the years I have accumulated several portfolios of drawings, watercolors, and opaque paintings. For purposes I don't yet fully understand it seems necessary for me to haul out these portfolios from time to time, to spread the pictures on the floors and around the walls, and gaze at these tidal traces of whatever midnight force has lived my life.

When I was about forty, living in a Greenwich Village apartment, I began to make model airplanes out of tissue and balsa, as I had between my tenth and fourteenth years. To tell the truth, this wasn't a hobby, and I was not greatly interested in the little flying toys, however beautifully they might climb into the Sunday morning light above a deserted Washington Square when my little boy and I took them there to fly. I was interested in what had passed with me, so many years ago, before I first quit building the models and went all out for basketball and girls. I made them in the same spirit of worshipful anxiety that comes on me when I spread out the watercolors made in Paris or from a sundeck in Bandol in the 1950's.

In such reviews I don't, in any simple sense, "see myself" as I was on those earlier occasions; and I don't, in any simple sense, recapture any lost times. And yet the return, the replication and the multiplicity of replications I have made through very many years of making model airplanes, painting and writing—these stubborn questionings—are part of the all-engaging processes by which the imagination makes time out of nothingness and places the always-dying creature in vistas it predicates as the structures of time.

Occasionally in trying to explain what I have glimpsed of the nature of the imagination, I have used the example of the palimpsest, or used the image of transparent film slides stacked one on top of the other, so that each single picture modifies as it unites with each of the other pictures beneath to become a new image.

Of course these analogies are poor approximations of what you—as well as I, or better—have experienced as imagination. But they still seem to have the merit of associating the imagination with memory and of focusing the question whether we can move toward understanding one without moving to understand the other.

Are memory and imagination the same thing? I suppose them to be, because I can't conceive of memory except as something moment by moment created, nor think of a product of the imagination not determined by the substance of past perceptions or events.

So in hauling out and considering once again an autobiographical story like "The Biggest Band" I am deliberately trying to do again—or still—the imaginative thing I was doing when I wrote the story, or maybe even what I was doing when I carried my trombone in its case to the World's Fair of 1933 in Chicago. "A child went forth. . . ." And goes forth. *Was* and *is* are deliberately confused by such events as writing a story. Are they not also deliberately confused by getting on a train, as I did once, and crossing a black river in the night, in an attempt to imagine the "Chicago" I remembered hearing about?

"In all the years since the Fair, I have told the story of our band a number of times, for laughs." These words are in the printed version of the story, and are literally true. Between the time I went to Chicago with the Southern Iowa Farm Bureau Band and the time I put the story on paper, when I was in college and looked back at the small town I had lived in, it seemed to me a matter for laughter and private tears that I had gone from it to Chicago expecting so much when I was ready to receive so little. When I was in the Army, later, telling the story again to this person or that, it seemed to me a matter for laughter and tears that the college boy repeating the tale had assumed that he had come all the way to the point where he might have seen the "Chicago" he missed the first time there. When I wrote it down—in 1952, I think—the language that I chose tried to mock and revive the self that had made this journey of the imagination often before.

I have talked about the written version of the story quite often since its publication. In such talk I have fallen into the habit of saying—for laughs, to try to make it more audible to myself or to anyone—that it was my little hymn to democracy. (I suppose most readers will note quickly that the language in it is cast to suggest that the band of the title is not a reference only to musicians but also to that conglomerate mass of camarados who have blundered their lives out on this continent like the "kindly, vegetarian dinosaurs that once roamed but never ruled the earth." It was *them*—us—I meant to salute with whatever drums I could invoke to thunder in the imagination, under a sky that—empty or not—never opened to acclaim their victory. "You know who's in this band? *Everybody.*")

And now I've read the story again. The words that came to me so strangely out of experiences while I was preparing to write it play on my memory as I suppose the band music once did. But now it seems that neither drums nor flags nor words convince me that democracy was ever a *we* or a *they* or ever will be. (In talking so, I am telling the same story again. What else could I possibly be doing? And this time, too, I am modifying the earlier words, straining for the same thing as always, trying to get to "Chicago" so I can see what it's really like behind its fans. I do want, at journey's end, to see what was so important that Sally Rand and her employers had to hide from us boys with so many agile fans.)

Now, in this latest modification, or review, I guess that democracy was essentially a yearning invested in us all. We were not it. It was and is in us—not a way of life but a recognition of possibilities, a flicker of the reality behind the fans which the imagination alone has a chance of apprehending.

Democracy, youth, possibility, memory—the terms fuse where they pass beyond the range of words, where I must relinquish that peculiar apprehension of time that words alone have made possible for me. When the words have been reviewed again we all go back into time through another door, through apprehensions of motion and the events around us. A turning page closes the door behind us—and we say that this story or the next one is over.

For me, what lingers when the page is turned from writing this modification of the story—or from writing the version reprinted with this comment—has never been much more than a sound of drumming, or a recollection of flags against the sky. But those lingering traces will maybe bring me again sometime to tell this story—for Mrs. Packer in imaginable circumstances—with different words, all part of the same.

Setting

Setting helps to give credibility to both action and plot, providing the illusion of spatial substance, the seemingly tangible dimension and coloration of locale which gives a certain solidity of texture to the narrated events. Setting is the physical background against which characters act out their lives. Thus, it is an element of place but also of time, for setting may impart a sense of history, the season of the year, or the hour of the day. The main thing about setting is that it must contribute to the development of character and plot; it must never be extraneous to them. It is not merely scenic or temporal but is inextricably connected to the people and happenings of the short story. Unless it has a dramatic use, it is no more than lifeless, superfluous window-dressing. But when it is dramatically functional, setting provokes thought, arouses feeling, and calls into play our visual imagination.

Setting performs, then, as an adjunct of character and plot, and so of mood and theme. It may also be the main source of atmosphere in the novel. This intangible quality, dependent for its effectiveness upon reader sensitivity and sophistication, is defined by the dictionary as a "mental or moral environment." But atmosphere, sometimes rendered as insubstantial as an essence, imparts the over-all mood or feeling of the short story. Eudora Welty offers a subjective but nonetheless practical explanation of atmosphere.

We are bearing in mind that the atmosphere in a story may be its chief glory—and for another thing, that it may be giving us an impression altogether contrary to what lies under it. The brightness may be the result of whizzing in a circle. Some action stories fling off the brightest clouds of obscuring and dazzling light, like ours here. Our penetrating look brings us the suspicion finally that this busy object is quite dark within, for all its clouds of speed, those primary colors of red and yellow and blue. It looks like one of Ernest Hemingway's stories, and it is.

Now a story behaves, it goes through motions—that's part of it. Some stories leave a train of light behind them, meteorlike, so that much later than they strike our eye we may see their meaning like an after-effect. These wildly careening stories are in many ways among the most interesting of all—the kind of story sometimes called apocalyptic. I think of Faulkner's stories as being not meteors but comets; in a way still beyond their extravagance and unexpectedness and disregard of the steadier laws of time and space, Faulkner's stories are cometlike in that they do have a wonderful course of their own: they reappear, in their own time they reiterate their meaning, and by reiteration show a whole further story over and beyond their single significance.

If we have thought of Hemingway's stories, then, as being bare and solid as billiard balls, so scrupulously cleaned of adjectives, of every unneeded word as they are, of being plain throughout as a verb in itself is plain, we may come to think twice about it. The atmosphere that cloaks D. H. Lawrence's stories is of sensation, which is a pure but thick cover, a cloak of self-luminous air, but the atmosphere that surrounds Hemingway's stories is just as thick and to some readers less illuminating. Action can be inscrutable, more than sensation can be. It can be just as voluptuous, too, just as vaporous, and much more desperately concealing.

So the first thing we see about a story is its mystery. And in the best stories, we return at the last to see mystery again. Every good story has mystery—not the puzzle kind, but the mystery of allurement. As we understand the story better, it is likely that the mystery does not necessarily decrease; rather it simply grows more beautiful.*

Setting may serve a variety of fictional purposes which can be illustrated by examples drawn from the stories which appear in this book. Sometimes it is worked discreetly and unobtrusively—perhaps even symbolically—into the short story. We *know,* for instance, that Faulkner's "Dry September" takes place in a small southern town; we can *feel* its dust and its heat. But we also infer from setting as much as from narrative details, that the inhumanity revealed in Jefferson is the world's inhumanity, that Jefferson is indeed a representation of the world. Sometimes setting—as in Conrad's "Secret Sharer"—functions as an arena in which a character fights a lonely struggle for self-recognition.

At other times place is kept deliberately vague, as in Melville's "Bell Tower," in order to create a sense—indeed, an atmosphere— of the mysterious and thus allow a focus upon the abstraction which gives meaning and form to the allegory. Yet in Hawthorne's "Ethan Brand," closely related to the Melville story in theme and characterization, setting is explicit and detailed, anchored to a specific time and place. Often setting serves as a symbolic correlative of theme. Thus the dark and dripping provincial city of "The Followers" captures the emptiness and sadness of vicarious existence; and it validates the presence of death. In Joyce Cary's "Growing Up," the garden, in part cultivated and in part wild, is like the adolescent girls who are neither adults nor children but struggling for their own kind of identity.

*"The Reading and Writing of Short Stories," *The Atlantic Monthly,* CLXXXIII (February, 1949), p. 56.

The Dead

James Joyce

Lily, the caretaker's daughter, was literally run off her feet. Hardly
had she brought one gentleman into the little pantry behind the
office on the ground floor and helped him off with his overcoat than
the wheezy hall-door bell clanged again and she had to scamper
along the bare hallway to let in another guest. It was well for her she
had not to attend to the ladies also. But Miss Kate and Miss Julia
had thought of that and had converted the bathroom upstairs into
a ladies' dressing-room. Miss Kate and Miss Julia were there, gossip-
ing and laughing and fussing, walking after each other to the head
of the stairs, peering down over the banisters and calling down to
Lily to ask her who had come.

It was always a great affair, the Misses Morkan's annual dance.
Everybody who knew them came to it, members of the family, old
friends of the family, the members of Julia's choir, any of Kate's
pupils that were grown up enough, and even some of Mary Jane's

pupils too. Never once had it fallen flat. For years and years it had gone off in splendid style, as long as anyone could remember; ever since Kate and Julia, after the death of their brother Pat, had left the house in Stoney Batter and taken Mary Jane, their only niece, to live with them in the dark, gaunt house on Usher's Island, the upper part of which they had rented from Mr. Fulham, the corn-factor on the ground floor. That was a good thirty years ago if it was a day. Mary Jane, who was then a little girl in short clothes, was now the main prop of the household, for she had the organ in Haddington Road. She had been through the Academy and gave a pupils' concert every year in the upper room of the Antient Concert Rooms. Many of her pupils belonged to the better-class families on the Kingstown and Dalkey line. Old as they were, her aunts also did their share. Julia, though she was quite grey, was still the leading soprano in Adam and Eve's, and Kate, being too feeble to go about much, gave music lessons to beginners on the old square piano in the back room. Lily, the caretaker's daughter, did housemaid's work for them. Though their life was modest, they believed in eating well; the best of everything: diamond-bone sirloins, three-shilling tea and the best bottled stout. But Lily seldom made a mistake in the orders, so that she got on well with her three mistresses. They were fussy, that was all. But the only thing they would not stand was back answers.

Of course, they had good reason to be fussy on such a night. And then it was long after ten o'clock and yet there was no sign of Gabriel and his wife. Besides they were dreadfully afraid that Freddy Malins might turn up screwed. They would not wish for worlds that any of Mary Jane's pupils should see him under the influence; and when he was like that it was sometimes very hard to manage him. Freddy Malins always came late, but they wondered what could be keeping Gabriel: and that was what brought them every two minutes to the banisters to ask Lily had Gabriel or Freddy come.

"O, Mr. Conroy," said Lily to Gabriel when she opened the door for him, "Miss Kate and Miss Julia thought you were never coming. Good-night, Mrs. Conroy."

"I'll engage they did," said Gabriel, "but they forget that my wife here takes three mortal hours to dress herself."

He stood on the mat, scraping the snow from his goloshes, while

Lily led his wife to the foot of the stairs and called out:

"Miss Kate, here's Mrs. Conroy."

Kate and Julia came toddling down the dark stairs at once. Both of them kissed Gabriel's wife, said she must be perished alive, and asked was Gabriel with her.

"Here I am as right as the mail, Aunt Kate! Go on up. I'll follow," called out Gabriel from the dark.

He continued scraping his feet vigorously while the three women went upstairs, laughing, to the ladies' dressing-room. A light fringe of snow lay like a cape on the shoulders of his overcoat and like toe-caps on the toes of his goloshes; and, as the buttons of his overcoat slipped with a squeaking noise through the snow-stiffened frieze, a cold, fragrant air from out-of-doors escaped from crevices and folds.

"Is it snowing again, Mr. Conroy?" asked Lily.

She had preceded him into the pantry to help him off with his overcoat. Gabriel smiled at the three syllables she had given his surname and glanced at her. She was a slim, growing girl, pale in complexion and with hay-coloured hair. The gas in the pantry made her look still paler. Gabriel had known her when she was a child and used to sit on the lowest step nursing a rag doll.

"Yes, Lily," he answered, "and I think we're in for a night of it."

He looked up at the pantry ceiling, which was shaking with the stamping and shuffling of feet on the floor above, listened for a moment to the piano and then glanced at the girl, who was folding his overcoat carefully at the end of a shelf.

"Tell me, Lily," he said in a friendly tone, "do you still go to school?"

"O no, sir," she answered. "I'm done schooling this year and more."

"O, then," said Gabriel gaily, "I suppose we'll be going to your wedding one of these fine days with your young man, eh?"

The girl glanced back at him over her shoulder and said with great bitterness:

"The men that is now is only all palaver and what they can get out of you."

Gabriel coloured, as if he felt he had made a mistake and, without looking at her, kicked off his goloshes and flicked actively with his muffler at his patent-leather shoes.

He was a stout, tallish young man. The high colour of his cheeks pushed upwards even to his forehead, where it scattered itself in a few formless patches of pale red; and on his hairless face there scintillated restlessly the polished lenses and the bright gilt rims of the glasses which screened his delicate and restless eyes. His glossy black hair was parted in the middle and brushed in a long curve behind his ears where it curled slightly beneath the groove left by his hat.

When he had flicked lustre into his shoes he stood up and pulled his waistcoat down more tightly on his plump body. Then he took a coin rapidly from his pocket.

"O Lily," he said, thrusting it into her hands, "it's Christmas-time, isn't it? Just . . . here's a little. . . ."

He walked rapidly towards the door.

"O no, sir!" cried the girl, following him. "Really, sir, I wouldn't take it."

"Christmas-time! Christmas-time!" said Gabriel, almost trotting to the stairs and waving his hand to her in deprecation.

The girl, seeing that he had gained the stairs, called out after him: "Well, thank you, sir."

He waited outside the drawing-room door until the waltz should finish, listening to the skirts that swept against it and to the shuffling of feet. He was still discomposed by the girl's bitter and sudden retort. It had cast a gloom over him which he tried to dispel by arranging his cuffs and the bows of his tie. He then took from his waistcoat pocket a little paper and glanced at the headings he had made for his speech. He was undecided about the lines from Robert Browning, for he feared they would be above the heads of his hearers. Some quotation that they would recognise from Shakespeare or from the Melodies would be better. The indelicate clacking of the men's heels and the shuffling of their soles reminded him that their grade of culture differed from his. He would only make himself ridiculous by quoting poetry to them which they could not understand. They would think that he was airing his superior education. He would fail with them just as he had failed with the girl in the pantry. He had taken up a wrong tone. His whole speech was a mistake from first to last, an utter failure.

Just then his aunts and his wife came out of the ladies' dressing-room. His aunts were two small, plainly dressed old women. Aunt Julia was an inch or so the taller. Her hair, drawn low over the tops of her ears, was grey; and grey also, with darker shadows, was her large flaccid face. Though she was stout in build and stood erect, her slow eyes and parted lips gave her the appearance of a woman who did not know where she was or where she was going. Aunt Kate was more vivacious. Her face, healthier than her sister's, was all puckers and creases, like a shrivelled red apple, and her hair, braided in the same old-fashioned way, had not lost its ripe nut colour.

They both kissed Gabriel frankly. He was their favourite nephew, the son of their dead elder sister, Ellen, who had married T. J. Conroy of the Port and Docks.

"Gretta tells me you're not going to take a cab back to Monkstown tonight, Gabriel," said Aunt Kate.

"No," said Gabriel, turning to his wife, "we had quite enough of that last year, hadn't we? Don't you remember, Aunt Kate, what a cold Gretta got out of it? Cab windows rattling all the way, and the east wind blowing in after we passed Merrion. Very jolly it was. Gretta caught a dreadful cold."

Aunt Kate frowned severely and nodded her head at every word.

"Quite right, Gabriel, quite right," she said. "You can't be too careful."

"But as for Gretta there," said Gabriel, "she'd walk home in the snow if she were let."

Mrs. Conroy laughed.

"Don't mind him, Aunt Kate," she said. "He's really an awful bother, what with green shades for Tom's eyes at night and making him do the dumb-bells, and forcing Eva to eat the stirabout. The poor child! And she simply hates the sight of it! . . . O, but you'll never guess what he makes me wear now!"

She broke out into a peal of laughter and glanced at her husband, whose admiring and happy eyes had been wandering from her dress to her face and hair. The two aunts laughed heartily, too, for Gabriel's solicitude was a standing joke with them.

"Goloshes!" said Mrs. Conroy. "That's the latest. Whenever it's wet underfoot I must put on my goloshes. Tonight even, he wanted me to put them on, but I wouldn't. The next thing he'll buy me will be a diving suit."

Gabriel laughed nervously and patted his tie reassuringly, while Aunt Kate nearly doubled herself, so heartily did she enjoy the joke. The smile soon faded from Aunt Julia's face and her mirthless eyes were directed towards her nephew's face. After a pause she asked:

"And what are goloshes, Gabriel?"

"Goloshes, Julia!" exclaimed her sister. "Goodness me, don't you know what goloshes are? You wear them over your . . . over your boots, Gretta, isn't it?"

"Yes," said Mrs. Conroy. "Guttapercha things. We both have a pair now. Gabriel says everyone wears them on the Continent."

"O, on the Continent," murmured Aunt Julia, nodding her head slowly.

Gabriel knitted his brows and said, as if he were slightly angered:

"It's nothing very wonderful, but Gretta thinks it very funny because she says the word reminds her of Christy Minstrels."

"But tell me, Gabriel," said Aunt Kate, with brisk tact. "Of course, you've seen about the room. Gretta was saying . . ."

"O, the room is all right," replied Gabriel. "I've taken one in the Gresham."

"To be sure," said Aunt Kate, "by far the best thing to do. And the children, Gretta, you're not anxious about them?"

"O, for one night," said Mrs. Conroy. "Besides, Bessie will look after them."

"To be sure," said Aunt Kate again. "What a comfort it is to have a girl like that, one you can depend on! There's that Lily, I'm sure I don't know what has come over her lately. She's not the girl she was at all."

Gabriel was about to ask her aunt some questions on this point, but she broke off suddenly to gaze after her sister, who had wandered down the stairs and was craning her neck over the banisters.

"Now, I ask you," she said almost testily, "where is Julia going? Julia! Julia! Where are you going?"

Julia, who had gone half way down one flight, came back and announced blandly:

"Here's Freddy."

At the same moment a clapping of hands and a final flourish of the pianist told that the waltz had ended. The drawing-room door was opened from within and some couples came out. Aunt Kate drew Gabriel aside hurriedly and whispered into his ear:

"Slip down, Gabriel, like a good fellow and see if he's all right, and don't let him up if he's screwed. I'm sure he's screwed. I'm sure he is."

Gabriel went to the stairs and listened over the banisters. He could hear two persons talking in the pantry. Then he recognised Freddy Malins' laugh. He went down the stairs noisily.

"It's such a relief," said Aunt Kate to Mrs. Conroy, "that Gabriel is here, I always feel easier in my mind when he's here.... Julia, there's Miss Daly and Miss Power will take some refreshment. Thanks for your beautiful waltz, Miss Daly. It made lovely time."

A tall wizen-faced man, with a stiff grizzled moustache and swarthy skin, who was passing out with his partner, said:

"And may we have some refreshment, too, Miss Morkan?"

"Julia," said Aunt Kate summarily, "and here's Mr. Browne and Miss Furlong. Take them in, Julia, with Miss Daly and Miss Power."

"I'm the man for the ladies," said Mr. Browne, pursing his lips until his moustache bristled and smiling in all his wrinkles. "You know, Miss Morkan, the reason they are so fond of me is—"

He did not finish his sentence, but, seeing that Aunt Kate was out of earshot, at once led the three young ladies into the back room. The middle of the room was occupied by two square tables placed end to end, and on these Aunt Julia and the caretaker were straightening and smoothing a large cloth. On the sideboard were arrayed dishes and plates, and glasses and bundles of knives and forks and spoons. The top of the closed square piano served also as a sideboard for viands and sweets. At a smaller sideboard in one corner two young men were standing, drinking hop-bitters.

Mr. Browne led his charges thither and invited them all, in jest, to some ladies' punch, hot, strong and sweet. As they said they never took anything strong, he opened three bottles of lemonade for them. Then he asked one of the young men to move aside, and, taking hold of the decanter, filled out for himself a goodly measure of whisky. The young men eyed him respectfully while he took a trial sip.

"God help me," he said, smiling, "it's the doctor's orders."

His wizened face broke into a broader smile, and the three young ladies laughed in musical echo to his pleasantry, swaying their bodies to and fro, with nervous jerks of their shoulders. The boldest said:

"O, now, Mr. Browne, I'm sure the doctor never ordered anything of the kind."

Mr. Browne took another sip of his whisky and said, with sidling mimicry:

"Well, you see, I'm like the famous Mrs. Cassidy, who is reported to have said: 'Now, Mary Grimes, if I don't take it, make me take it, for I feel I want it.' "

His hot face had leaned forward a little too confidentially and he had assumed a very low Dublin accent so that the young ladies, with one instinct, received his speech in silence. Miss Furlong, who was one of Mary Jane's pupils, asked Miss Daly what was the name of the pretty waltz she had played; and Mr. Browne, seeing that he was ignored, turned promptly to the two young men who were more appreciative.

A red-faced young woman, dressed in pansy, came into the room, excitedly clapping her hands and crying:

"Quadrilles! Quadrilles!"

Close on her heels came Aunt Kate, crying:

"Two gentlemen and three ladies, Mary Jane!"

"O, here's Mr. Bergin and Mr. Kerrigan," said Mary Jane. "Mr. Kerrigan, will you take Miss Power? Miss Furlong, may I get you a partner, Mr. Bergin. O, that'll just do now."

"Three ladies, Mary Jane," said Aunt Kate.

The two young gentlemen asked the ladies if they might have the pleasure, and Mary Jane turned to Miss Daly.

"O, Miss Daly, you're awfully good, after playing for the last two dances, but really we're so short of ladies tonight."

"I don't mind in the least, Miss Morkan."

"But I've a nice partner for you, Mr. Bartell D'Arcy, the tenor. I'll get him to sing later on. All Dublin is raving about him."

"Lovely voice, lovely voice!" said Aunt Kate.

As the piano had twice begun the prelude to the first figure Mary Jane led her recruits quickly from the room. They had hardly gone when Aunt Julia wandered slowly into the room, looking behind her at something.

"What is the matter, Julia?" asked Aunt Kate anxiously. "Who is it?"

Julia, who was carrying in a column of table-napkins, turned to her sister and said, simply, as if the question had surprised her:

"It's only Freddy, Kate, and Gabriel with him."

In fact right behind her Gabriel could be seen piloting Freddy Malins across the landing. The latter, a young man of about forty, was of Gabriel's size and build, with very round shoulders. His face was fleshy and pallid, touched with colour only at the thick hanging lobes of his ears and at the wide wings of his nose. He had coarse features, a blunt nose, a convex and receding brow, tumid and protruded lips. His heavy-lidded eyes and the disorder of his scanty hair made him look sleepy. He was laughing heartily in a high key at a story which he had been telling Gabriel on the stairs and at the same time rubbing the knuckles of his left fist backwards and forwards into his left eye.

"Good-evening, Freddy," said Aunt Julia.

Freddy Malins bade the Misses Morkan good-evening in what seemed an offhand fashion by reason of the habitual catch in his voice and then, seeing that Mr. Browne was grinning at him from the sideboard, crossed the room on rather shaky legs and began to repeat in an undertone the story he had just told to Gabriel.

"He's not so bad, is he?" said Aunt Kate to Gabriel.

Gabriel's brows were dark, but he raised them quickly and answered: "O, no, hardly noticeable."

"Now, isn't he a terrible fellow!" she said. "And his poor mother made him take the pledge on New Year's Eve. But come on, Gabriel, into the drawing-room."

Before leaving the room with Gabriel she signalled to Mr. Browne by frowning and shaking her forefinger in warning to and fro. Mr. Browne nodded in answer and, when she had gone, said to Freddy Malins:

"Now, then, Teddy, I'm going to fill you out a good glass of lemonade just to buck you up."

Freddy Malins, who was nearing the climax of his story, waved the offer aside impatiently but Mr. Browne, having first called Freddy Malins' attention to a disarray in his dress, filled out and handed him a full glass of lemonade. Freddy Malins' left hand accepted the glass mechanically, his right hand being engaged in the mechanical re-adjustment of his dress. Mr. Browne, whose face was once more wrinkling with mirth, poured out for himself a glass of whisky while Freddy Malins exploded, before he had well reached the climax of his story, in a kink of high-pitched bronchitic laughter and, setting down his untasted and overflowing glass, began to rub the knuckles of his left fist backwards and forwards into his left eye, repeating words of his last phrase as well as his fit of laughter would allow him.

Gabriel could not listen while Mary Jane was playing her Academy piece, full of runs and difficult passages, to the hushed drawing-room. He liked music but the piece she was playing had no melody for him and he doubted whether it had any melody for the other listeners, though they had begged Mary Jane to play something. Four young men, who had come from the refreshment-room to stand in the doorway at the sound of the piano, had gone away quietly in couples after a few minutes. The only persons who seemed to follow the music were Mary Jane herself, her hands racing along the keyboard or lifted from it at the pauses like those of a priestess in momentary imprecation, and Aunt Kate standing at her elbow to turn the page.

Gabriel's eyes, irritated by the floor, which glittered with beeswax under the heavy chandelier, wandered to the wall above the piano. A picture of the balcony scene in *Romeo and Juliet* hung there and beside it was a picture of the two murdered princes in the Tower which Aunt Julia had worked in red, blue and brown wools when she was a girl. Probably in the school they had gone to as girls that kind of work had been taught for one year. His mother had worked for him as a birthday present a waistcoat of purple tabinet, with little foxes' heads upon it, lined with brown satin and having round mulberry buttons. It was strange that his mother had had no musical talent though Aunt Kate used to call her the brains carrier of the Morkan family. Both she and Julia had always seemed a little proud of their serious and matronly sister. Her photograph stood before the pierglass. She held an open book on her knees and was pointing out something in it to Constantine who, dressed in a man-o'-war suit, lay at her feet. It was she who had chosen the names of her sons for she was very sensible of the dignity of family life. Thanks to her, Constantine was now senior curate in Balbriggan and, thanks to her, Gabriel himself had taken his degree in the Royal University. A shadow passed over his face as he remembered her sullen opposition to his marriage. Some slighting phrases she had used still rankled in his memory; she had once spoken of Gretta as being country cute and that was not true of Gretta at all. It was Gretta who had nursed her during all her last long illness in their house at Monkstown.

He knew that Mary Jane must be near the end of her piece for she was playing again the opening melody with runs of scales after every bar and while he waited for the end the resentment died down in his heart. The piece ended with a trill of octaves in the treble and a final deep octave in the bass. Great applause greeted Mary Jane as, blushing and rolling up her music nervously, she escaped from the room. The most vigorous clapping came from the four young men in the doorway who had gone away to the refreshment-room at the beginning of the piece but had come back when the piano had stopped.

Lancers were arranged. Gabriel found himself partnered with Miss Ivors. She was a frank-mannered talkative young lady, with a freckled face and prominent brown eyes. She did not wear a low-cut bodice and the large brooch which was fixed in the front of her collar bore on it an Irish device and motto.

When they had taken their places she said abruptly:

"I have a crow to pluck with you."

"With me?" said Gabriel.

She nodded her head gravely.

"What is it?" asked Gabriel, smiling at her solemn manner.

"Who is G. C.?" answered Miss Ivors, turning her eyes upon him.

Gabriel coloured and was about to knit his brows, as if he did not understand, when she said bluntly:

"O, innocent Amy! I have found out that you write for *The Daily Express*. Now, aren't you ashamed of yourself?"

"Why should I be ashamed of myself?" asked Gabriel, blinking his eyes and trying to smile.

"Well, I'm ashamed of you," said Miss Ivors frankly. "To say you'd write for a paper like that. I didn't think you were a West Briton."

A look of perplexity appeared on Gabriel's face. It was true that he wrote a literary column every Wednesday in *The Daily Express,* for which he was paid fifteen shillings. But that did not make him a West Briton surely. The books he received for review were almost more welcome than the paltry cheque. He loved to feel the covers and turn over the pages of newly printed books. Nearly every day when his teaching in the college was ended he used to wander down the quays to the second-hand booksellers, to Hickey's on Bachelor's Walk, to Web's or Massey's on Aston's Quay, or to O'Clohissey's in the bystreet. He did not know how to meet her charge. He wanted to say that literature was above politics. But they were friends of many years' standing and their careers had been parallel, first at the University and then as teachers: he could not risk a grandiose phrase with her. He continued blinking his eyes and trying to smile and murmured lamely that he saw nothing political in writing reviews of books.

When their turn to cross had come he was still perplexed and inattentive. Miss Ivors promptly took his hand in a warm grasp and said in a soft friendly tone:

"Of course, I was only joking. Come, we cross now."

When they were together again she spoke of the University question and Gabriel felt more at ease. A friend of hers had shown her his review of Browning's poems. That was how she had found out the secret: but she liked the review immensely. Then she said suddenly:

"O, Mr. Conroy, will you come for an excursion to the Aran Isles this summer? We're going to stay there a whole month. It will be splendid out in the Atlantic. You ought to come. Mr. Clancy is coming, and Mr. Kilkelly and Kathleen Kearney. It would be splendid for Gretta too if she'd come. She's from Connacht, isn't she?"

"Her people are," said Gabriel shortly.

"But you will come, won't you?" said Miss Ivors, laying her warm hand eagerly on his arm.

"The fact is," said Gabriel, "I have just arranged to go—"

"Go where?" asked Miss Ivors.

"Well, you know, every year I go for a cycling tour with some fellows and so—"

"But where?" asked Miss Ivors.

"Well, we usually go to France or Belgium or perhaps Germany," said Gabriel awkwardly.

"And why do you go to France and Belgium," said Miss Ivors, "instead of visiting your own land?"

"Well," said Gabriel, "it's partly to keep in touch with the languages and partly for a change."

"And haven't you your own language to keep in touch with— Irish?" asked Miss Ivors.

"Well," said Gabriel, "if it comes to that, you know, Irish is not my language."

Their neighbours had turned to listen to the cross-examination. Gabriel glanced right and left nervously and tried to keep his good humour under the ordeal which was making a blush invade his forehead.

"And haven't you your own land to visit," continued Miss Ivors, "that you know nothing of, your own people, and your own country?"

"O, to tell you the truth," retorted Gabriel suddenly, "I'm sick of my own country, sick of it!"

"Why?" asked Miss Ivors.

Gabriel did not answer for his retort had heated him.

"Why?" repeated Miss Ivors.

They had to go visiting together and, as he had not answered her, Miss Ivors said warmly:

"Of course, you've no answer."

Gabriel tried to cover his agitation by taking part in the dance with great energy. He avoided her eyes for he had seen a sour expression on her face. But when they met in the long chain he was surprised to feel his hand firmly pressed. She looked at him from under her brows for a moment quizzically until he smiled. Then, just as the chain was about to start again, she stood on tiptoe and whispered into his ear:

"West Briton!"

When the lancers were over Gabriel went away to a remote corner of the room where Freddy Malins' mother was sitting. She was a stout feeble old woman with white hair. Her voice had a catch in it like her son's and she stuttered slightly. She had been told that Freddy had come and that he was nearly all right. Gabriel asked her whether she had had a good crossing. She lived with her married daughter in Glasgow and came to Dublin on a visit once a year. She answered placidly that she had had a beautiful crossing and that the captain had been most attentive to her. She spoke also of the beautiful house her daughter kept in Glasgow, and of all the friends they had there. While her tongue rambled on Gabriel tried to banish from his mind all memory of the unpleasant incident with Miss Ivors. Of course the girl or woman, or whatever she was, was an enthusiast but there was a time for all things. Perhaps he ought not to have answered her like that. But she had no right to call him a West Briton before people, even in joke. She had tried to make him ridiculous before people, heckling him and staring at him with her rabbit's eyes.

He saw his wife making her way towards him through the waltzing couples. When she reached him she said into his ear:

"Gabriel, Aunt Kate wants to know won't you carve the goose as usual. Miss Daly will carve the ham and I'll do the pudding."

"All right," said Gabriel.

"She's sending in the younger ones first as soon as this waltz is over so that we'll have the table to ourselves."

"Were you dancing?" asked Gabriel.

"Of course I was. Didn't you see me? What row had you with Molly Ivors?"

"No row. Why? Did she say so?"

"Something like that. I'm trying to get that Mr. D'Arcy to sing. He's full of conceit, I think."

"There was no row," said Gabriel moodily, "only she wanted me to go for a trip to the west of Ireland and I said I wouldn't."

His wife clasped her hand excitedly and gave a little jump.

"O, do go, Gabriel," she cried. "I'd love to see Galway again."

"You can go if you like," said Gabriel coldly.

She looked at him for a moment, then turned to Mrs. Malins and said:

"There's a nice husband for you, Mrs. Malins."

While she was threading her way back across the room Mrs. Malins, without adverting to the interruption, went on to tell Gabriel what beautiful places there were in Scotland and beautiful scenery. Her son-in-law brought them every year to the lakes and they used to go fishing. Her son-in-law was a splendid fisher. One day he caught a beautiful big fish and the man in the hotel cooked it for their dinner.

Gabriel hardly heard what she said. Now that supper was coming near he began to think again about his speech and about the quotation. When he saw Freddy Malins coming across the room to visit his mother Gabriel left the chair free for him and retired into the embrasure of the window. The room had already cleared and from the back room came the clatter of plates and knives. Those who still remained in the drawing-room seemed tired of dancing and were conversing quietly in little groups. Gabriel's warm trembling fingers tapped the cold pane of the window. How cool it must be outside! How pleasant it would be to walk out alone, first along by the river and then through the park! The snow would be lying on the branches of the trees and forming a bright cap on the top of the Wellington Monument. How much more pleasant it would be there than at the supper-table!

He ran over the headings of his speech: Irish hospitality, sad memories, the Three Graces, Paris, the quotation from Browning. He repeated to himself a phrase he had written in his review: "One feels that one is listening to a thought-tormented music." Miss Ivors had praised the review. Was she sincere? Had she really any life of her own behind all her propagandism? There had never been any ill-feeling between them until that night. It unnerved him to think that she would be at the supper-table, looking up at him while he spoke with her critical quizzing eyes. Perhaps she would not be sorry to see him fail in his speech. An idea came into his mind and gave him courage. He would say, alluding to Aunt Kate and Julia: "Ladies and Gentlemen, the generation which is now on the wane among us may have had its faults but for my part I think it had certain qualities of hospitality, of humour, of humanity, which the new and very serious and hypereducated generation that is growing up around us seems to me to lack." Very good: that was one for Miss

Ivors. What did he care that his aunts were only two ignorant old women?

A murmur in the room attracted his attention. Mr. Browne was advancing from the door, gallantly escorting Aunt Julia, who leaned upon his arm, smiling and hanging her head. An irregular musketry of applause escorted her also as far as the piano and then, as Mary Jane seated herself on the stool, and Aunt Julia, no longer smiling, half turned so as to pitch her voice fairly into the room, gradually ceased. Gabriel recognised the prelude. It was that of an old song of Aunt Julia's—*Arrayed for the Bridal*. Her voice, strong and clear in tone, attacked with great spirit the runs which embellish the air and though she sang very rapidly she did not miss even the smallest of the grace notes. To follow the voice, without looking at the singer's face, was to feel and share the excitement of swift and secure flight. Gabriel applauded loudly with all the others at the close of the song and loud applause was borne in from the invisible supper-table. It sounded so genuine that a little colour struggled into Aunt Julia's face as she bent to replace in the music-stand the old leather-bound songbook that had her initials on the cover. Freddy Malins, who had listened with his head perched sideways to hear her better, was still applauding when everyone else had ceased and talking animatedly to his mother who nodded her head gravely and slowly in acquiescence. At last, when he could clap no more, he stood up suddenly and hurried across the room to Aunt Julia whose hand he seized and held in both his hands, shaking it when words failed him or the catch in his voice proved too much for him.

"I was just telling my mother," he said, "I never heard you sing so well, never. No, I never heard your voice so good as it is tonight. Now! Would you believe that now? That's the truth. Upon my word and honour that's the truth. I never heard your voice sound so fresh and so . . . so clear and fresh, never."

Aunt Julia smiled broadly and murmured something about compliments as she released her hand from his grasp. Mr. Browne extended his open hand towards her and said to those who were near him in the manner of a showman introducing a prodigy to an audience:

"Miss Julia Morkan, my latest discovery!"

He was laughing very heartily at this himself when Freddy Malins turned to him and said:

"Well, Browne, if you're serious you might make a worse discovery. All I can say is I never heard her sing half so well as long as I am coming here. And that's the honest truth."

"Neither did I," said Mr. Browne. "I think her voice has greatly improved."

Aunt Julia shrugged her shoulders and said with meek pride: "Thirty years ago I hadn't a bad voice as voices go."

"I often told Julia," said Aunt Kate emphatically, "that she was simply thrown away in that choir. But she never would be said by me."

She turned as if to appeal to the good sense of the others against a refractory child while Aunt Julia gazed in front of her, a vague smile of reminiscence playing on her face.

"No," continued Aunt Kate, "she wouldn't be said or led by anyone, slaving there in that choir night and day, night and day. Six o'clock on Christmas morning! And all for what?"

"Well, isn't it for the honour of God, Aunt Kate?" asked Mary Jane, twisting round on the piano-stool and smiling.

Aunt Kate turned fiercely on her niece and said:

"I know all about the honour of God, Mary Jane, but I think it's not at at all honourable for the pope to turn out the women out of the choirs that have slaved there all their lives and put little whippersnappers of boys over their heads. I suppose it is for the good of the Church if the pope does it. But it's not just, Mary Jane, and it's not right."

She had worked herself into a passion and would have continued in defence of her sister for it was a sore subject with her but Mary Jane, seeing that all the dancers had come back, intervened pacifically:

"Now, Aunt Kate, you're giving scandal to Mr. Browne who is of the other persuasion."

Aunt Kate turned to Mr. Browne, who was grinning at this allusion to his religion, and said hastily:

"O, I don't question the pope's being right. I'm only a stupid old woman and I wouldn't presume to do such a thing. But there's such a thing as common everyday politeness and gratitude. And if I were in Julia's place I'd tell that Father Healey straight up to his face . . ."

"And besides, Aunt Kate," said Mary Jane, "we really are all hungry and when we are hungry we are all very quarrelsome."

"And when we are thirsty we are also quarrelsome," added Mr. Browne.

"So that we had better go to supper," said Mary Jane, "and finish the discussion afterwards."

On the landing outside the drawing-room Gabriel found his wife and Mary Jane trying to persuade Miss Ivors to stay for supper. But Miss Ivors, who had put on her hat and was buttoning her cloak, would not stay. She did not feel in the least hungry and she had already overstayed her time.

"But only for ten minutes, Molly," said Mrs. Conroy. "That won't delay you."

"To take a pick itself," said Mary Jane, "after all your dancing."

"I really couldn't," said Miss Ivors.

"I am afraid you didn't enjoy yourself at all," said Mary Jane hopelessly.

"Ever so much, I assure you," said Miss Ivors, "but you really must let me run off now."

"But how can you get home?" asked Mrs. Conroy.

"O, it's only two steps up the quay."

Gabriel hesitated a moment and said:

"If you will allow me, Miss Ivors, I'll see you home if you are really obliged to go."

But Miss Ivors broke away from them.

"I won't hear of it," she cried. "For goodness' sake go in to your suppers and don't mind me. I'm quite well able to take care of myself."

"Well, you're the comical girl, Molly," said Mrs. Conroy frankly.

"*Beannacht libh*," cried Miss Ivors, with a laugh, as she ran down the staircase.

Mary Jane gazed after her, a moody puzzled expression on her face, while Mrs. Conroy leaned over the banisters to listen for the hall-door. Gabriel asked himself was he the cause of her abrupt departure. But she did not seem to be in ill humour: she had gone away laughing. He stared blankly down the staircase.

At the moment Aunt Kate came toddling out of the supper-room, almost wringing her hands in despair.

"Where is Gabriel?" she cried. "Where on earth is Gabriel? There's everyone waiting in there, stage to let, and nobody to carve the goose!"

"Here I am, Aunt Kate!" cried Gabriel, with sudden animation, "ready to carve a flock of geese, if necessary."

A fat brown goose lay at one end of the table and at the other end, on a bed of creased paper strewn with sprigs of parsley, lay a great ham, stripped of its outer skin and peppered over with crust crumbs, a neat paper frill round its shin and beside this was a round of spiced beef. Between these rival ends ran parallel lines of side-dishes: two little minsters of jelly, red and yellow; a shallow dish full of blocks of blancmange and red jam, a large green leaf-shaped dish with a stalk-shaped handle, on which lay bunches of purple raisins and peeled almonds, a companion dish on which lay a solid rectangle of Smyrna figs, a dish of custard topped with grated nutmeg, a small bowl full of chocolates and sweets wrapped in gold and silver papers and a glass vase in which stood some tall celery stalks. In the centre of the table there stood, as sentries to a fruit-stand which upheld a pyramid of oranges and American apples, two squat old-fashioned decanters of cut glass, one containing port and the other dark sherry. On the closed square piano a pudding in a huge yellow dish lay in waiting and behind it were three squads of bottles of stout and ale and minerals, drawn up according to the colours of their uniforms, the first two black, with brown and red labels, the third and smallest squad white, with transverse green sashes.

Gabriel took his seat boldly at the head of the table and, having looked to the edge of the carver, plunged his fork firmly into the goose. He felt quite at ease now for he was an expert carver and liked nothing better than to find himself at the head of a well-laden table.

"Miss Furlong, what shall I send you?" he asked. "A wing or a slice of the breast?"

"Just a small slice of the breast."

"Miss Higgins, what for you?"

"O, anything at all, Mr. Conroy."

While Gabriel and Miss Daly exchanged plates of goose and plates of ham and spiced beef Lily went from guest to guest with a dish of hot floury potatoes wrapped in a white napkin. This was Mary Jane's idea and she had also suggested apple sauce for the goose but Aunt Kate had said that plain roast goose without any apple sauce had always been good enough for her and she hoped she might never eat worse. Mary Jane waited on her pupils and saw that they got the best slices and Aunt Kate and Aunt Julia opened and carried across from the piano bottles of stout and ale for the gentlemen and bottles of minerals for the ladies. There was a great deal of confusion and laughter and noise, the noise of orders and counter-orders, of knives and forks, of corks and glass-stoppers. Gabriel began to carve second helpings as soon as he had finished the first round without serving himself. Everyone protested loudly so that he compromised by taking a long draught of stout for he had found the carving hot work. Mary Jane settled down quietly to her supper but Aunt Kate and Aunt Julia were still toddling round the table, walking on each other's heels, getting in each other's way and giving each other unheeded orders. Mr. Browne begged of them to sit down and eat their suppers and so did Gabriel but they said there was time enough, so that, at last, Freddy Malins stood up and, capturing Aunt Kate, plumped her down on her chair amid general laughter.

When everyone had been well served Gabriel said, smiling:

"Now, if anyone wants a little more of what vulgar people call stuffing let him or her speak."

A chorus of voices invited him to begin his own supper and Lily came forward with three potatoes which she had reserved for him.

"Very well," said Gabriel amiably, as he took another preparatory draught, "kindly forget my existence, ladies and gentlemen, for a few minutes."

He set to his supper and took no part in the conversation with which the table covered Lily's removal of the plates. The subject of talk was the opera company which was then at the Theatre Royal. Mr. Bartell D'Arcy, the tenor, a dark-complexioned young man with a smart moustache, praised very highly the leading contralto of the company but Miss Furlong thought she had a rather vulgar style of production. Freddy Malins said there was a Negro chieftain singing in the second part of the Gaiety pantomime who had one of the finest tenor voices he had ever heard.

"Have you heard him?" he asked Mr. Bartell D'Arcy across the table.

"No," answered Mr. Bartell D'Arcy carelessly.

"Because," Freddy Malins explained, "now I'd be curious to hear your opinion of him. I think he has a grand voice."

"It takes Teddy to find out the really good things," said Mr. Browne familiarly to the table.

"And why couldn't he have a voice too?" asked Freddy Malins sharply. "Is it because he's only a black?"

Nobody answered this question and Mary Jane led the table back to the legitimate opera. One of her pupils had given her a pass for *Mignon.* Of course it was very fine, she said, but it made her think of poor Georgina Burns. Mr. Browne could go back farther still, to the old Italian companies that used to come to Dublin—Tietjens, Ilma de Murzka, Campanini, the great Trebelli, Giuglini, Ravelli, Aramburo. Those were the days, he said, when there was something like singing to be heard in Dublin. He told too of how the top gallery of the old Royal used to be packed night after night, of how one night an Italian tenor had sung five encores to *Let me like a Soldier fall*, introducing a high C every time, and of how the gallery boys would sometimes in their enthusiasm unyoke the horses from the carriage of some great *prima donna* and pull her themselves through the streets to her hotel. Why did they never play the grand old operas now, he asked, *Dinorah, Lucrezia Borgia*? Because they could not get the voices to sing them: that was why.

"Oh, well," said Mr. Bartell D'Arcy, "I presume there are as good singers today as there were then."

"Where are they?" asked Mr. Browne defiantly.

"In London, Paris, Milan," said Mr. Bartell D'Arcy warmly. "I suppose Caruso, for example, is quite as good, if not better than any of the men you have mentioned."

"Maybe so," said Mr. Browne. "But I may tell you I doubt it strongly."

"O, I'd give anything to hear Caruso sing," said Mary Jane.

"For me," said Aunt Kate, who had been picking a bone, "there was only one tenor. To please me, I mean. But I suppose none of you ever heard of him."

"Who was he, Miss Morkan?" asked Mr. Bartell D'Arcy politely.

"His name," said Aunt Kate, "was Parkinson. I heard him when he was in his prime and I think he had then the purest tenor voice that was ever put into a man's throat."

"Strange," said Mr. Bartell D'Arcy. "I never even heard of him."

"Yes, yes, Miss Morkan is right," said Mr. Browne. "I remember hearing of old Parkinson but he's too far back for me."

"A beautiful, pure, sweet, mellow English tenor," said Aunt Kate with enthusiasm.

Gabriel having finished, the huge pudding was transferred to the table. The clatter of forks and spoons began again. Gabriel's wife served out spoonfuls of the pudding and passed the plates down the table. Midway down they were held up by Mary Jane, who replenished them with raspberry or orange jelly or with blancmange and jam. The pudding was of Aunt Julia's making and she received praises for it from all quarters. She herself said that it was not quite brown enough.

"Well, I hope, Miss Morkan," said Mr. Browne, "that I'm brown enough for you because, you know, I'm all brown."

All the gentlemen, except Gabriel, ate some of the pudding out of compliment to Aunt Julia. As Gabriel never ate sweets the celery had been left for him. Freddy Malins also took a stalk of celery and ate it with his pudding. He had been told that celery was a capital thing for the blood and he was just then under doctor's care. Mrs. Malins, who had been silent all through the supper, said that her son was going down to Mount Melleray in a week or so. The table then spoke of Mount Melleray, how bracing the air was down there, how hospitable the monks were and how they never asked for a penny-piece from their guests.

"And do you mean to say," asked Mr. Browne incredulously, "that a chap can go down there and put up there as if it were a hotel and live on the fat of the land and then come away without paying anything?"

"O, most people give some donation to the monastery when they leave," said Mary Jane

"I wish we had an institution like that in our Church," said Mr. Browne candidly.

He was astonished to hear that the monks never spoke, got up at two in the morning and slept in their coffins. He asked what they did it for.

"That's the rule of the order," said Aunt Kate firmly.

"Yes, but why?" asked Mr. Browne.

Aunt Kate repeated that it was the rule, that was all. Mr. Browne still seemed not to understand. Freddy Malins explained to him, as best he could, that the monks were trying to make up for the sins committed by all the sinners in the outside world. The explanation was not very clear for Mr. Browne grinned and said:

"I like that idea very much but wouldn't a comfortable spring bed do them as well as a coffin?"

"The coffin," said Mary Jane, "is to remind them of their last end."

As the subject had grown lugubrious it was buried in a silence of the table during which Mrs. Malins could be heard saying to her neighbour in an indistinct undertone:

"They are very good men, the monks, very pious men."

The raisins and almonds and figs and apples and oranges and chocolates and sweets were now passed about the table and Aunt Julia invited all the guests to have either port or sherry. At first Mr. Bartell D'Arcy refused to take either but one of his neighbours nudged him and whispered something to him upon which he allowed his glass to be filled. Gradually as the last glasses were being filled the conversation ceased. A pause followed, broken only by the noise of the wine and by unsettlings of chairs. The Misses Morkan, all three, looked down at the tablecloth. Someone coughed once or twice and then a few gentlemen patted the table gently as a signal for silence. The silence came and Gabriel pushed back his chair and stood up.

The patting at once grew louder in encouragement and then ceased altogether. Gabriel leaned his ten trembling fingers on the tablecloth and smiled nervously at the company. Meeting a row of upturned faces he raised his eyes to the chandelier. The piano was playing a waltz tune and he could hear the skirts sweeping against the drawing-room door. People, perhaps, were standing in the snow on the quay outside, gazing up at the lighted windows and listening to the waltz music. The air was pure there. In the distance lay the park where the trees were weighted with snow. The Wellington Monument wore a gleaming cap of snow that flashed westward over the white field of Fifteen Acres.

He began:

"Ladies and Gentlemen,

"It has fallen to my lot this evening, as in years past, to perform a very pleasing task but a task for which I am afraid my poor powers as a speaker are all too inadequate."

"No, no!" said Mr. Browne.

"But, however that may be, I can only ask you tonight to take the will for the deed and to lend me your attention for a few moments while I endeavour to express to you in words what my feelings are on this occasion.

"Ladies and Gentlemen, it is not the first time that we have gathered together under this hospitable roof, around this hospitable board. It is not the first time that we have been the recipients—or perhaps, I had better say, the victims—of the hospitality of certain good ladies."

He made a circle in the air with his arm and paused. Everyone laughed or smiled at Aunt Kate and Aunt Julia and Mary Jane who all turned crimson with pleasure. Gabriel went on more boldly:

"I feel more strongly with every recurring year that our country has no tradition which does it so much honour and which it should guard so jealously as that of its hospitality. It is a tradition that is unique as far as my experience goes (and I have visited not a few places abroad) among the modern nations. Some would say, perhaps, that with us it is rather a failing than anything to be boasted of. But granted even that, it is, to my mind, a princely failing, and one that I trust will long be cultivated among us. Of one thing, at least, I am sure. As long as this one roof shelters the good ladies aforesaid—and I wish from my heart it may do so for many and many a long year to come—the tradition of genuine warm-hearted courteous Irish hospitality, which our forefathers have handed down to us and which we in turn must hand down to our descendants, is still alive among us."

A hearty murmur of assent ran round the table. It shot through Gabriel's mind that Miss Ivors was not there and that she had gone away discourteously: and he said with confidence in himself:

"Ladies and Gentlemen,

"A new generation is growing up in our midst, a generation actuated by new ideas and new principles. It is serious and enthusiastic for these new ideas and its enthusiasm, even when it is misdirected, is, I believe, in the main sincere. But we are living in a sceptical and, if I may use the phrase, a thought-tormented age: and sometimes I fear that this new generation, educated or hypereducated as it is, will lack those qualities of humanity, of hospitality, of kindly humour which belonged to an older day. Listening tonight to the names of all those great singers of the past it seemed to me, I must confess, that we were living in a less spacious age. Those days might, without exaggeration, be called spacious days: and if they are gone beyond recall let us hope, at least, that in gatherings such as this we shall still speak of them with pride and affection, still cherish in our hearts the memory of those dead and gone great ones whose fame the world will not willingly let die."

"Hear, hear!" said Mr. Browne loudly.

"But yet," continued Gabriel, his voice falling into a softer inflection, "there are always in gatherings such as this sadder thoughts that will recur to our minds: thoughts of the past, of youth, of changes, of absent faces that we miss here tonight. Our path through life is strewn with many such sad memories: and were we to brood upon them always we could not find the heart to go on bravely with our work among the living. We have all of us living duties and living affections which claim, and rightly claim, our strenuous endeavours.

"Therefore, I will not linger on the past. I will not let any gloomy moralising intrude upon us here tonight. Here we are gathered together for a brief moment from the bustle and rush of our everyday routine. We are met here as friends, in the spirit of good-fellowship, as colleagues, also to a certain extent, in the true spirit of *camaraderie*, and as the guests of—what shall I call them?—the Three Graces of the Dublin musical world."

The table burst into applause and laughter at this allusion. Aunt Julia vainly asked each of her neighbours in turn to tell her what Gabriel had said.

"He says we are the Three Graces, Aunt Julia," said Mary Jane.

Aunt Julia did not understand but she looked up, smiling, at Gabriel, who continued in the same vein:

"Ladies and Gentlemen,

"I will not attempt to play the part that Paris played on another occasion. I will not attempt to choose between them. The task would be an invidious one and one beyond my poor powers. For when I view them in turn, whether it be our chief hostess herself, whose good heart, whose too good heart, has become a byword with all who know her, or her sister, who seems to be gifted with perennial youth and whose singing must have been a surprise and a revelation to us all tonight, or, last but not least, when I consider our youngest hostess, talented, cheerful, hard-working and the best of nieces, I confess, Ladies and Gentlemen, that I do not know to which of them I should award the prize."

Gabriel glanced down at his aunts and, seeing the large smile on Aunt Julia's face and the tears which had risen to Aunt Kate's eyes, hastened to his close. He raised his glass of port gallantly, while every member of the company fingered a glass expectantly, and said loudly:

"Let us toast them all three together. Let us drink to their health, wealth, long life, happiness and prosperity and may they long continue to hold the proud and self-won position which they hold in their profession and the position of honour and affection which they hold in our hearts."

All the guests stood up, glass in hand, and turning towards the three seated ladies, sang in unison, with Mr. Browne as leader:

> *For they are jolly gay fellows,*
> *For they are jolly gay fellows,*
> *For they are jolly gay fellows,*
> *Which nobody can deny.*

Aunt Kate was making frank use of her handkerchief and even Aunt Julia seemed moved. Freddy Malins beat time with his pudding-fork and the singers turned towards one another, as if in melodious conference, while they sang with emphasis:

> *Unless he tells a lie,*
> *Unless he tells a lie,*

Then, turning once more towards their hostesses, they sang:

> *For they are jolly gay fellows,*
> *For they are jolly gay fellows,*
> *For they are jolly gay fellows,*
> *Which nobody can deny.*

The acclamation which followed was taken up beyond the door of the supper-room by many of the other guests and renewed time after time. Freddy Malins acting as officer with his fork on high.

The piercing morning air came into the hall where they were standing so that Aunt Kate said:

"Close the door, somebody. Mrs. Malins will get her death of cold."

"Browne is out there, Aunt Kate," said Mary Jane.

"Browne is everywhere," said Aunt Kate, lowering her voice.

Mary Jane laughed at her tone.

"Really," she said archly, "he is very attentive."

"He has been laid on here like the gas," said Aunt Kate in the same tone, "all during the Christmas."

She laughed herself this time good-humouredly and then added quickly:

"But tell him to come in, Mary Jane, and close the door. I hope to goodness he didn't hear me."

At that moment the hall-door was opened and Mr. Browne came in from the doorstep, laughing as if his heart would break. He was dressed in a long green overcoat with mock astrakhan cuffs and collar and wore on his head an oval fur cap. He pointed down the snow-covered quay from where the sound of shrill prolonged whistling was borne in.

"Teddy will have all the cabs in Dublin out," he said.

Gabriel advanced from the little pantry behind the office, struggling into his overcoat and, looking round the hall, said:

"Gretta not down yet?"

"She's getting on her things, Gabriel," said Aunt Kate.

"Who's playing up there?" asked Gabriel.

"Nobody. They're all gone."

"O no, Aunt Kate," said Mary Jane. "Bartell D'Arcy and Miss O'Callaghan aren't gone yet."

"Someone is fooling at the piano anyhow," said Gabriel.

Mary Jane glanced at Gabriel and Mr. Browne and said with a shiver:

"It makes me feel cold to look at you two gentlemen muffled up like that. I wouldn't like to face your journey home at this hour."

"I'd like nothing better this minute," said Mr. Browne stoutly, "than a rattling fine walk in the country or a fast drive with a good spanking goer between the shafts."

"We used to have a very good horse and trap at home," said Aunt Julia sadly.

"The never-to-be-forgotten Johnny," said Mary Jane, laughing.

Aunt Kate and Gabriel laughed too.

"Why, what was wonderful about Johnny?" asked Mr. Browne.

"The late lamented Patrick Morkan, our grandfather, that is," explained Gabriel, "commonly known in his later years as the old gentleman, was a glue-boiler."

"Oh, now, Gabriel," said Aunt Kate, laughing, "he had a starch mill."

"Well, glue or starch," said Gabriel, "the old gentleman had a horse by the name of Johnny. And Johnny used to work in the old gentleman's mill, walking round and round in order to drive the mill. That was all very well; but now comes the tragic part about Johnny. One fine day the old gentleman thought he'd like to drive out with the quality to a military review in the park."

"The Lord have mercy on his soul," said Aunt Kate compassionately.

"Amen," said Gabriel. "So the old gentleman, as I said, harnessed Johnny and put on his very best tall hat and his very best stock collar and drove out in grand style from his ancestral mansion somewhere near Back Lane, I think."

Everyone laughed, even Mrs. Malins, at Gabriel's manner and Aunt Kate said:

"O, now, Gabriel, he didn't live in Back Lane, really. Only the mill was there."

"Out from the mansion of his forefathers," continued Gabriel, "he drove with Johnny. And everything went on beautifully until Johnny came in sight of King Billy's statue: and whether he fell in love with the horse King Billy sits on or whether he thought he was back again in the mill, anyhow he began to walk round the statue."

Gabriel paced in a circle round the hall in his goloshes amid the laughter of the others.

"Round and round he went," said Gabriel, "and the old gentleman, who was a very pompous old gentleman, was highly indignant. 'Go on, sir! What do you mean, sir? Johnny! Johnny! Most extraordinary conduct! Can't understand the horse!' "

The peal of laughter which followed Gabriel's imitation of the incident was interrupted by a resounding knock at the hall door. Mary Jane ran to open it and let in Freddy Malins. Freddy Malins, with his hat well back on his head and his shoulders humped with cold, was puffing and steaming after his exertions.

"I could only get one cab," he said.

"O, we'll find another along the quay," said Gabriel.

"Yes," said Aunt Kate. "Better not keep Mrs. Malins standing in the draught."

Mrs. Malins was helped down the front steps by her son and Mr. Browne and, after many manoeuvres, hoisted into the cab. Freddy Malins clambered in after her and spent a long time settling her on the seat, Mr. Browne helping him with advice. At last she was settled comfortably and Freddy Malins invited Mr. Browne into the cab. There was a good deal of confused talk, and then Mr. Browne got into the cab. The cabman settled his rug over his knees, and bent down for the address. The confusion grew greater and the cabman was directed differently by Freddy Malins and Mr. Browne, each of whom had his head out through a window of the cab. The difficulty was to know where to drop Mr. Browne along the route, and Aunt Kate, Aunt Julia and Mary Jane helped the discussion from the doorstep with cross-directions and contradictions and abundance of laughter. As for Freddy Malins he was speechless with laughter. He popped his head in and out of the window every moment to the great danger of his hat, and told his mother how the discussion was progressing, till at last Mr. Browne shouted to the bewildered cabman above the din of everybody's laughter:

"Do you know Trinity College?"

"Yes, sir," said the cabman.

"Well, drive bang up against Trinity College gates," said Mr. Browne, "and then we'll tell you where to go. You understand now?"

"Yes, sir," said the cabman.

"Make like a bird for Trinity College."

"Right, sir," said the cabman.

The horse was whipped up and the cab rattled off along the quay amid a chorus of laughter and adieus.

Gabriel had not gone to the door with the others. He was in a dark part of the hall gazing up the staircase. A woman was standing near the top of the first flight, in the shadow also. He could not see her face but he could see the terra-cotta and salmon-pink panels of her skirt which the shadow made appear black and white. It was his wife. She was leaning on the banisters, listening to something. Gabriel was surprised at her stillness and strained his ear to listen also. But he could hear little save the noise of laughter and dispute on the front steps, a few chords struck on the piano and a few notes of a man's voice singing.

He stood still in the gloom of the hall, trying to catch the air that the voice was singing and gazing up at his wife. There was grace and mystery in her attitude as if she were a symbol of something. He asked himself what is a woman standing on the stairs in the shadow, listening to distant music, a symbol of. If he were a painter he would paint her in that attitude. Her blue felt hat would show off the bronze of her hair against the darkness and the dark panels of her skirt would show off the light ones. *Distant Music* he would call the picture if he were a painter.

The hall-door was closed; and Aunt Kate, Aunt Julia and Mary Jane came down the hall, still laughing.

"Well, isn't Freddy terrible?" said Mary Jane. "He's really terrible."

Gabriel said nothing but pointed up the stairs towards where his wife was standing. Now that the hall-door was closed the voice and the piano could be heard more clearly. Gabriel held up his hand for them to be silent. The song seemed to be in the old Irish tonality and the singer seemed uncertain both of his words and of his voice. The voice, made plaintive by distance and by the singer's hoarseness, faintly illuminated the cadence of the air with words expressing grief:

> *O, the rain falls on my heavy locks*
> *And the dew wets my skin,*
> *My babe lies cold . . .*

"O," exclaimed Mary Jane. "It's Bartell D'Arcy singing and he wouldn't sing all the night. O, I'll get him to sing a song before he goes."

"O, do, Mary Jane," said Aunt Kate.

Mary Jane brushed past the others and ran to the staircase, but before she reached it the singing stopped and the piano was closed abruptly.

"O, what a pity!" she cried. "Is he coming down, Gretta?"

Gabriel heard his wife answer yes and saw her come down towards them. A few steps behind her were Mr. Bartell D'Arcy and Miss O'Callaghan.

"O, Mr. D'Arcy," cried Mary Jane, "it's downright mean of you to break off like that when we were all in raptures listening to you."

"I have been at him all the evening," said Miss O'Callaghan, "and Mrs. Conroy, too, and he told us he had a dreadful cold and couldn't sing."

"O, Mr. D'Arcy," said Aunt Kate, "now that was a great fib to tell."

"Can't you see that I'm as hoarse as a crow?" said Mr. D'Arcy roughly.

He went into the pantry hastily and put on his overcoat. The others, taken aback by his rude speech, could find nothing to say.

Aunt Kate wrinkled her brows and made signs to the others to drop the subject. Mr. D'Arcy stood swathing his neck carefully and frowning.

"It's the weather," said Aunt Julia, after a pause.

"Yes, everybody has colds," said Aunt Kate readily, "everybody."

"They say," said Mary Jane, "we haven't had snow like it for thirty years; and I read this morning in the newspapers that the snow is general all over Ireland."

"I love the look of snow," said Aunt Julia sadly.

"So do I," said Miss O'Callaghan. "I think Christmas is never really Christmas unless we have the snow on the ground."

"But poor Mr. D'Arcy doesn't like the snow," said Aunt Kate smiling.

Mr. D'Arcy came from the pantry, fully swathed and buttoned, and in a repentant tone told them the history of his cold. Everyone gave him advice and said it was a great pity and urged him to be very careful of his throat in the night air. Gabriel watched his wife, who did not join in the conversation. She was standing right under the dusty fanlight and the flame of the gas lit up the rich bronze of her hair, which he had seen her drying at the fire a few days before. She was in the same attitude and seemed unaware of the talk about her. At last she turned towards them and Gabriel saw that there was colour on her cheeks and that her eyes were shining. A sudden tide of joy went leaping out of his heart.

"Mr. D'Arcy," she said, "what is the name of that song you were singing?"

"It's called *The Lass of Aughrim*," said Mr. D'Arcy, "but I couldn't remember it properly. Why? Do you know it?"

"*The Lass of Aughrim*," she repeated. "I couldn't think of the name."

"It's a very nice air," said Mary Jane. "I'm sorry you were not in voice tonight."

"Now, Mary Jane," said Aunt Kate, "don't annoy Mr. D'Arcy. I won't have him annoyed."

Seeing that all were ready to start she shepherded them to the door, where good-night was said:

"Well, good-night, Aunt Kate, and thanks for the pleasant evening."

"Good-night, Gabriel. Good-night, Gretta!"

"Good-night, Aunt Kate, and thanks ever so much. Good-night, Aunt Julia."

"O, good-night, Gretta, I didn't see you."

"Good-night, Mr. D'Arcy. Good-night, Miss O'Callaghan."

"Good-night, Miss Morkan."

"Good-night, again."

"Good-night, all. Safe home."

"Good-night. Good night."

The morning was still dark. A dull, yellow light brooded over the houses and the river; and the sky seemed to be descending. It was slushy underfoot; and only streaks and patches of snow lay on the roofs, on the parapets of the quay and on the area railings. The lamps were still burning redly in the murky air and, across the river, the palace of the Four Courts stood out menacingly against the heavy sky.

She was walking on before him with Mr. Bartell D'Arcy, her shoes in a brown parcel tucked under one arm and her hands holding her skirt up from the slush. She had no longer any grace of attitude, but Gabriel's eyes were still bright with happiness. The blood went bounding along his veins; and the thoughts went rioting through his brain, proud, joyful, tender, valorous.

She was walking on before him so lightly and so erect that he longed to run after her noiselessly, catch her by the shoulder and say something foolish and affectionate into her ear. She seemed to him so frail that he longed to defend her against something and then to be alone with her. Moments of their secret life together burst like stars upon his memory. A heliotrope envelope was lying beside his breakfast-cup and he was caressing it with his hand. Birds were twittering in the ivy and the sunny web of the curtain was shimmering along the floor: he could not eat for happiness. They were standing on the crowded platform and he was placing a ticket inside the warm palm of her glove. He was standing with her in the cold, looking in through a grated window at a man making bottles in a roaring furnace. It was very cold. Her face, fragrant in the cold air, was quite close to his; and suddenly he called out to the man at the furnace:

"Is the fire hot, sir?"

But the man could not hear with the noise of the furnace. It was just as well. He might have answered rudely.

A wave of yet more tender joy escaped from his heart and went coursing in warm flood along his arteries. Like the tender fire of stars moments of their life together, that no one knew of or would ever know of, broke upon and illuminated his memory. He longed to recall to her those moments, to make her forget the years of their dull existence together and remember only their moments of ecstasy. For the years, he felt, had not quenched his soul or hers. Their children, his writing, her household cares had not quenched all their souls' tender fire. In one letter that he had written to her then he had said: "Why is it that words like these seem to me so dull and cold? Is it because there is no word tender enough to be your name?"

Like distant music these words that he had written years before were borne towards him from the past. He longed to be alone with her. When the others had gone away, when he and she were in the room in the hotel, then they would be alone together. He would call her softly:

"Gretta!"

Perhaps she would not hear at once: she would be undressing. Then something in his voice would strike her. She would turn and look at him. . . .

At the corner of Winetavern Street they met a cab. He was glad of its rattling noise as it saved him from conversation. She was looking out of the window and seemed tired. The others spoke only a few words, pointing out some building or street. The horse galloped along wearily under the murky morning sky, dragging his old rattling box after his heels, and Gabriel was again in a cab with her, galloping to catch the boat, galloping to their honeymoon.

As the cab drove across O'Connell Bridge Miss O'Callaghan said:

"They say you never cross O'Connell Bridge without seeing a white horse."

"I see a white man this time," said Gabriel.

"Where?" asked Mr. Bartell D'Arcy.

Gabriel pointed to the statue, on which lay patches of snow. Then he nodded familiarly to it and waved his hand.

"Good-night, Dan," he said gaily.

When the cab drew up before the hotel, Gabriel jumped out and, in spite of Mr. Bartell D'Arcy's protest, paid the driver. He gave the man a shilling over his fare. The man saluted and said:

"A prosperous New Year to you, sir."

"The same to you," said Gabriel cordially.

She leaned for a moment on his arm in getting out of the cab and while standing at the curbstone, bidding the others good-night. She leaned lightly on his arm, as lightly as when she had danced with him a few hours before. He had felt proud and happy then, happy that she was his, proud of her grace and wifely carriage. But now, after the kindling again of so many memories, the first touch of her body, musical and strange and perfumed, sent through him a keen pang of lust. Under cover of her silence he pressed her arm closely to his side; and, as they stood at the hotel door, he felt that they had escaped from their lives and duties, escaped from home and friends and run away together with wild and radiant hearts to a new adventure.

An old man was dozing in a great hooded chair in the hall. He lit a candle in the office and went before them to the stairs. They followed him in silence, their feet falling in soft thuds on the thickly carpeted stairs. She mounted the stairs behind the porter, her head bowed in the ascent, her frail shoulders curved as with a burden, her skirt girt tightly about her. He could have flung his arms about her hips and held her still, for his arms were trembling with desire to seize her and only the stress of his nails against the palms of his hands held the wild impulse of his body in check. The porter halted on the stairs to settle his guttering candle. They halted, too, on the steps below him. In the silence Gabriel could hear the falling of the molten wax into the tray and the thumping of his own heart against his ribs.

The porter led them along a corridor and opened a door. Then he set his unstable candle down on a toilet-table and asked at what hour they were to be called in the morning.

"Eight," said Gabriel.

The porter pointed to the tap of the electric-bulb and began a muttered apology, but Gabriel cut him short.

"We don't want any light. We have light enough from the street. And I say," he added, pointing to the candle, "you might remove that handsome article, like a good man."

The porter took up his candle again, but slowly, for he was surprised by such a novel idea. Then he mumbled good-night and went out. Gabriel shot the lock to.

A ghastly light from the street lamp lay in a long shaft from one window to the door. Gabriel threw his overcoat and hat on a couch and crossed the room towards the window. He looked down into the street in order that his emotion might calm a little. Then he turned and leaned against a chest of drawers with his back to the light. She had taken off her hat and cloak and was standing before a large swinging mirror, unhooking her waist. Gabriel paused for a few moments, watching her, and then said:

"Gretta!"

She turned away from the mirror slowly and walked along the shaft of light towards him. Her face looked so serious and weary that the words would not pass Gabriel's lips. No, it was not the moment yet.

"You looked tired," he said.

"I am a little," she answered

"You don't feel ill or weak?"

"No, tired: that's all."

She went on to the window and stood there, looking out. Gabriel waited again and then, fearing that diffidence was about to conquer him, he said abruptly:

"By the way, Gretta!"

"What is it?"

"You know that poor fellow Malins?" he said quickly.

"Yes. What about him?"

"Well, poor fellow, he's a decent sort of chap, after all," continued Gabriel in a false voice. "He gave me back that sovereign I lent him, and I didn't expect it, really. It's a pity he wouldn't keep away from that Browne, because he's not a bad fellow, really."

He was trembling now with annoyance. Why did she seem so abstracted? He did not know how he could begin. Was she annoyed, too, about something? If she would only turn to him or come to him of her own accord! To take her as she was would be brutal. No, he must see some ardour in her eyes first. He longed to be master of her strange mood.

"When did you lend him the pound?" she asked, after a pause.

Gabriel strove to restrain himself from breaking out into brutal language about the sottish Malins and his pound. He longed to cry to her from his soul, to crush her body against his, to overmaster her. But he said:

"O, at Christmas, when he opened that little Christmas-card shop in Henry Street."

He was in such a fever of rage and desire that he did not hear her come from the window. She stood before him for an instant, looking at him strangely. Then, suddenly raising herself on tiptoe and resting her hands lightly on his shoulders, she kissed him.

"You are a very generous person, Gabriel," she said.

Gabriel, trembling with delight at her sudden kiss and at the quaintness of her phrase, put his hands on her hair and began smoothing it back, scarcely touching it with his fingers. The washing had made it fine and brilliant. His heart was brimming over with happiness. Just when he was wishing for it she had come to him of her own accord. Perhaps her thoughts had been running with his. Perhaps she had felt the impetuous desire that was in him, and then the yielding mood had come upon her. Now that she had fallen to him so easily, he wondered why he had been so diffident.

He stood, holding her head between his hands. Then, slipping one arm swiftly about her body and drawing her towards him, he said softly:

"Gretta, dear, what are you thinking about?"

She did not answer nor yield wholly to his arm. He said again, softly:

"Tell me what it is, Gretta. I think I know what is the matter. Do I know?"

She did not answer at once. Then she said in an outburst of tears:

"O, I am thinking about that song, *The Lass of Aughrim*."

She broke loose from him and ran to the bed and, throwing her arms across the bed-rail, hid her face. Gabriel stood stock-still for a moment in astonishment and then followed her. As he passed in the way of the cheval-glass he caught sight of himself in full length, his broad, well-filled shirt-front, the face whose expression always puzzled him when he saw it in a mirror, and his glimmering gilt-rimmed eyeglasses. He halted a few paces from her and said:

"What about the song? Why does that make you cry?"

She raised her head from her arms and dried her eyes with the back of her hand like a child. A kinder note than he had intended went into his voice.

"Why, Gretta?" he asked.

"I am thinking about a person long ago who used to sing that song.'

"And who was the person long ago?" asked Gabriel, smiling.

"It was a person I used to know in Galway when I was living with my grandmother," she said.

The smile passed away from Gabriel's face. A dull anger began to gather again at the back of his mind and the dull fires of his lust began to glow angrily in his veins.

"Someone you were in love with?" he asked ironically.

"It was a young boy I used to know," she answered, "named Michael Furey. He used to sing that song *The Lass of Aughrim*. He was very delicate."

Gabriel was silent. He did not wish her to think that he was interested in this delicate boy.

"I can see him so plainly," she said, after a moment. "Such eyes as he had: big, dark eyes! And such an expression in them—an expression!"

"O, then you are in love with him?" said Gabriel.

"I used to go out walking with him," she said, "when I was in Galway."

A thought flew across Gabriel's mind.

"Perhaps that was why you wanted to go to Galway with that Ivors girl?" he said coldly.

She looked at him and asked in surprise:

"What for?"

Her eyes made Gabriel feel awkward. He shrugged his shoulders and said:

"How do I know? To see him, perhaps."

She looked away from him along the shaft of light towards the window in silence.

"He is dead," she said at length. "He died when he was only seventeen. Isn't it a terrible thing to die so young as that?"

"What was he?" asked Gabriel, still ironically.

"He was in the gasworks," she said.

Gabriel felt humiliated by the failure of his irony and by the evocation of this figure from the dead, a boy in the gasworks. While he had been full of memories of their secret life together, full of tenderness and joy and desire, she had been comparing him in her mind with another. A shameful consciousness of his own person assailed him. He saw himself as a ludicrous figure, acting as a penny-boy for his aunts, a nervous, well-meaning sentimentalist, orating to vulgarians and idealising his own clownish lusts, the pitiable fatuous fellow he had caught a glimpse of in the mirror. Instinctively he turned his back more to the light lest she might see the shame that burned upon his forehead.

He tried to keep up his tone of cold interrogation, but his voice when he spoke was humble and indifferent.

"I suppose you were in love with this Michael Furey, Gretta," he said.

"I was great with him at that time," she said.

Her voice was veiled and sad. Gabriel, feeling now how vain it would be to try to lead her whither he had purposed, caressed one of her hands and said, also sadly:

"And what did he die of so young, Gretta? Consumption, was it?"

"I think he died for me," she answered.

A vague terror seized Gabriel at this answer, as if, at that hour when he had hoped to triumph, some impalpable and vindictive being was coming against him, gathering forces against him in its vague world. But he shook himself free of it with an effort of reason and continued to caress her hand. He did not question her again, for he felt that she would tell him of herself. Her hand was warm and moist: it did not respond to his touch, but he continued to caress it just as he had caressed her first letter to him that spring morning.

"It was in the winter," she said, "about the beginning of the winter when I was going to leave my grandmother's and come up here to the convent. And he was ill at the time in his lodgings in Galway and wouldn't be let out, and his people in Oughterard were written to. He was in decline, they said, or something like that. I never knew rightly."

She paused for a moment and sighed.

"Poor fellow," she said. "He was very fond of me and he was such a gentle boy. We used to go out together, walking, you know, Gabriel, like the way they do in the country. He was going to study singing only for his health. He had a very good voice, poor Michael Furey."

"Well; and then?" asked Gabriel.

"And then when it came to the time for me to leave Galway and come up to the convent he was much worse and I wouldn't be let see him so I wrote a letter saying I was going up to Dublin and would be back in the summer, and hoping he would be better then."

She paused for a moment to get her voice under control, and then went on:

"Then the night before I left, I was in my grandmother's house in Nuns' Island, packing up, and I heard gravel thrown up against the window. The window was so wet I couldn't see, so I ran downstairs as I was and slipped out the back into the garden and there was the poor fellow at the end of the garden, shivering."

"And did you not tell him to go back?" asked Gabriel.

"I implored of him to go home at once and I told him he would get his death in the rain. But he said he did not want to live. I can see his eyes as well as well! He was standing at the end of the wall where there was a tree."

"And did he go home?" asked Gabriel.

"Yes, he went home. And when I was only a week in the convent he died and he was buried in Oughterard, where his people came from. O, the day I heard that, that he was dead!"

She stopped, choking with sobs, and, overcome by emotion, flung herself face downward on the bed, sobbing in the quilt. Gabriel held her hand for a moment longer, irresolutely, and then, shy of intruding on her grief, let it fall gently and walked quietly to the window.

She was fast asleep.

Gabriel, leaning on his elbow, looked for a few moments unresentfully on her tangled hair and half-open mouth, listening to her deep-drawn breath. So she had had that romance in her life: a man had died for her sake. It hardly pained him now to think how poor a part he, her husband, had played in her life. He watched her while she slept, as though he and she had never lived together as man and wife. His curious eyes rested long upon her face and on her hair; and, as he thought of what she must have been then, in that time of her first girlish beauty, a strange, friendly pity for her entered his soul. He did not like to say even to himself that her face was no longer beautiful, but he knew that it was no longer the face for which Michael Furey had braved death.

Perhaps she had not told him all the story. His eyes moved to the chair over which she had thrown some of her clothes. A petticoat string dangled to the floor. One boot stood upright, its limp upper fallen down: the fellow of it lay upon its side. He wondered at his riot of emotions of an hour before. From what had it proceeded? From his aunt's supper, from his own foolish speech, from the wine and dancing, the merry-making when saying good-night in the hall, the pleasure of the walk along the river in the snow. Poor Aunt Julia! She, too, would soon be a shade with the shade of Patrick Morkan and his horse. He had caught that haggard look upon her face for a moment when she was singing *Arrayed for the Bridal*. Soon, perhaps, he would be sitting in that same drawing-room, dressed in black, his silk hat on his knees. The blinds would be drawn down and Aunt Kate would be sitting beside him, crying and blowing her nose and telling him how Julia had died. He would cast about in his mind for some words that might console her, and would find only lame and useless ones. Yes, yes: that would happen very soon.

The air of the room chilled his shoulders. He stretched himself cautiously along under the sheets and lay down beside his wife. One by one, they were all becoming shades. Better pass boldly into that other world, in the full glory of some passion, than fade and wither dismally with age. He thought of how she who lay beside him had locked in her heart for so many years that image of her lover's eyes when he had told her that he did not wish to live.

Generous tears filled Gabriel's eyes. He had never felt like that himself towards any woman, but he knew that such a feeling must be love. The tears gathered more thickly in his eyes and in the partial darkness he imagined he saw the form of a young man standing under a dripping tree. Other forms were near. His soul had approached that region where dwell the vast hosts of the dead. He was conscious of, but could not apprehend, their wayward and flickering existence. His own identity was fading out into a grey impalpable world: the solid world itself, which these dead had one time reared and lived in, was dissolving and dwindling.

A few light taps upon the pane made him turn to the window. It had begun to snow again. He watched sleepily the flakes, silver and dark, falling obliquely against the lamplight. The time had come for him to set out on his journey westward. Yes, the newspapers were right: snow was general all over Ireland. It was falling on every part of the dark central plain, on the treeless hills, falling softly upon the Bog of Allen and, farther westward, softly falling into the dark mutinous Shannon waves. It was falling, too, upon every part of the lonely churchyard on the hill where Michael Furey lay buried. It lay thickly drifted on the crooked crosses and headstones, on the spears of the little gate, on the barren thorns. His soul swooned slowly as he heard the snow falling faintly through the universe and faintly falling, like the descent of their last end, upon all the living and the dead.

Old Man at the Bridge
Ernest Hemingway

An old man with steel rimmed spectacles and very dusty clothes sat by the side of the road. There was a pontoon bridge across the river and carts, trucks, and men, women and children were crossing it. The mule-drawn carts staggered up the steep bank from the bridge with soldiers helping push against the spokes of the wheels. The trucks ground up and away heading out of it all and the peasants plodded along in the ankle deep dust. But the old man sat there without moving. He was too tired to go any farther.

It was my business to cross the bridge, explore the bridgehead beyond and find out to what point the enemy had advanced. I did this and returned over the bridge. There were not so many carts now and very few people on foot, but the old man was still there.

"Where do you come from?" I asked him.

"From San Carlos," he said, and smiled.

That was his native town and so it gave him pleasure to mention it and he smiled.

"I was taking care of animals," he explained.

"Oh," I said, not quite understanding.

"Yes," he said, "I stayed, you see, taking care of animals. I was the last one to leave the town of San Carlos."

He did not look like a shepherd nor a herdsman and I looked at his black dusty clothes and his gray dusty face and his steel rimmed spectacles and said, "What animals were they?"

"Various animals," he said, and shook his head. "I had to leave them."

I was watching the bridge and the African looking country of the Ebro Delta and wondering how long now it would be before we would see the enemy, and listening all the while for the first noises that would signal that ever mysterious event called contact, and the old man still sat there.

"What animals were they?" I asked.

"There were three animals altogether," he explained. "There were two goats and a cat and then there were four pairs of pigeons."

"And you had to leave them?" I asked.

"Yes. Because of the artillery. The captain told me to go because of the artillery."

"And you have no family?" I asked, watching the far end of the bridge where a few last carts were hurrying down the slope of the bank.

"No," he said, "only the animals I stated. The cat, of course, will be all right. A cat can look out for itself, but I cannot think what will become of the others."

"What politics have you?" I asked.

"I am without politics," he said. "I am seventy-six years old. I have come twelve kilometers now and I think now I can go no further."

"This is not a good place to stop," I said. "If you can make it, there are trucks up the road where it forks for Tortosa."

"I will wait a while," he said, "and then I will go. Where do the trucks go?"

"Towards Barcelona," I told him.

"I know no one in that direction," he said. "but thank you very much. Thank you again very much."

He looked at me very blankly and tiredly, then said, having to share his worry with some one, "The cat will be all right, I am sure. There is no need to be unquiet about the cat. But the others. Now what do you think about the others?"

"Why they'll probably come through it all right."

"You think so?"

"Why not," I said, watching the far bank where now there were no carts.

"But what will they do under the artillery when I was told to leave because of the artillery?"

"Did you leave the dove cage unlocked?" I asked.

"Yes."

"Then they'll fly."

"Yes, certainly they'll fly. But the others. It's better not to think about the others," he said.

"If you are rested I would go," I urged. "Get up and try to walk now."

"Thank you," he said and got to his feet, swayed from side to side and then sat down backwards in the dust.

"I was taking care of animals," he said dully, but no longer to me. "I was only taking care of animals."

There was nothing to do about him. It was Easter Sunday and the Fascists were advancing toward the Ebro. It was a gray overcast day with a low ceiling so their planes were not up. That and the fact that cats know how to look after themselves was all the good luck that old man would ever have.

Categories of Order

1. SELECTION, ARRANGEMENT, AND STYLE

The material of fiction does not just "happen" on the pages of the short story. It abets the author's intention, but only after a process of selection and arrangement which tests his capacity for controlled, subjective economy or discrimination. For it is he as an individual who looks at the raw ingredients of his story and says to himself: "This detail I shall use but that I shall ignore; this one I shall build upon but this I shall only mention." And he continues: "This item shall go first while others will be casually interspersed throughout the story." In short, it is the author and only he who, confronted with his material, chooses what he shall retain, what he shall reject and then consciously arranges what he has for the determination of his specific purpose. It is he who decides whether the time sequence will satisfy conventional expectations or will defy them. It is he who decides which characters will be "flat" and which "round," "static," or "dynamic." It is he who decides whether the plot will be constructed

on a linear plan like the deceptively simple one of Vladimir Nabokov's "Signs and Symbols," or the openly more complex one of
Nadine Gordimer's "Message in a Bottle" with its crosshatching of
metaphoric analogies, of events experienced, surmised, and imagined.
The author alone must determine whether the proper form of his
story is best sustained by the conventional logic of chronology and
thought, or by the indirection of digressive action and thought, of
time-shifts and streams-of-consciousness.

What we have said here would suggest that the process of selection
is thoroughly conscious, clearly rational. This is not necessarily so.
Virginia Woolf, for example, correctly looks upon artistic selectivity
as a paradoxical blend of intuitive sensitivity and a firm sense of intellectual discipline.

The novelist—it is his distinction and his danger—is terribly exposed
to life. Other artists, partially at least, withdraw; they shut themselves up
for weeks alone with a dish of apples and a paint-box, or a roll of music
paper and a piano. When they emerge it is to forget and distract themselves. But the novelist never forgets and is seldom distracted. He fills
his glass and lights his cigarette, he enjoys presumably all the pleasures
of talk and table, but always with a sense that he is being stimulated and
played upon by the subject matter of his art. Taste, sound, movement, a
few words here, a gesture there, a man coming in, a woman going out,
even the motor that passes in the street or the beggar who shuffles along
the pavement, and all the reds and blues and lights and shades of the
scene claim his attention and rouse his curiosity. He can no more cease
to receive impressions than a fish in mid-ocean can cease to let the
water rush through his gills.

But if this sensibility is one of the conditions of the novelist's life, it
is obvious that all writers whose books survive have known how to
master it and make it serve their purposes. They have finished the wine
and paid the bill and gone off, alone, into some solitary room where,
with toil and pause, in agony (like Flaubert), with struggle and rush,
tumultuously (like Dostoevsky) they have mastered their perceptions,
hardened them, and changed them into the fabrics of their art.

So drastic is the process of selection that in its final state we can often
find no trace of the actual scene upon which the chapter was based. For
in that solitary room, whose door the critics are for ever trying to un-
lock, processes of the strangest kind are gone through. Life is subjected

to a thousand disciplines and exercises. It is curbed; it is killed. It is mixed with this, stiffened with that, brought into contrast with something else; so that when we get our scene at a cafe a year later the surface signs by which we remembered it have disappeared. There emerges from the mist something stark, something formidable and enduring, the bone and substance upon which our rush of indiscriminating emotion was founded.*

A writer's "style"—one of the most subjective of literary concepts—emerges from the manner in which he selects and arranges his words upon the page, from the manner in which he reconciles language and meaning. Style emerges therefore with the same inevitability as does every other aspect of the short story. To be sure, the author is not indifferent to the principles laid down by grammarians. But they have only limited relevance for him because his purpose is not served by strict insistence upon "clarity" and "correctness." Denotation is a function of daily communication in which expository precision is always valuable. The artist, contrarily, projects his imagination through the connotative resources of language—ambiguity, metaphor, image, and the like— and through the subjective manipulation of syntax. He refuses, in short, to be limited by verbal and grammatical formality. That is why Faulkner can say of fictional style, there is "no rule to it." Style is a manner of writing that exacts critical tolerance and sympathy, for the critic must judge this variable, individualistic condition by its ultimate effects.

Perhaps we should leave off trying to define what style is in order to determine what it does within a short story. Certainly style helps to set the mood of a narrative. We can feel the despair of the old man at the bridge with every one of Hemingway's reticent words. Yet the old man never speaks openly of his state of mind. He just sits in his "very dusty clothes . . . by the side of the road." And over and over again he says like a feeling robot, "I was taking care of the animals." Or "I stayed, you see, taking care of animals, . . . I was only taking care of the animals." Using this same story as an illustration, we can be sure that style prompts us to judge an author's

*Virginia Woolf, "Life and the Novelist," New York *Herald Tribune,* 7 November 1926.

materials as he would wish us to judge them. We are moved by the simplicity and repression in the old man's manner of speaking. There is in it a deliberately dulled tonality that elicits our sympathy for him and arouses anger over those conditions which have brought him to this state. We are made to hate as passionately as Hemingway the inhumanity of war and its sacrifice of the innocent.

Style further sharpens our awareness of the characters within a story, of their emotional and intellectual complexity or simplicity, of their ability to undergo change. It is style which permits us to understand the chivalric decision of Sammy in Updike's "A & P." Because the story is told in the first person, the very words used reveal the personality of the narrator. Like his language, the boy himself is half-flippant, half-sensitive. His quitting, his repudiation of the supermarket and its self-righteous manager, is the gesture of a knight errant who in an unlikely mercenary setting is prepared to defend the beautiful and the innocent. But it is also a quixotic gesture and no one knows this better than the boy who has grown up in a cynical modernity.

"You'll feel this for the rest of your life," Lengel says, and I know that's true, too, but remembering how he made that pretty girl blush makes me so scrunchy inside I punch the No Sale tab and the machine whirs "peepul" and the drawer splats out. One advantage to this scene taking place in summer, I can follow this up with a clean exit, there's no fumbling around getting your coat and galoshes, I just saunter into the electric eye in my white shirt that my mother ironed the night before, and the door heaves itself open, and outside the sunshine is skating around on the asphalt.

Finally, style, which is among other things the mark of a writer's individuality, provides the unity of any piece of fiction and its atmosphere. For someone like Edgar Allan Poe style *is* atmosphere or "effect" as he chooses to call it. In his review of Hawthorne's *Twice-Told Tales*, he speaks of style without mentioning the word. "A skilful literary artist," he says, "has constructed a tale. If wise, he has not fashioned his thought to accommodate his incidents; but having conceived, with deliberate care, a certain unique or single *effect* to be wrought out, he then invents such incidents—he then combines such events as may best aid him in establishing this preconceived effect. If his very initial sentence tend not to the outbringing of this effect, then he has failed in his first step. In the whole composition there should be no word written, of which the tendency, direct or indirect, is not to the one pre-established design. And by such means, with such care and skill, a picture is at length painted which leaves in the mind of him who contemplates it with a kindred art, a sense of the fullest satisfaction. The idea of the tale has been presented unblemished, because undisturbed . . . ."

Signs and Symbols
Vladimir Nabokov

1

For the fourth time in as many years they were confronted with
the problem of what birthday present to bring a young man who was
incurably deranged in his mind. He had no desires. Man-made
objects were to him either hives of evil, vibrant with a malignant
activity that he alone could perceive, or gross comforts for which no
use could be found in his abstract world. After eliminating a number of articles that might offend him or frighten him (anything in
the gadget line for instance was taboo), his parents chose a dainty
and innocent trifle: a basket with ten different fruit jellies in ten
little jars.

At the time of his birth they had been married already for a long
time; a score of years had elapsed, and now they were quite old.
Her drab gray hair was done anyhow. She wore cheap black dresses.
Unlike other women of her age (such as Mrs. Sol, their next-door

neighbor, whose face was all pink and mauve with paint and whose hat was a cluster of brookside flowers), she presented a naked white countenance to the fault-finding light of spring days. Her husband, who in the old country had been a fairly successful business man, was now wholly dependent on his brother Issac, a real American of almost forty years standing. They seldom saw him and had nicknamed him "the Prince."

That Friday everything went wrong. The underground train lost its life current between two stations, and for a quarter of an hour one could hear nothing but the dutiful beating of one's heart and the rustling of newspapers. The bus they had to take next kept them waiting for ages; and when it did come, it was crammed with garrulous high-school children. It was raining hard as they walked up the brown path leading to the sanitarium. There they waited again; and instead of their boy shuffling into the room as he usually did (his poor face blotched with acne, ill-shaven, sullen, and confused), a nurse they knew, and did not care for, appeared at last and brightly explained that he had again attempted to take his life. He was all right, she said, but a visit might disturb him. The place was so miserably understaffed, and things got mislaid or mixed up so easily, that they decided not to leave their present in the office but to bring it to him next time they came.

She waited for her husband to open his umbrella and then took his arm. He kept clearing his throat in a special resonant way he had when he was upset. They reached the bus-stop shelter on the other side of the street and he closed his umbrella. A few feet away, under a swaying and dripping tree, a tiny half-dead unfledged bird was helplessly twitching in a puddle.

During the long ride to the subway station, she and her husband did not exchange a word; and every time she glanced at his old hands (swollen veins, brown-spotted skin), clasped and twitching upon the handle of his umbrella, she felt the mounting pressure of tears. As she looked around trying to hook her mind onto something, it gave her a kind of soft shock, a mixture of compassion and wonder, to notice that one of the passengers, a girl with dark hair and grubby red toenails, was weeping on the shoulder of an older woman. Whom did that woman resemble? She resembled Rebecca Borisovna, whose daughter had married one of the Soloveichiks—in Minsk, years ago.

The last time he had tried to do it, his method had been, in the doctor's words, a masterpiece of inventiveness; he would have succeeded, had not an envious fellow patient thought he was learning to fly—and stopped him. What he really wanted to do was to tear a hole in his world and escape.

The system of his delusions had been the subject of an elaborate paper in a scientific monthly, but long before that she and her husband had puzzled it out for themselves. "Referential mania," Herman Brink had called it. In these very rare cases the patient imagines that everything happening around him is a veiled reference to his personality and existence. He excludes real people from the conspiracy—because he considers himself to be so much more intelligent than other men. Phenomenal nature shadows him wherever he goes. Clouds in the staring sky transmit to one another, by means of slow signs, incredibly detailed information regarding him. His inmost thoughts are discussed at nightfall, in manual alphabet, by darkly gesticulating trees. Pebbles or stains or sun flecks form patterns representing in some awful way messages which he must intercept. Everything is a cipher and of everything he is the theme. Some of the spies are detached observers, such are glass surfaces and still pools; others, such as coats in store windows, are prejudiced witnesses, lynchers at heart; others again (running water, storms) are hysterical to the point of insanity, have a distorted opinion of him and grotesquely misinterpret his actions. He must be always on his guard and devote every minute and module of life to the decoding of the undulation of things. The very air he exhales is indexed and filed away. If only the interest he provokes were limited to his immediate surroundings—but alas it is not! With distance the torrents of wild scandal increase in volume and volubility. The silhouettes of his blood corpuscles, magnified a million times, flit over vast plains; and still farther, great mountains of unbearable solidity and height sum up in terms of granite and groaning firs the ultimate truth of his being.

2

When they emerged from the thunder and foul air of the subway, the last dregs of the day were mixed with the street lights. She wanted to buy some fish for supper, so she handed him the basket of jelly jars, telling him to go home. He walked up to the third landing and then remembered he had given her his keys earlier in the day.

In silence he sat down on the steps and in silence rose when some ten minutes later she came, heavily trudging upstairs, wanly smiling, shaking her head in deprecation of her silliness. They entered their two-room flat and he at once went to the mirror. Straining the corners of his mouth apart by means of his thumbs, with a horrible masklike grimace, he removed his new hopelessly uncomfortable dental plate and severed the long tusks of saliva connecting him to it. He read his Russian-language newspaper while she laid the table. Still reading, he ate the pale victuals that needed no teeth. She knew his moods and was also silent.

When he had gone to bed, she remained in the living room with her pack of soiled cards and her old albums. Across the narrow yard where the rain tinkled in the dark against some battered ash cans, windows were blandly alight and in one of them a black-trousered man with his bare elbows raised could be seen lying supine on an untidy bed. She pulled the blind down and examined the photographs. As a baby he looked more surprised than most babies. From a fold in the album, a German maid they had had in Leipzig and her fat-faced fiancé fell out. Minsk, the Revolution, Leipzig, Berlin, Leipzig, a slanting house front badly out of focus. Four years old, in a park: moodily, shyly, with puckered forehead, looking away from an eager squirrel as he would from any other stranger. Aunt Rosa, a fussy, angular, wild-eyed old lady, who had lived in a tremulous world of bad news, bankruptcies, train accidents, cancerous growths— until the Germans put her to death, together with all the people she had worried about. Age six—that was when he drew wonderful birds with human hands and feet, and suffered from insomnia like a grown-up man. His cousin, now a famous chess player. He again, aged about eight, already difficult to understand, afraid of the wallpaper in the passage, afraid of a certain picture in a book which merely showed an idyllic landscape with rocks on a hillside and an old cart wheel hanging from the branch of a leafless tree. Aged ten: the year they left Europe. The shame, the pity, the humiliating difficulties, the ugly, vicious, backward children he was with in that special school. And then came a time in his life, coinciding with a long convalescence after pneumonia, when those little phobias of his which his parents had stubbornly regarded as the eccentricities of a prodigiously gifted child hardened as it were into a dense tangle of logically interacting illusions, making him totally inaccessible to normal minds.

This, and much more, she accepted—for after all living did mean accepting the loss of one joy after another, not even joys in her case—mere possibilities of improvement. She thought of the endless waves of pain that for some reason or other she and her husband had to endure; of the invisible giants hurting her boy in some unimaginable fashion; of the incalculable amount of tenderness contained in the world; of the fate of this tenderness, which is either crushed, or wasted, or transformed into madness; of neglected children humming to themselves in unswept corners; of beautiful weeds that cannot hide from the farmer and helplessly have to watch the shadow of his simian stoop leave mangled flowers in its wake, as the monstrous darkness approaches.

3

It was past midnight when from the living room she heard her husband moan; and presently he staggered in, wearing over his nightgown the old overcoat with astrakhan collar which he much preferred to the nice blue bathrobe he had.

"I can't sleep," he cried.

"Why," she asked, "why can't you sleep? You were so tired."

"I can't sleep because I am dying," he said and lay down on the couch.

"Is it your stomach? Do you want me to call Dr. Solov?"

"No doctors, no doctors," he moaned, "To the devil with doctors! We must get him out of there quick. Otherwise we'll be responsible.

Responsible!" he repeated and hurled himself into a sitting position, both feet on the floor, thumping his forehead with his clenched fist.

"All right," she said quietly, "we shall bring him home tomorrow morning."

"I would like some tea," said her husband and retired to the bathroom.

Bending with difficulty, she retrieved some playing cards and a photograph or two that had slipped from the couch to the floor: knave of hearts, nine of spades, ace of spades, Elsa and her bestial beau.

He returned in high spirits, saying in a loud voice:

"I have it all figured out. We will give him the bedroom. Each of us will spend part of the night near him and the other part on this couch. By turns. We will have the doctor see him at least twice a week. It does not matter what the Prince says. He won't have to say much anyway because it will come out cheaper."

The telephone rang. It was an unusual hour for their telephone to ring. His left slipper had come off and he groped for it with his heel and toe as he stood in the middle of the room, and childishly, toothlessly, gaped at his wife. Having more English than he did, it was she who attended to calls.

"Can I speak to Charlie," said a girl's dull little voice.

"What number you want? No. That is not the right number."

The receiver was gently cradled. Her hand went to her old tired heart.

"It frightened me," she said.

He smiled a quick smile and immediately resumed his excited monologue. They would fetch him as soon as it was day. Knives would have to be kept in a locked drawer. Even at his worst he presented no danger to other people.

The telephone rang a second time. The same toneless anxious young voice asked for Charlie.

"You have the incorrect number. I will tell you what you are doing: you are turning the letter O instead of the zero."

They sat down to their unexpected festive midnight tea. The birthday present stood on the table. He sipped noisily; his face was flushed; every now and then he imparted a circular motion to his raised glass so as to make the sugar dissolve more thoroughly. The vein on the side of his bald head where there was a large birthmark stood out conspicuously and, although he had shaved that morning, a silvery bristle showed on his chin. While she poured him another glass of tea, he put on his spectacles and re-examined with pleasure the luminous yellow, green, red little jars. His clumsy moist lips spelled out their eloquent labels: apricot, grape, beech plum, quince. He had got to crab apple, when the telephone rang again.

Message in a Bottle
Nadine Gordimer

There are days when the world pauses, gets stuck, senselessly, like one of those machines that ought to give cigarettes or make balls bump round but simply becomes an object that takes kicks, shakes, unyieldingly. You drop out of step with the daily work or habit that carries you along and stare about. Halt, halt! It's fatal. This is not Sunday, with cows beside winter willows and dried-up streams, and white egrets catching up with their own forward-jerking necks. I notice a face in the strip of mirror attached with crystal knobs to the pillar in the coffee shop. An uneven face, looks as if it's been up all night for years: my own. Once I had no face to speak of, only a smile, bright eyes and powdered cheeks, nicely arranged. I order two coffees, one for myself, one for the child—"Would you like a cup of coffee?": it is a piece of clumsy flattery, a status I confer upon her because she has just been to a doctor and suffered a painful treatment. She accepts it, her token smile knowing its worth.

She shivers a little, from shock, in her dusty school clothes; at this time of the morning, she ought to be doing mental arithmetic. I am in my work clothes too, interrupted by necessity. I do not know what to talk to the child about because she has plumbed cheerful, jollying reassurances over months of pain, and efforts at distraction she takes as a kind of insult. She resents my sympathy because I have not her pain; my solicitously gentle voice is easy enough for me, it does not help her, she has discovered. So we don't talk, and I eat a piece of cheesecake, not so much because I want it, but to show her that life must go on. By such moves and signals do we conduct the battle that is waged between the sick and the well.

I eat the cheesecake and look again at the only other two customers in the place at this time on a Wednesday morning. I half-saw them when we came in, but my awareness was merely of a presence that brought to light my old trousers and cardigan. An oldish man and a blonde girl out of a fashion magazine. She is tall as they always are and she sits not with her knees under the table but with the length of her body from seat to head turned diagonally toward him and supported by her elbow on the table. From the door, without detail, they fell into an image of a girl making up to a man. But she is weeping. Tears fill and refract marvellously the one eye I can see and then run slowly down the pale beige cheek. She stretches the muscles of her face to hold them and puts up the forefinger of a clenched hand to catch them. One distinctly runs over the finger and drops to the tablecloth. There will be a little splotch there, where it fell.

I look away, but when I look back again the tears are still coming, in slow twos and threes down the matte and perfect cheek. She is talking all the time to the man, not looking at him but talking without a sound that I can hear, directly to his ear with the dark shadow in it that must be a tuft of hair. That tense tendon in her neck may become permanent when she is older; but there is no reason why she will be so unhappy often. It looks like the kind of misery one grows out of.

She is a beautiful girl dressed from head to foot in pale beige that matches her face and hair. He would be ugly if he were a poor man, sucked dry, at his age, and leathery; but his crowded features, thin ridged nose and eyes and line of mouth, are filled out, smoothly built up, deal by deal, as a sculptor adds clay daub by daub, by ease and money-making. He has never been a good-looking young man, never. While she talks he looks out across the room, listening.

He does not look at her but at the waiters passing, the door opening, the woman at the cash register ringing up the sale of a packet of cigarettes. It is a face that has put love into making money. Yes, he is ugly, but I do not know whether I imagine that she already has the look of one of those lovely creatures whose beauty—that makes them feel they may have any man—brings them nothing but one of these owners of textile factories; while we others, who are ignored by the many, carry off the particular prizes, the distinguished, the gentle, the passionately attractive, the adventurous. Is she pleading with him not to break off an affair? The one remark I do hear belies this: "...what about that boy friend of yours, doesn't he..." The very tone of his voice, raised plainly above the confidential, is that of the confidant importuned, stonily turning nasty and wanting to give up his privilege to anyone who seems under a more valid obligation to deal with the situation. Yet I don't know. She is still pleading, clearly going over and over what she has said a dozen times before. How beautifully she weeps, without a bloated nose; why should one feel not moved by her just because she is beautiful, why, in spite of everything, is there the obstinate cold resentment that her face is more than she deserves?

The man's eyes (he is obviously keenly long-sighted) follow the passing of someone on the other side of the glass barrier, in the street. As he changes focus we meet, my piece of cheesecake halfway to my mouth. We know each other, this morning, above the heads of the child and the weeping one. I should never have thought it; but you don't always choose the ones you know. The girl has not paused in her desperate monologue and the child, beside me, has her one uncovered eye screwed up, nuzzling toward brightness without seeing, like a mole.

I pay and the child and I walk out just behind the other two. There is a big black car outside the door and a black chauffeur, fat henchman, opens the door for them. One feels the girl likes this, it turns up the fragment of a fairy tale. She steps inside elegantly, with a certain melancholy pleasure, balanced like a brimming glass.

I drive out of the city to an address where the child is to have a culture made from the infected tissues in her eyelids. The doctor has drawn a little map for me; through suburbs, past country clubs and chicken farms, everywhere the sun shines evenly through a bloom of blue smoke that marks the position of the city, from far off, like the spout of a whale. The research institute is spread out pleasantly on a rise; there are gardens, and horses standing in a field. We get out of the car and it's as if a felt-lined door has been shut—the sound of life in the city comes only as a slight vibration under one's feet. I take her by the arm and we cross some grass, city people in the sunlight, and wander from building to building. They are white inside and, although we hear voices through frosted doors, all desks are empty. We see an African in a white coat blocking the light at the end of corridor. He directs us to another building. He has a kind of trolley full of small cages with dark shapes in them that don't move. Out of the clean buildings, round the goldfish ponds (she is too old to want to linger beside them any more), we come into a courtyard full of gray monkeys in cages. She forgets about her eye and breaks away from me, finding her way: "Oh aren't they sweet!" They swing from gray tails, they have black masks through which amber eyes shine with questions. They have patches where the fur has been shaved and the skin has been punctured again and again and painted with medicaments; oh why, but why? She pulls back from my arm when I tell her. There are rats, crouched guinea pigs, piles of empty cages in yards. The horses, that were standing so peacefully in the field, have glazed eyes and the hopelessness of working animals who have come out of the shafts for good. On their rumps and necks are the shaved and painted patches. Their stalls are being swilled out and scrubbed by men in rubber boots; it is so clean, all this death and disease.

"Now we're going to try and grow these nasty goggas from your eye, dear, we're going to grow them in an egg and see whether we can make you well." The woman in the white coat talks soothingly as she works on the eye. While she is out of the laboratory for a moment we listen to a kettle that is singing up to the boil, and I say, "Don't rub it." The child says after a silence, "I wish I could be the one who sits and watches." Pain is taking her innocence, she is getting to know me. But if she indicts, she begins at the same time to take on some of the guilt: "They will grow mine in an egg? Only in an egg?" The sun is high; we do not know what time it is, driving back. She tells time by the school bell, I by the cardboard file growing thinner.

My husband has a story to tell when he comes home in the evening. An acquaintance, who took him out shooting, last weekend, has committed suicide. He does not tell it baldly like this but begins slowly at what led up to the beginning, although we can tell, almost from the beginning, what is coming. "He was in wonderful form. I stood next to him and watched him bring down four birds with five cartridges. Alba worked so well and he asked me whether I couldn't ask Jack Strahan to sell him one from the next litter. He couldn't get over the way Alba worked; he said he'd never seen a dog like it, for range. And he asked when I was going to bring you on a shoot again, when're you going to bring your wife out here with you, he said; he remembered that time last year when we had such a good time in the camp."

The man kissed his wife, dropped his children at their school, telephoned his office to say he would be a little late, and then drove out into the veld. "Shut himself in the boot of the car and shot himself through the head." I scarcely knew the man, met him only that once at the camp, but, at this detail of the manner of his death, I suddenly think of something: "But don't you remember, he used to shut his hunting dogs in the boot? He did it that day, and when I picked him out about it he said it wasn't cruel and they didn't mind being shut up in there!" Nobody knows why he killed himself, he has gone without a word to anyone—except this. The stranger who cannot remember clearly what he looked like is the one into whose hands his last message has fallen. What can I do with it? It's like a message picked up on the beach, that may be a joke, a hoax, or a genuine call of distress—one can't tell, and ends by throwing the bottle back into the sea. If it's genuine, the sender is beyond help already. Or someone else may pick it up and know what it's all about.

If I keep it perhaps I might crack the code one day? If only it were the sort of code that children or spies use, made out of numbers or lines from the Bible. But it is made of what couldn't be equated or spelled out to anyone in the world, that could leave communication only in the awkward movement of his body through the air as he scrambled into the smell of dust and petrol, where the dogs had crouched, and closed the lid over his head.

For no reason at all, my mind begins to construct a dialogue with the girl—that girl. I see her somewhere, years later. She is laughing, she is conscious of her beauty. I say to her quite abruptly, "What happened that morning, anyway?—You know, he has developed hardened arteries and his teeth are giving him trouble. He's on a strict diet—no wine, no red meat—and his old wife cooks for him again. He never goes out."

The child comes in and stands squarely before me. She has put her dark glasses on and I can't see her eyes. "And if the egg should hatch, " she says, "if the egg hatches?"

A & P
John Updike

In walks these three girls in nothing but bathing suits. I'm in the third checkout slot, with my back to the door, so I don't see them until they're over by the bread. The one that caught my eye first was the one in the plaid green two-piece. She was a chunky kid, with a good tan and a sweet broad soft-looking can with those two crescents of white just under it, where the sun never seems to hit, at the top of the backs of her legs. I stood there with my hand on a box of HiHo crackers trying to remember if I rang it up or not. I ring it up again and the customer starts giving me hell. She's one of these cash-register-watchers, a witch about fifty with rouge on her cheekbones and no eyebrows, and I know it made her day to trip me up. She'd been watching cash registers for fifty years and probably never seen a mistake before.

By the time I got her feathers smoothed and her goodies into a bag—she gives me a little snort in passing, if she'd been born at the right time they would have burned her over in Salem—by the time I get her on her way the girls had circled around the bread and were coming back, without a pushcart, back my way along the counters, in the aisle between the checkouts and the Special bins. They didn't even have shoes on. There was this chunky one, with the two-piece—it was bright green and the seams on the bra were still sharp and her belly was still pretty pale so I guessed she just got it (the suit)—there was this one, with one of those chubby berry-faces, the lips all bunched together under her nose, this one, and a tall one, with black hair that hadn't quite frizzed right, and one of these sunburns right across under the eyes, and a chin that was too long—you know, the kind of girl other girls think is very "striking" and "attractive" but never quite makes it, as they very well know, which is why they like her so much—and then the third one, that wasn't quite so tall. She was the queen. She kind of led them, the other two peeking around and making their shoulders round. She didn't look around, not this queen, she just walked straight on slowly, on these long white prima-donna legs. She came down a little hard on her heels, as if she didn't walk in her bare feet that much, putting down her heels and then letting the weight move along to her toes as if she was testing the floor with every step, putting a little deliberate extra action into it. You never know for sure how girls' minds work (do you really think it's a mind in there or just a little buzz like a bee in a glass jar?) but you got the idea she had talked the other two into coming in here with her, and now she was showing them how to do it, walk slow and hold yourself straight.

She had on a kind of dirty-pink—beige maybe, I don't know—bathing suit with a little nubble all over it and, what got me, the straps were down. They were off her shoulders looped loose around the cool tops of her arms, and I guess as a result the suit had slipped a little on her, so all around the top of the cloth there was this shining rim. If it hadn't been there you wouldn't have known there could have been anything whiter than those shoulders. With the straps pushed off, there was nothing between the top of the suit and the top of her head except just *her,* this clean bare plane of the top of her chest down from the shoulder bones like a dented sheet of metal tilted in the light. I mean, it was more than pretty.

She had sort of oaky hair that the sun and salt had bleached, done up in a bun that was unravelling, and a kind of prim face. Walking into the A & P with your straps down, I suppose it's the only kind of face you *can* have. She held her head so high her neck, coming up out of those white shoulders, looked kind of stretched, but I didn't mind. The longer her neck was, the more of her there was.

She must have felt in the corner of her eye me and over my shoulder Stokesie in the second slot watching, but she didn't tip. Not this queen. She kept her eyes moving across the racks, and stopped, and turned so slow it made my stomach rub the inside of my apron, and buzzed to the other two, who kind of huddled against her for relief, and then they all three of them went up the cat - and - dog - food - breakfast - cereal - macaroni - rice - raisins - seasonings - spreads - spaghetti - soft - drinks - crackers - and - cookies aisle. From the third slot I look straight up this aisle to the meat counter, and I watched them all the way. The fat one with the tan sort of fumbled with the cookies, but on second thought she put the package back. The sheep pushing their carts down the aisle—the girls were walking against the usual traffic (not that we have one-way signs or anything) —were pretty hilarious. You could see them, when Queenie's white shoulders dawned on them, kind of jerk, or hop, or hiccup, but their eyes snapped back to their own baskets and on they pushed. I bet you could set off dynamite in an A & P and the people would by and large keep reaching and checking oatmeal off their lists and muttering "Let me see, there was a third thing, began with A, asparagus, no, ah, yes, applesauce!" or whatever it is they do mutter. But there was no doubt, this jiggled them. A few houseslaves in pin curlers even looked around after pushing their carts past to make sure what they had seen was correct.

You know, it's one thing to have a girl in a bathing suit down on the beach, where what with the glare nobody can look at each other much anyway, and another thing in the cool of the A & P, under the fluorescent lights, against all those stacked packages, with her feet paddling along naked over our checkerboard green-and-cream rubber-tile floor.

"Oh Daddy," Stokesie said beside me. "I feel so faint."

"Darling," I said. "Hold me tight." Stokesie's married, with two babies chalked up on his fuselage already, but as far as I can tell that's the only difference. He's twenty-two, and I was nineteen this April.

"Is it done?" he asks, the responsible married man finding his voice. I forgot to say he thinks he's going to be manager some sunny day, maybe in 1990 when it's called the Great Alexandrov and Petrooshki Tea Company or something.

What he meant was, our town is five miles from a beach, with a big summer colony out on the Point, but we're right in the middle of town, and the women generally put on a shirt or shorts or something before they get out of the car into the street. And anyway these are usually women with six children and varicose veins mapping their legs and nobody, including them, could care less. As I say, we're right in the middle of town, and if you stand at our front doors you can see two banks and the Congregational church and the newspaper store and three real-estate offices and about twenty-seven old freeloaders tearing up Central Street because the sewer broke again. It's not as if we're on the Cape; we're north of Boston and there's people in this town haven't seen the ocean for twenty years.

The girls had reached the meat counter and were asking McMahon something. He pointed, they pointed, and they shuffled out of sight behind a pyramid of Diet Delight peaches. All that was left for us to see was old McMahon patting his mouth and looking after them sizing up their joints. Poor kids, I began to feel sorry for them, they couldn't help it.

Now here comes the sad part of the story, at least my family says it's sad, but I don't think it's so sad myself. The store's pretty empty, it being Thursday afternoon, so there was nothing much to do except lean on the register and wait for the girls to show up again. The whole store was like a pinball machine and I didn't know which tunnel they'd come out of. After a while they come around out of the far aisle, around the light bulbs, records at discount of the Caribbean Six or Tony Martin Sings or some such gunk you wonder they waste the wax on, sixpacks of candy bars, and plastic toys done up in cellophane that fall apart when a kid looks at them anyway. Around they come, Queenie still leading the way, and holding a little gray jar in her hand. Slots Three through Seven are unmanned and I could see her wondering between Stokes and me, but Stokesie with his usual luck draws an old party in baggy pants who stumbles up with four giant cans of pineapple juice (what do these bums *do* with all that pineapple juice? I've often asked myself) so the girls come to me. Queenie puts down the jar and I take it into my fingers icy cold. Kingfish Fancy Herring Snacks in Pure Sour Cream: 49¢. Now her hands are empty, not a ring or a bracelet, bare as God made them, and I wonder where the money's coming from. Still with that prim look she lifts a folded dollar bill out of the hollow at the center of her nubbled pink top. The jar went heavy in my hand. Really, I thought that was so cute.

Then everybody's luck begins to run out. Lengel comes in from haggling with a truck full of cabbages on the lot and is about to scuttle into that door marked MANAGER behind which he hides all day when the girls touch his eye. Lengel's pretty dreary, teaches Sunday school and the rest, but he doesn't miss that much. He comes over and says, "Girls, this isn't the beach."

Queenie blushes, though maybe it's just a brush of sunburn I was noticing for the first time, now that she was so close. "My mother asked me to pick up a jar of herring snacks." Her voice kind of startled me, the way voices do when you see the people first, coming out so flat and dumb yet kind of tony, too, the way it ticked over "pick up" and "snacks." All of a sudden I slid right down her voice into her living room. Her father and the other men were standing around in ice-cream coats and bow ties and the women were in sandals picking up herring snacks on toothpicks off a big glass plate and they were all holding drinks the color of water with olives and sprigs of mint in them. When my parents have somebody over they get lemonade and if it's a real racy affair Schlitz in tall glasses with "They'll Do It Every Time" cartoons stencilled on.

"That's all right," Lengel said. "But this isn't the beach." His repeating this struck me as funny, as if it had just occurred to him, and he had been thinking all these years the A & P was a great big dune and he was the head lifeguard. He didn't like my smiling—as I say he doesn't miss much—but he concentrates on giving the girls that sad Sunday-school-superintendent stare.

Queenie's blush is no sunburn now, and the plump one in plaid, that I liked better from the back—a really sweet can—pipes up, "We weren't doing any shopping. We just came in for the one thing."

"That makes no difference," Lengel tells her, and I could see from the way his eyes went that he hadn't noticed she was wearing a two-piece before. "We want you decently dressed when you come in here."

"We *are* decent," Queenie says suddenly, her lower lip pushing, getting sore now that she remembers her place, a place from which the crowd that runs the A & P must look pretty crummy. Fancy Herring Snacks flashed in her very blue eyes.

"Girls, I don't want to argue with you. After this come in here with your shoulders covered. It's our policy." He turns his back. That's policy for you. Policy is what the kingpins want. What the others want is juvenile delinquency.

All this while, the customers had been showing up with their carts but, you know, sheep, seeing a scene, they had all bunched up on Stokesie, who shook open a paper bag as gently as peeling a peach, not wanting to miss a word. I could feel in the silence everybody getting nervous, most of all Lengel, who asks me, "Sammy, have you rung up their purchase?"

I thought and said "No" but it wasn't about that I was thinking. I go through the punches, 4, 9, GROC, TOT—it's more complicated than you think, and after you do it often enough, it begins to make a little song, that you hear words to, in my case "Hello (*bing*) there, you (*gung*) hap-py *pee*-pul (*splat*)!"—the *splat* being the drawer flying out. I uncrease the bill, tenderly as you may imagine, it just having come from between the two smoothest scoops of vanilla I had ever known were there, and pass a half and a penny into her narrow pink palm, and nestle the herrings in a bag and twist its neck and hand it over, all the time thinking.

The girls, and who'd blame them, are in a hurry to get out, so I say "I quit" to Lengel quick enough for them to hear, hoping they'll stop and watch me, their unsuspected hero. They keep right on going, into the electric eye; the door flies open and they flicker across the lot to their car, Queenie and Plaid and Big Tall Goony-Goony (not that as raw material she was so bad), leaving me with Lengel and a kink in his eyebrow.

"Did you say something, Sammy?"

"I said I quit."

"I thought you did."

"You didn't have to embarrass them."

"It was they who were embarrassing us."

I started to say something that came out "Fiddle-de-doo." It's a saying of my grandmother's, and I know she would have been pleased.

"I don't think you know what you're saying," Lengel said.

"I know you don't," I said. "But I do." I pull the bow at the back of my apron and start shrugging it off my shoulders. A couple customers that had been heading for my slot begin to knock against each other, like scared pigs in a chute.

Lengel sighs and begins to look very patient and old and gray. He's been a friend of my parents for years. "Sammy, you don't want to do this to your Mom and Dad," he tells me. It's true, I don't. But it seems to me that once you begin a gesture it's fatal not to go through with it. I fold the apron, "Sammy" stitched in red on the pocket, and put it on the counter, and drop the bow tie on top of it. The bow tie is theirs, if you've ever wondered. "You'll feel this for the rest of your life," Lengel says, and I know that's true, too, but remembering how he made that pretty girl blush makes me so scrunchy inside I punch the No Sale tab and the machine whirs "pee-pul" and the drawer splats out. One advantage to this scene taking place in summer, I can follow this up with a clean exit, there's no fumbling around getting your coat and galoshes, I just saunter into the electric eye in my white shirt that my mother ironed the night before, and the door heaves itself open, and outside the sunshine is skating around on the asphalt.

I look around for my girls, but they're gone, of course. There wasn't anybody but some young married screaming with her children about some candy they didn't get by the door of a powder-blue Falcon station wagon. Looking back in the big windows, over the bags of peat moss and aluminum lawn furniture stacked on the pavement, I could see Lengel in my place in the slot, checking the sheep through.

His face was dark gray and his back stiff, as if he'd just had an injection of iron, and my stomach kind of fell as I felt how hard the world was going to be to me hereafter.

2. MOOD AND TONE

The creator of a short story writes because he has a compulsion to express feelings which merge with rational attitudes toward a subject and his reader. Otherwise he simply would not bother to write. Or if he forced himself to make the effort, his composition would be an emotionally or intellectually arid product. Occasionally the author's involvement with the subject *(mood)* is at variance with his response toward his audience *(tone)*. That is, as a generalized instance, his sympathy on behalf of a suffering protagonist may be countered by a feeling—expressed or implied—of indignation or contempt for the members of society whom he equates with the source of oppressive responsibility. Again, however, mood and tone may blend so completely as to lose distinction.

Let us consider mood first. A difficult term to define, it is essentially the author's feeling reaction to the materials with which his narration deals. In some cases the mood of a story undergoes no change. Such is true of the O'Flaherty story, "Mother and Son," which poses no significant alteration of mood. From the beginning of the account, the author accents the drabness, the poverty-ridden desperation of the cottage which is alleviated by the love between the mother and child and even transcended by the imagination shared by the two. On the other hand, some short stories evoke mixed feelings because their authors assign varying emotional values to successive actions and/or to different characters. In "The Liar," for example, Henry James employs a multiple mood. Obviously, he feels—and therefore we feel—pity for Colonel Capadose, who is a thoroughly decent man, yet flawed morally by a disease. James, on the other hand, admires Mrs. Capadose for her sensitivity and her ability to make the best of an agonizing situation. Finally, he etches the figure of Oliver Lyon in a contempt bordering on hatred as the painter pursues his plan to expose the liar—and only to enhance his own ego.

When we point out that a mood may be single or multiple, we are not making a value judgment based on quantity or complexity. What is important is that the author be able to impress his feelings upon his readers. If he has communicated well, that is, if his characters, setting, and plot are integrated sufficiently to express the total design of the story, then the writer will probably be able to share his mood with his reader. If, however, he has not worked out his symbols of transference, then the reader may not understand the author's mood or he may even refuse to participate in it.

Mood, to repeat, consists of the artist's feelings toward his materials; tone involves his reaction toward his reader. According to I. A. Richards, the writer "chooses or arranges his words differently as his audience varies, in automatic or deliberate *recognition of his relation* to them. The tone of his utterance reflects his awareness of this relation, his sense of how he stands towards those he is addressing. Again the exceptional case of dissimulation, or instances in which the speaker unwittingly reveals an attitude he is not consciously desirous of expressing, will come to mind."

Tone is not more subtle than mood but it is more difficult to isolate and recognize. We are so aware of the author in terms of his subject that we ordinarily fail to be sensitive to him in relation to ourselves. Occasionally an author will be so involved with his materials that he will divest himself of anonymity, then speaking directly to his readers and telling them what to feel. This is usually so in short stories conceived to fulfill a propagandistic purpose, in, for example, Steinbeck's or Farrell's narratives of social protest. Sometimes the tone is not stated but is so deliberately implied that the reader cannot miss it.

Let us try to illustrate this last premise. In "The Nuisance," Doris Lessing implies her compassion for the Cross-Eyed Woman who, ugly and undesirable, is murdered by a cruel and barbaric husband. At the same time that the author is capable of pity for the black victim, she is also capable of sustained ire toward those white settlers of Rhodesia who look upon the natives as a source either of amusement or annoyance but never as incentives for their humanity. Implicitly she asks her readers—many of whom share the attitudes of white Rhodesia—to revise their thinking, to fight against such prejudice, and to accept all men as brothers. In a more abstract fashion Herman Melville in "The Bell Tower" creates a mood of fearful anticipation as Bannadonna builds his tower higher and higher in order to challenge God's own creativity. Concurrently, his tone is one of awe mingled with pessimism as he makes us aware of human pride and the daring of evil.

Mother and Son
Liam O'Flaherty

Although it was only five o'clock, the sun had already set and the evening was very still, as all spring evenings are, just before the birds begin to sing themselves to sleep; or maybe tell one another bedside stories. The village was quiet. The men had gone away to fish for the night after working all the morning with the sowing. Women were away milking the cows in the little fields among the crags.

Brigid Gill was alone in her cottage waiting for her little son to come home from school. He was now an hour late, and as he was only nine years she was very nervous about him, especially as he was her only child and he was a wild boy, always getting into mischief, mitching from school, fishing minnows on Sunday and building stone "castles" in the great crag above the village. She kept telling herself that she would give him a good scolding and beating when he came in, but at the same time her heart was thumping with anxiety and she started at every sound, rushing out to the door and looking down the winding road, that was now dim with the shadows of evening. So many things could happen to a little boy.

His dinner of dried fish and roast potatoes was being kept warm in the oven among the peat ashes beside the fire on the hearth, and on the table there was a plate, a knife and a little mug full of buttermilk.

At last she heard the glad cries of the schoolboys afar off, and rushing out she saw their tiny forms scampering, not up the road, but across the crags to the left, their caps in their hands.

"Thank God," she said, and then she persuaded herself that she was very angry. Hurriedly she got a small dried willow rod, sat down on a chair within the door and waited for her little Stephen.

He advanced up the yard very slowly, walking near the stone fence that bounded the vegetable garden, holding his satchel in his left hand by his side, with his cap in his right hand, a red-cheeked slim boy, dressed in close-fitting grey frieze trousers that reached a little below his knees and a blue sweater. His feet were bare and covered with all sorts of mud. His face perspired and his great soft blue eyes were popping out of his head with fright. He knew his mother would be angry.

At last he reached the door and, holding down his head, he entered the kitchen. The mother immediately jumped up and seized him by the shoulder. The boy screamed, dropped his satchel and his cap and clung to her apron. The mother raised the rod to strike, but when she looked down at the little trembling body, she began to tremble herself and she dropped the stick. Stooping down, she raised him up and began kissing him, crying at the same time with tears in her eyes.

"What's going to become of you atall, atall? God save us, I haven't the courage to beat you and you're breaking my heart with your wickedness."

The boy sobbed, hiding his head in his mother's bosom.

"Go away," she said, thrusting him away from her, "and eat your dinner. Your father will give to you a good thrashing in the morning. I've spared you often and begged him not to beat you, but this time I'm not going to say a word for you. You've my heart broken, so you have. Come here and eat your dinner."

She put the dinner on the plate and pushed the boy into the chair. He sat down sobbing, but presently he wiped his eyes with his sleeve and began to eat ravenously. Gradually his face brightened and he moved about on the chair, settling himself more comfortably and forgetting all his fears of his mother and the thrashing he was going to get next morning in the joy of satisfying his hunger. The mother sat on the doorstep, knitting in silence and watching him lovingly under her long black eyelashes.

All her anger had vanished by now and she felt glad that she had thrust all the responsibility for punishment on to her husband. Still, she wanted to be severe, and although she wanted to ask Stephen what he had been doing, she tried to hold her tongue. At last, however, she had to talk.

"What kept you, Stephen?" she said softly.

Stephen swallowed the last mouthful and turned around with his mug in his hand.

"We were only playing ball," he said excitedly, "and then Red Michael ran after us and chased us out of his field where we were playing. And we had to run an awful way; oh, a long, long way we had to run, over crags where I never was before."

"But didn't I often tell you not to go into people's fields to play ball?"

"Oh, mother, sure it wasn't me but the other boys that wanted to go, and if I didn't go with them they'd say I was afraid, and father says I mustn't be afraid."

"Yes, you pay heed to your father but you pay no heed to your mother that has all the trouble with you. Now and what would I do if you fell running over the crags and sprained your ankle?"

And she put her apron to her eyes to wipe away a tear.

Stephen left his chair, came over to her and put his arms around her neck.

"Mother," he said, "I'll tell you what I saw on the crags if you promise not to tell father about me being late and playing ball in Red Michael's field."

"I'll do no such thing," she said.

"Oh, do, mother," he said, "and I'll never be late again, never never, never."

"All right, Stephen; what did you see, my little treasure?"

He sat down beside her on the threshold and, looking wistfully out into the sky, his eyes became big and dreamy and his face assumed an expression of mystery and wonder.

"I saw a great big black horse," he said, "running in the sky over our heads, but none of the other boys saw it but me, and I didn't tell them about it. The horse had seven tails and three heads and its belly was so big that you could put our house into it. I saw it with my two eyes. I did, mother. And then it soared and galloped away, away, ever so far. Isn't that a great thing I saw, mother?"

"It is, darling," she said dreamily, looking out into the sky, thinking of something with soft eyes. There was silence. Then Stephen spoke again without looking at her.

"Sure you won't tell on me, mother?"

"No, treasure, I won't."

"On your soul you won't?"

"Hush! little one. Listen to the birds. They are beginning to sing. I won't tell at all. Listen to the beautiful ones."

They both sat in silence, listening and dreaming, both of them.

The Curate's Friend

E. M. Forster

It is uncertain how the Faun came to be in Wiltshire. Perhaps he came over with the Roman legionaries to live with his friends in camp, talking to them of Lucretilis, or Garganus or of the slopes of Etna; they in the joy of their recall forgot to take him on board, and he wept in exile; but at last he found that our hills also understood his sorrows, and rejoiced when he was happy. Or, perhaps he came to be there because he had been there always. There is nothing particularly classical about a faun: it is only that the Greeks and Italians have ever had the sharpest eyes. You will find him in the "Tempest" and the "Benedicite"; and any country which has beech clumps and sloping grass and very clear streams may reasonably produce him.

How I came to see him is a more difficult question. For to see him there is required a certain quality, for which truthfulness is too cold a name and animal spirits too coarse a one, and he alone knows how this quality came to be in me. No man has the right to call himself a fool, but I may say that I then presented the perfect semblance of one. I was facetious without humour and serious without conviction. Every Sunday I would speak to my rural parishioners about the other world in the tone of one who has been behind the scenes, or I would explain to them the errors of the Pelagians, or I would warn them against hurrying from one dissipation to another. Every Tuesday I gave what I called "straight talks to my lads"—talks which led straight past anything awkward. And every Thursday I addressed the Mothers' Union on the duties of wives or widows, and gave them practical hints on the management of a family of ten.

I took myself in, and for a time I certainly took in Emily. I have never known a girl attend so carefully to my sermons, or laugh so heartily at my jokes. It is no wonder that I became engaged. She has made an excellent wife, freely correcting her husband's absurdities, but allowing no one else to breathe a word against them; able to talk about the subconscious self in the drawing-room, and yet have an ear for the children crying in the nursery, or the plates breaking in the scullery. An excellent wife—better than I ever imagined. But she has not married me.

Had we stopped indoors that afternoon nothing would have happened. It was all owing to Emily's mother, who insisted on our teaing out. Opposite the village, across the stream, was a small chalk down, crowned by a beech copse, and a few Roman earthworks. (I lectured very vividly on those earthworks: they have since proved to be Saxon.) Hither did I drag up a tea-basket and a heavy rug for Emily's mother, while Emily and a little friend went on in front. The little friend—who has played all through a much less important part than he supposes—was a pleasant youth, full of intelligence and poetry, especially of what he called the poetry of earth. He longed to wrest earth's secret from her, and I have seen him press his face passionately into the grass, even when he has believed himself to be alone. Emily was at that time full of vague aspirations, and, though I should have preferred them all to centre in me, yet it seemed unreasonable to deny her such other opportunities for self-culture as the neighbourhood provided.

It was then my habit, on reaching the top of any eminence, to exclaim facetiously "And who will stand on either hand and keep the bridge with me?" at the same moment violently agitating my arms or casting my wide-awake at an imaginary foe. Emily and the friend received my sally as usual, nor could I detect any insincerity in their mirth. Yet I was convinced that some one was present who did not think I had been funny, and any public speaker will understand my growing uneasiness.

I was somewhat cheered by Emily's mother, who puffed up exclaiming, "Kind Harry, to carry the things! What should we do without you, even now! Oh, what a view! Can you see the dear Cathedral? No. Too hazy. Now I'm going to sit right on the rug." She smiled mysteriously. "The downs in September, you know."

We gave some perfunctory admiration to the landscape, which is indeed only beautiful to those who admire land, and to them perhaps the most beautiful in England. For here is the body of the great chalk spider who straddles over our island—whose legs are the south downs and the north downs and the Chilterns, and the tips of whose toes poke out at Cromer and Dover. He is a clean creature, who grows as few trees as he can, and those few in tidy clumps, and he loves to be tickled by quickly flowing streams. He is pimpled all over with earthworks, for from the beginning of time men have fought for the privilege of standing on him, and the oldest of our temples is built upon his back.

But in those days I liked my country snug and pretty, full of gentlemen's residences and shady bowers and people who touch their hats. The great sombre expanses on which one may walk for miles and hardly shift a landmark or meet a genteel person were still intolerable to me. I turned away as soon as propriety allowed and said, "And may I now prepare the cup that cheers?"

Emily's mother replied: "Kind man, to help me. I always do say that tea out is worth the extra effort. I wish we led simpler lives." We agreed with her. I spread out the food. "Won't the kettle stand? Oh, but *make* it stand." I did so. There was a little cry, faint but distinct, as of something in pain.

"How silent it all is up here!" said Emily.

I dropped a lighted match on the grass, and again I heard the little cry.

"What is that?" I asked.

"I only said it was so silent," said Emily.

"Silent, indeed," echoed the little friend.

Silent! the place was full of noises. If the match had fallen in a drawing-room it could not have been worse, and the loudest noise came from beside Emily herself. I had exactly the sensation of going to a great party, of waiting to be announced in the echoing hall, where I could hear the voices of the guests, but could not yet see their faces. It is a nervous moment for a self-conscious man, especially if all the voices should be strange to him, and he has never met his host.

"My dear Harry!" said the elder lady, "never mind about that match. That'll smoulder away and harm no one. Tea-ee-ee! I always say—and you will find Emily the same—that as the magic hour of five approaches, no matter how good a lunch, one begins to feel a sort of —"

Now the Faun is of the kind who capers upon the Neo-Attic reliefs, and if you do not notice his ears or see his tail, you take him for a man and are horrified.

"Bathing!" I cried wildly. "Such a thing for our village lads, but I quite agree—more supervision—I blame myself. Go away, bad boy, go away!"

"What will he think of next!" said Emily, while the creature beside her stood up and beckoned to me. I advanced struggling and gesticulating with tiny steps and horrified cries, exorcising the apparition with my hat. Not otherwise had I advanced the day before, when Emily's nieces showed me their guinea pigs. And by no less hearty laughter was I greeted now. Until the strange fingers closed upon me, I still thought that here was one of my parishioners and did not cease to exclaim, "Let me go, naughty boy, let go!" And Emily's mother, believing herself to have detected the joke, replied, "Well I must confess they are naughty boys and reach one even on the rug: the downs in September, as I said before."

Here I caught sight of the tail, uttered a wild shriek and fled into the beech copse behind.

"Harry would have been a born actor," said Emily's mother as I left them.

I realized that a great crisis in my life was approaching, and that if I failed in it I might permanently lose my self-esteem. Already in the wood I was troubled by a multitude of voices—the voices of the hill beneath me, of the trees over my head, of the very insects in the bark of the tree. I could even hear the stream licking little pieces out of the meadows, and the meadows dreamily protesting. Above the din—which is no louder than the flight of a bee—rose the Faun's voice saying, "Dear priest, be placid, be placid: why are you frightened?"

"I am not frightened," said I—and indeed I was not. "But I am grieved: you have disgraced me in the presence of ladies."

"No one else has seen me," he said, smiling idly. "The women have tight boots and the man has long hair. Those kinds never see. For years I have only spoken to children, and they lose sight of me as soon as they grow up. But you will not be able to lose sight of me, and until you die you will be my friend. Now I begin to make you happy: lie upon your back or run races, or climb trees, or shall I get you blackberries, or harebells, or wives—"

In a terrible voice I said to him, "Get thee behind me!" He got behind me. "Once for all," I continued, "let me tell you that it is vain to tempt one whose happiness consists in giving happiness to others."

"I cannot understand you," he said ruefully. "What is to tempt?"

"Poor woodland creature!" said I, turning round. "How could you understand? It was idle of me to chide you. It is not your little nature to comprehend a life of self-denial. Ah! if only I could reach you!"

"You have reached him," said the hill.

"If only I could touch you!"

"You have touched him," said the hill.

"But I will never leave you," burst out the Faun. "I will sweep out your shrine for you, I will accompany you to the meetings of matrons. I will enrich you at the bazaars."

I shook my head. "For these things I care not at all. And indeed I was minded to reject your offer of service altogether. There I was wrong. You shall help me—you shall help me to make others happy."

"Dear priest, what a curious life! People whom I have never seen—people who cannot see me—why should I make them happy?"

"My poor lad—perhaps in time you will learn why. Now begone: commence. On this very hill sits a young lady for whom I have a high regard. Commence with her. Aha! your face falls. I thought as much. You *cannot* do anything. Here is the conclusion of the whole matter!"

"I can make her happy," he replied, "if you order me! and when I have done so, perhaps you will trust me more."

Emily's mother had started home, but Emily and the little friend still sat beside the tea-things—she in her white piqué dress and biscuit straw, he in his rough but well-cut summer suit. The great pagan figure of the Faun towered insolently above them.

The friend was saying, "And have you never felt the appalling loneliness of a crowd?"

"All that," replied Emily, "have I felt, and very much more—"

Then the Faun laid his hands upon them. They, who had only intended a little cultured flirtation, resisted him as long as they could, but were gradually urged into each other's arms, and embraced with passion.

"Miscreant!" I shouted, bursting from the wood. "You have betrayed me."

"I know it: I care not," cried the little friend. "Stand aside. You are in the presence of that which you do not understand. In the great solitude we have found ourselves at last."

"Remove your accursed hands!" I shrieked to the Faun.

He obeyed and the little friend continued more calmly: "It is idle to chide. What should you know, poor clerical creature, of the mystery of love of the eternal man and the eternal woman, of the self-effectuation of a soul?"

"That is true," said Emily angrily. "Harry, you would never have made me happy. I shall treat you as a friend, but how could I give myself to a man who makes such silly jokes? When you played the buffoon at tea, your hour was sealed. I must be treated seriously: I must see infinities broadening around me as I rise. You may not approve of it, but so I am. In the great solitude I have found myself at last."

"Wretched girl!" I cried. "Great solitude! O pair of helpless puppets—"

The little friend began to lead Emily away, but I heard her whisper to him: "Dear, we can't possibly leave the basket for Harry after this: and mother's rug; do you mind having that in the other hand?"

So they departed and I flung myself upon the ground with every appearance of despair.

"Does he cry?" said the Faun.

"He does not cry," answered the hill. "His eyes are as dry as pebbles."

My tormentor made me look at him. "I see happiness at the bottom of your heart," said he.

"I trust I have my secret springs," I answered stiffly. And then I prepared a scathing denunciation, but of all the words I might have said, I only said one and it began with "D."

He gave a joyful cry, "Oh, now you really belong to us. To the end of your life you will swear when you are cross and laugh when you are happy. Now laugh!"

There was a great silence. All nature stood waiting, while a curate tried to conceal his thoughts not only from nature but from himself. I thought of my injured pride, of my baffled unselfishness, of Emily, whom I was losing through no fault of her own, of the little friend, who just then slipped beneath the heavy tea basket, and that decided me, and I laughed.

That evening, for the first time, I heard the chalk downs singing to each other across the valleys, as they often do when the air is quiet and they have had a comfortable day. From my study window I could see the sunlit figure of the Faun, sitting before the beech copse as a man sits before his house. And as night came on I knew for certain that not only was he asleep, but that the hills and woods were asleep also. The stream, of course, never slept, any more than it ever freezes. Indeed, the hour of darkness is really the hour of water, which has been somewhat stifled all day by the great pulsings of the land. That is why you can feel it and hear it from a greater distance in the night, and why a bath after sundown is most wonderful.

The joy of that first evening is still clear in my memory, in spite of all the happy years that have followed. I remember it when I ascend my pulpit—I have a living now—and look down upon the best people sitting beneath me pew after pew, generous and contented, upon the worst people, crowded in the aisles, upon the whiskered tenors of the choir, and the high-browed curates and the church-wardens fingering their bags, and the supercilious vergers who turn late comers from the door. I remember it also when I sit in my comfortable bachelor rectory, amidst the carpet slippers that good young ladies have worked for me, and the oak brackets that have been carved for me by good young men; amidst my phalanx of presentation teapots and my illuminated testimonials and all the other offerings of people who believe that I have given them a helping hand, and who really have helped me out of the mire themselves. And though I try to communicate that joy to others—as I try to communicate anything else that seems good—and though I sometimes succeed, yet I can tell no one exactly how it came to me. For if I breathed one word of that, my present life, so agreeable and profitable, would come to an end, my congregation would depart, and so should I, and instead of being an asset to my parish, I might find myself an expense to the nation. Therefore in the place of the lyrical and rhetorical treatment, so suitable to the subject, so congenial to my profession, I have been forced to use the unworthy medium of a narrative, and to delude you by declaring that this is a short story, suitable for reading in the train.

COMMENTARIES
by Virginia Woolf and Elizabeth Bowen

E. M. Forster's friend Virginia Woolf greatly admired his work. When she wrote about the character of supernatural fiction, she undoubtedly had in mind certain of Forster's stories, like "The Curate's Friend." According to Mrs. Woolf, "it would be a mistake to suppose that supernatural fiction always seeks to produce fear, or that the best ghost stories are those which most accurately and medically describe abnormal states of mind. On the contrary, a vast amount of fiction both in prose and in verse now assures us that the world to which we shut our eyes is far more friendly and inviting, more beautiful by day and more holy by night, than the world which we persist in thinking the real world. The contrary is peopled with nymphs and dryads, and Pan, far from being dead, is at his pranks in all the villages of England. Much of this mythology is used not for its own sake, but for the purposes of satire and allegory; but there exists a group of writers who have the sense of the unseen without such alloy. Such a sense may bring visions of fairies or phantoms, or it may lead to a quickened perception of the relations existing between men and plants, or houses and their inhabitants, or any one of those innumerable alliances which somehow or other we spin between ourselves and other objects in our passage."*

More specifically Elizabeth Bowen claims that "in his supernatural stories E. M. Forster has added to a terribly likely world, whose oddness has a super-rationality, which is waiting just at the edge of

*"The Supernatural in Fiction," in *Granite and Rainbow* (London, 1958), p. 64. (The essay first appeared in the *Times Literary Supplement,* 31 January 1918.)

normal experience.... The fantasy story has often a literary beauty that is disarming; the one test one can apply is: does the imagination find this credible? Any crazy house against moonlight might, like the House of Usher, split right down to show the moon: there is assent at once, but no way to check up. Fancy has an authority reason cannot challenge. The pure fantasy writer works in a free zone; he has not to reconcile inner and outer images."*

The Followers
Dylan Thomas

It was six o'clock on a winter's evening. Thin, dingy rain spat and drizzled past the lighted street lamps. The pavements shone long and yellow. In squeaking goloshes, with mackintosh collars up and bowlers and trilbies weeping, youngish men from the offices bundled home against the thistly wind—

"Night, Mr. Macey."

"Going my way, Charlie?"

"Ooh, there's a pig of a night!"

"Goodnight, Mr. Swan"—

and older men, clinging on to the big, black circular birds of their umbrellas, were wafted back, up the gaslit hills, to safe, hot, slippered, weather proof hearths, and wives called Mother, and old, fond, fleabag dogs, and the wireless babbling.

Young women from the offices, who smelt of scent and powder and wet pixie hoods and hair, scuttled, giggling, arm-in-arm, after the hissing trams, and screeched as they splashed their stockings in the puddles rainbowed with oil between the slippery lines.

*"Preface" to The Faber Book of Modern Short Stories, ed. Elizabeth Bowen (London, 1937).

In a shopwindow, two girls undressed the dummies:

"Where are you going tonight?"

"Depends on Arthur. Up she comes."

"Mind her cami-knicks, Edna..."

The blinds came down over another window.

A newsboy stood in a doorway, calling the news to nobody, very softly:

"Earthquake. Earthquake in Japan."

Water from a chute dripped on to his sacking. He waited in his own pool of rain.

A flat, long girl drifted, snivelling into her hanky, out of a jeweller's shop, and slowly pulled the steel shutters down with a hooked pole. She looked, in the grey rain, as though she were crying from top to toe.

A silent man and woman, dressed in black, carried the wreaths away from the front of their flower shop into the scented deadly darkness behind the window lights. Then the lights went out.

A man with a balloon tied to his cap pushed a shrouded barrow up a dead end.

A baby with an ancient face sat in its pram outside the wine vaults, quiet, very wet, peering cautiously all round it.

It was the saddest evening I had ever known.

A young man, with his arm round his girl, passed by me, laughing; and she laughed back, right into his handsome, nasty face. That made the evening sadder still.

I met Leslie at the corner of Crimea Street. We were both about the same age: too young and too old. Leslie carried a rolled umbrella, which he never used, though sometimes he pressed doorbells with it. He was trying to grow a moustache. I wrote a check ratting cap at a Saturday angle. We greeted each other formally:

"Good evening, old man."

"Evening, Leslie."

"Right on the dot, boy."

"That's right," I said. "Right on the dot."

A plump blonde girl, smelling of wet rabbits, self-conscious even in that dirty night, minced past on high-heeled shoes. The heels clicked, the soles squelched.

Leslie whistled after her, low and admiring.

"Business first," I said.

"Oh, boy!" Leslie said.

"And she's too fat as well."

"I like them corpulent," Leslie said. "Remember Penelope Bogan? a Mrs. too."

"Oh, come *on*. That old bird of Paradise Alley! How's the exchequer, Les?"

"One and a penny. How you fixed?"

"Tanner."

"What'll it be, then? The Compasses?"

"Free cheese at the Marlborough."

We walked towards the Marlborough, dodging umbrella spokes, smacked by our windy macs, stained by steaming lamplight, seeing the sodden, blown scourings and street-wash of the town, papers, rags, dregs, rinds, fag-ends, balls of fur, flap, float, and cringe along the gutters, hearing the sneeze and rattle of the bony trams and a ship hoot like a fog-ditched owl in the bay, and Leslie said:

"What'll we do after?"

"We'll follow someone," I said.

"Remember following that old girl up Kitchener Street? The one who dropped her handbag?"

"You should have given it back."

"There wasn't anything in it, only a piece of bread-and-jam."

"Here we are," I said.

The Marlborough saloon was cold and empty. There were notices on the damp walls: No Singing. No Dancing. No Gambling. No Peddlers.

"You sing," I said to Leslie, "and I'll dance, then we'll have a game of nap and I'll peddle my braces."

The barmaid, with gold hair and two gold teeth in front, like a well-off rabbit's, was blowing on her nails and polishing them on her black marocain. She looked up as we came in, then blew on her nails again and polished them without hope.

"You can tell it isn't Saturday night," I said. "Evening, Miss. Two pints."

"And a pound from the till," Leslie said.

"Give us your one-and-a-penny, Les," I whispered, and then said aloud: "Anybody can tell it isn't Saturday night. Nobody sick."

"Nobody here to *be* sick," Leslie said.

The peeling, liver-coloured room might never have been drunk in at all. Here, commercials told jokes and had Scotches and sodas with happy, dyed, port-and-lemon women; dejected regulars grew grand and muzzy in the corners, inventing their pasts, being rich, important, and loved; reprobate grannies in dustbin black cackled and nipped; influential nobodies revised the earth; a party, with earrings, called "Frilly Willy," played the crippled piano, which sounded like a hurdy-gurdy playing under water, until the publican's nosy wife said, No. Strangers came and went, but mostly went. Men from the valleys dropped in for nine or ten; sometimes there were fights; and always there was something doing, some argie-bargie, giggle and bluster, horror or folly, affection, explosion, nonsense, peace, some wild goose flying in the boozy air of that comfortless, humdrum nowhere in the dizzy, ditchwater town at the end of the railway lines. But that evening it was the saddest room I had ever known.

Leslie said, in a low voice: "Think she'll let us have one on tick?"

"Wait a bit, boy," I murmured. "Wait for her to thaw."

But the barmaid heard me, and looked up. She looked clean through me, back through my small history to the bed I was born in, then shook her gold head.

"I don't know what it is," said Leslie as we walked up Crimea Street in the rain, "but I feel kind of depressed tonight."

"It's the saddest night in the world," I said.

We stopped, soaked and alone, to look at the stills outside the cinema we called the Itch-pit. Week after week, for years and years, we had sat on the edges of the springless seats there, in the dank but snug, flickering dark, first with toffees and monkey-nuts that crackled for the dumb guns, and then with cigarettes: a cheap special kind that would make a fire-swallower cough up the cinders of his heart. "Let's go in and see Lon Chaney," I said, "and Richard Talmadge and Milton Sills and ... and Noah Beery," I said, "and Richard Dix ... and Slim Summerville and Hoot Gibson."

We both sighed.

"Oh for our vanished youth," I said.

We walked on heavily, with wilful feet, splashing the passers-by.

"Why don't you open your brolly?" I said.

"It won't open. You try."

We both tried, and the umbrella suddenly bellied out, the spokes tore through the soaking cover; the wind danced its tatters; it wrangled above us in the wind like a ruined, mathematical bird. We tried to tug it down; an unseen, new spoke sprang through its ragged ribs. Leslie dragged it behind him, along the pavement, as though he had shot it.

A girl called Dulcie, scurrying to the Itch-pit, sniggered hallo, and we stopped her.

"A rather terrible thing has happened," I said to her. She was so silly that, even when she was fifteen, we had told her to eat soap to make her straw hair crinkle, and Les took a piece from the bathroom, and she did.

"I know," she said, "you broke your gamp."

"No, you're wrong there," Leslie said. "It isn't *our* umbrella at all. It fell off the roof. *You* feel," he said. "You can feel it fell off the roof." She took the umbrella gingerly by its handle.

"There's someone up there throwing umbrellas down," I said. "It may be serious."

She began to titter, and then grew silent and anxious as Leslie said: "You never know. It might be walking-sticks next."

"Or sewing-machines," I said.

"You wait here, Dulcie, and we'll investigate," Leslie said.

We hurried on down the street, turned a blowing corner, and then ran.

Outside Rabiotti's café, Leslie said: "It isn't fair on Dulcie." We never mentioned it again.

A wet girl brushed by. Without a word, we followed her. She catered, long-legged, down Inkerman Street and through Paradise Passage, and we were at her heels.

"I wonder what's the point in following people," Leslie said, "it's kind of daft. It never gets you anywhere. All you do is follow them home and then try to look through the window and see what they're doing and mostly there's curtains anyway. I bet nobody else does things like that."

"You never know," I said. The girl turned into St. Augustus Crescent, which was a wide lamplit mist. "People are always following people. What shall we call her?"

"Hermione Weatherby," Leslie said. He was never wrong about names. Hermione was fey and stringy, and walked like a long gymmistress, full of love, through the stinging rain.

"You never know. You never know what you'll find out. Perhaps she lives in a huge house with all her sisters—"

"How many?"

"Seven. All full of love. And when she gets home they all change into kimonos and lie on divans with music and whisper to each other and all they're doing is waiting for somebody like us to walk in, lost, and then they'll all chatter round us like starlings and put us in kimonos too, and we'll never leave the house until we die. Perhaps it's so beautiful and soft and noisy—like a warm bath full of birds . . ."

"I don't want birds in my bath," said Leslie. "Perhaps she'll slit her throat if they don't draw the blinds. I don't care what happens so long as it's interesting."

She slip-slopped round a corner into an avenue where the neat trees were sighing and the cosy windows shone.

"I don't want old feathers in the tub," Leslie said.

Hermione turned in at number thirteen, Beach-view.

"You can see the beach all right," Leslie said, "if you got a periscope."

We waited on the pavement opposite, under a bubbling lamp, as Hermione opened her door, and then we tip-toed across and down the gravel path and were at the back of the house, outside an uncurtained window.

Hermione's mother, a round, friendly, owlish woman in a pinafore, was shaking a chip-pan on the kitchen stove.

"I'm hungry," I said.

"Ssh!"

We edged to the side of the window as Hermione came into the kitchen. She was old, nearly thirty, with a mouse-brown shingle and big earnest eyes. She wore horn-rimmed spectacles and a sensible tweed costume, and a white shirt with a trim bow-tie. She looked as though she tried to look like a secretary in domestic films, who had only to remove her spectacles and have her hair cherished, and be dressed like a silk dog's dinner, to turn into a dazzler and make her employer, Warner Baxter, gasp, woo, and marry her; but if Hermione took off her glasses, she wouldn't be able to tell if he was Warner Baxter or the man who read the meters.

We stood so near the window, we could hear the chips spitting.

"Have a nice day in the office, dear? There's weather," Hermione's mother said, worrying the chip-pan.

"What's *her* name, Les?"

"Hetty."

Everything there in the warm kitchen, from the tea-caddy and the grandmother clock, to the tabby that purred like a kettle, was good, dull, and sufficient.

"Mr. Truscott was something awful," Hermione said as she put on slippers.

"Where's her kimono?" Leslie said.

"Here's a nice cup of tea," said Hetty.

"Everything's nice in that old hole," said Leslie, grumbling. "Where's the seven sisters like starlings?"

It began to rain much more heavily. It bucketed down on the black backyard, and the little comfy kennel of a house, and us, and the hidden, hushed town, where, even now, in the haven of the Marlborough, the submarine piano would be tinning "Daisy," and the happy henna'd women squealing into their port.

Hetty and Hermione had their supper. Two drowned boys watched them enviously.

"Put a drop of Worcester on the chips," Leslie whispered; and by God she did.

"Doesn't anything happen anywhere?" I said, "in the whole wide world? I think the *News of the World* is all made up. Nobody murders no one. There isn't any sin any more, or love, or death, or pearls and divorces and mink coats or anything, or putting arsenic in the cocoa..."

"Why don't they put on some music for us," Leslie said, "and do a dance? It isn't every night they got two fellows watching them in the rain. Not *every* night, anyway!"

All over the dripping town, small lost people with nowhere to go and nothing to spend were gooseberrying in the rain outside wet windows, but nothing happened.

"I'm getting pneumonia," Leslie said.

The cat and the fire were purring, grandmother time tick-tocked our lives away. The supper was cleared, and Hetty and Hermione, who had not spoken for many minutes, they were so confident and close in their little lighted box, looked at one another and slowly smiled.

They stood still in the decent, purring kitchen, facing one another.

"There's something funny going to happen," I whispered very softly.

"It's going to begin," Leslie said.

We did not notice the sour, racing rain any more.

The smiles stayed on the faces of the two still, silent women.

"It's going to begin."

And we heard Hetty say in a small secret voice: "Bring out the album, dear."

Hermione opened a cupboard and brought out a big, stiff-coloured photograph album, and put it in the middle of the table. Then she and Hetty sat down at the table, side by side, and Hermione opened the album.

"That's Uncle Eliot who died in Porthcawl, the one who had the cramp," said Hetty.

They looked with affection at Uncle Eliot, but we could not see him.

"That's Martha-the-woolshop, you wouldn't remember her, dear, it was wool, wool, wool, with her all the time; she wanted to be buried in her jumper, the mauve one, but her husband put his foot down. He'd been in India. That's your Uncle Morgan," Hetty said, "one of the Kidwelly Morgans, remember him in the snow?"

Hermione turned a page. "And that's Myfanwy, she got queer all of a sudden, remember. It was when she was milking. That's your cousin Jim, the Minister, until they found out. And that's our Beryl," Hetty said.

But she spoke all the time like somebody repeating a lesson: a well-loved lesson she knew by heart.

We knew that she and Hermione were only waiting.

Then Hermione turned another page. And we knew, by their secret smiles, that this was what they had been waiting for.

"My sister Katinka," Hetty said.

"Auntie Katinka," Hermione said. They bent over the photograph.

"Remember that day in Aberystwyth, Katinka?" Hetty said softly. "The day we went on the choir outing."

"I wore my new white dress," a new voice said.

Leslie clutched at my hand.

"And a straw hat with birds," said the clear, new voice.

Hermione and Hetty were not moving their lips.

"I was always a one for birds on my hat. Just the plumes of course. It was August the third, and I was twenty-three."

"Twenty-three come October, Katinka," Hetty said.

"That's right, love," the voice said. "Scorpio I was. And we met Douglas Pugh on the Prom and he said, 'You look like a queen today, Katinka,' he said. 'You look like a queen, Katinka,' he said. Why are those two boys looking in at the window?"

We ran up the gravel drive, and around the corner of the house, and into the avenue and out on to St. Augustus Crescent. The rain roared down to drown the town. There we stopped for breath. We did not speak or look at each other. Then we walked on through the rain. At Victoria corner, we stopped again.

"Good-night, old man," Leslie said.

"Good-night," I said.

And we went our different ways.

COMMENTARY
by the Editors

Dylan Thomas has created a middle world of suspended experience in which neither childish fantasy nor adult reason can quite come to terms. It is a world from which the two youthful protagonists try to wrest meaning but cannot because they are "too young" to penetrate the barriers of mature customs and attitudes and "too old" to prolong the fabled visions of childhood. And yet, precisely because they are in this indeterminate center of being, they at first confront their dilemma exuberantly. What must seem to many of their elders a bitter taste of reality, they treat with an irreverence and joy made possible by romantic imagination. Theirs is like that Wordsworthian stage of development in which instinctual responses, though already modified by the encroachment of experience, still dominate the rational. The narrator and Leslie absorb the preoccupations of adulthood through the skin, as it were, but not through the mind. They have access to only a closely circumscribed field of human responsibility, of course, but they are not a part of that field—they are "followers."

Awareness, then, is for them sensation and desire, a yearning to look behind the barrier; it is feeling without the perception that comes with participation. Implicitly, if unintentionally, Thomas has opened our eyes to a dramatic irony, for he reveals what his protagonists are not yet prepared to grasp—the literal truths of a shoddy, indeed, futile, reality. That revelation intensifies the sense of our own lost innocence, and it makes us envious of the capacity these boys still have for joyously sensuous fulfillment. Conversely, we are a little saddened, anticipating as we do the inexorable shift toward which they are moving from the roles of uncommitted spectators to those of troubled agents in a world impatient of imagination. With the guilelessness of inexperience, the narrator can make a refrain of his own regret: "It was the saddest evening I had ever known." ... "It's the saddest night in the world." This too is in the nature of the irony, for he is uttering words borrowed from adult experience which soon enough will become true for him. This is the formality of language, as mechanical perhaps as the chorus of "*good*-nights" which contradicts what we know cannot be true much longer.

As long as the two boys can remain followers, they are free to play their games of imagination. Like children who put on the attire of their parents, they move safely on the periphery of adult conventions—even as the pub interlude is a parody by adolescents, a game they skip in and out of with the same impish zest they apply to teasing Dulcie. The hard facts of life are all about them, but only as entertaining sensations. The Marlborough saloon brings them no closer to the weaknesses and aspirations of grownups than do the two-dimensional exploits of their cinema favorites. Intuitively, however, they are impelled away from the bright sanctuary of fantasy and onto the dark edges of experience. They are no longer satisfied with merely sensing reality; imagination must give way to tangible participation. We are sad for them because they are preparing to relinquish the happiness—the imaginative freedom—of spontaneous, unencumbered lives. They, meanwhile, are sad for themselves because in their restless groping for as yet unfelt sensations the daily, familiar sensations are no longer enough.

They are followers, hence, but with a frustrated, to them inexplicable longing for something more—paradoxically the infinitely poorer initiation into adulthood. " 'I wonder what's the point in following people,' Leslie said, 'it's kind of daft. It never gets you anywhere. All you do is follow them home and then try to look through the windows and see what they're doing and mostly there's curtains anyway.' " But the power of imagination is still strong within them, and once again they look for that elusive magic of rich sensation. This time, however, they do penetrate the curtain and are brought up short by the painful, initiatory discovery that fantasy can bring its own kind of sadness, one that impinges upon the ultimate truth of experience. For the first time they have left the safety of impersonal, harmless imaginings and intruded into the privacy of individual lives. And for the first time fantasy has betrayed them, for it has swept them from the vicarious pleasures of imagination to an apprehension of their mortality. For the first time they have evoked in themselves an awareness of death and are frightened by this sudden insight.

The mood of "The Followers," then, is a bittersweet one in which gaiety vies with melancholy (though not with gloom) and the sense of companionship fades into that of isolation. The social friendliness with which adults take their leave of each other—"Goodnight, Mr. Swan"—becomes a presage of discovery for the two initiates. The affectionate ritual of parting is also an acknowledgment of the separateness which must finally take them their lonely, separate ways. The mood, further, is enforced by settings whose wet discomfort and squalor emphasize the subtle drift of simple events which sweep the boys toward consciousness of their destiny. Thomas allows this mood to work itself out gradually and inevitably without visible interference. The young narrator holds the key to the reader's responses, inducing credibility by an unaffected presentation that reflects his movement toward self-recognition. Familiarity with Thomas' attitudes about the progression from life to death, however, inescapably adds an autobiographical dimension to the mood. That is, we accept him as a hovering presence or, for better artistic effect, as the participating creator behind the persona's mask. Consequently, we are encouraged to interpret, to draw forth implications which we would not expect to be enunciated by a boy on the threshold of experience. The mood, hence, is self-generating as a complex of sensations. But it is amplified beyond its narrative circumstances through identification with the author.

The Outing
James Baldwin

Each summer the church gave an outing. It usually took place on the Fourth of July, that being the day when most of the church-members were free from work; it began quite early in the morning and lasted all day. The saints referred to it as the 'whosoever will' outing, by which they meant that, though it was given by the Mount of Olives Pentecostal Assembly for the benefit of its members, all men were free to join them, Gentile, Jew or Greek or sinner. The Jews and the Greeks, to say nothing of the Gentiles—on whom, for their livelihood, most of the saints depended—showed themselves, year after year, indifferent to the invitation; but sinners of the more expected hue were seldom lacking. This year they were to take a boat trip up the Hudson as far as Bear Mountain where they would spend the day and return as the moon rose over the wide river. Since on other outings they had merely taken a subway ride as far as Pelham Bay or Van Cortlandt Park, this year's outing was more than ever a special occasion and even the deacon's two oldest boys, Johnnie and Roy, and their friend, David Jackson, were reluctantly thrilled. These three tended to consider themselves sophisticates, no longer, like the old folks, at the mercy of the love or the wrath of God.

The entire church was going and for weeks in advance talked of nothing else. And for weeks in the future the outing would provide interesting conversation. They did not consider this frivolous. The outing, Father James declared from his pulpit a week before the event, was for the purpose of giving the children of God a day of relaxation; to breathe a purer air and to worship God joyfully beneath the roof of heaven; and there was nothing frivolous about *that*. And, rather to the alarm of the captain, they planned to hold church services aboard the ship. Last year Sister McCandless had held an impromptu service in the unbelieving subway car; she played the tambourine and sang and exhorted sinners and passed through the train distributing tracts. Not everyone had found this admirable, to some it seemed that Sister McCandless was being a little ostentatious. "I praise my Redeemer wherever I go," she retorted defiantly. "Holy Ghost don't leave *me* when I leave the church. I got a every day religion."

Sylvia's birthday was on the third, and David and Johnnie and Roy had been saving money for her birthday present. Between them they had five dollars but they could not decide what to give her. Roy's suggestion that they give her underthings was rudely shouted down: did he want Sylvia's mother to kill the girl? They were all frightened of the great, rawboned, outspoken Sister Daniels and for Sylvia's sake went to great pains to preserve what remained of her good humor. Finally, at the suggestion of David's older sister, Lorraine, they bought a small, gold-plated pin cut in the shape of a butterfly. Roy thought that it was cheap and grumbled angrily at their combined bad taste ("Wait till it starts turning her clothes green!" he cried) but David did not think it was so bad; Johnnie thought it pretty enough and he was sure that Sylvia would like it anyway; ("When's *your* birthday?" he asked David). It was agreed that David should present it to her on the day of the outing in the presence of them all.

("Man, I'm the oldest cat here," David said, "you know that girl's crazy about me"). This was the summer in which they all abruptly began to grow older, their bodies becoming troublesome and awkward and even dangerous and their voices not to be trusted. David perpetually boasted of the increase of down on his chin and professed to have hair on his chest—"and somewhere else, too," he added slyly, whereat they all laughed. "You ain't the only one," Roy said. "No," Johnnie said, "I'm almost as old as you are." "Almost ain't got it," David said. "Now ain't this a hell of a conversation for church boys?" Roy wanted to know.

The morning of the outing they were all up early; their father sang in the kitchen and their mother, herself betraying an excitement nearly youthful, scrubbed and dressed the younger children and laid the plates for breakfast. In the bedroom which they shared Roy looked wistfully out of the window and turned to Johnnie.

"Got a good mind to stay home," he said. "Probably have more fun." He made a furious gesture toward the kitchen. "Why doesn't *he* stay home?"

Johnnie, who was looking forward to the day with David and who had not the remotest desire to stay home for any reason and who knew, moreover, that Gabriel was not going to leave Roy alone in the city, not even if the heavens fell, said lightly, squirming into clean underwear: "Oh, he'll probably be busy with the old folks. We can stay out of his way."

Roy sighed and began to dress. "Be glad when I'm a man," he said.

Lorraine and David and Mrs. Jackson were already on the boat when they arrived. They were among the last; most of the church, Father James, Brother Elisha, Sister McCandless, Sister Daniels and Sylvia were seated near the rail of the boat in a little semi-circle, conversing in strident tones. Father James and Sister McCandless were remarking the increase of laxity among God's people and debating whether or not the church should run a series of revival meetings. Sylvia sat there, saying nothing, smiling painfully now and then at young Brother Elisha, who spoke loudly of the need for a revival and who continually attempted to include Sylvia in the conversation. Elsewhere on the boat similar conversations were going on. The saints of God were together and very conscious this morning of their being together and of their sainthood; and were determined that the less enlightened world should know who they were and remark upon it. To this end there were a great many cries of "Praise the Lord!" in greeting and the formal holy kiss. The children, bored with the familiar spectacle, had already drawn apart and amused themselves by loud cries and games that were no less exhibitionistic than that being played by their parents. Johnnie's nine year old sister, Lois, since she professed salvation, could not very well behave as the other children did; yet no degree of salvation could have equipped her to enter into the conversation of the grown-ups; and she was very violently disliked among the adolescents and could not join them either. She wandered about, therefore, unwillingly forlorn, contenting herself to some extent by a great display of virtue in her encounters with the unsaved children and smiling brightly at the grown-ups. She came to Brother Elisha's side. "Praise the Lord," he cried, stroking her head and continuing his conversation.

Lorraine and Mrs. Jackson met Johnnie's mother for the first time as she breathlessly came on board, dressed in the airy and unreal blue which Johnnie would forever associate with his furthest memories of her. Johnnie's baby brother, her youngest, happiest child, clung round her neck; she made him stand, staring in wonder at the strange, endless deck, while she was introduced. His mother, on all social occasions, seemed fearfully distracted, as though she awaited, at any moment, some crushing and irrevocable disaster. This disaster might be the sudden awareness of a run in her stocking or private knowledge that the trump of judgment was due, within five minutes, to sound: but, whatever it was, it lent her a certain agitated charm and people, struggling to guess what it might be that so claimed her inward attention, never failed, in the process, to be won over. She talked with Lorraine and Mrs. Jackson for a few moments, the child tugging at her skirts, Johnnie watching her with a smile; and at last, the child becoming always more restive, said that she must go—into what merciless arena one dared not imagine—but hoped, with a despairing smile which clearly indicated the improbability of such happiness, that she would be able to see them later. They watched her as she walked slowly to the other end of the boat, sometimes pausing in conversation, always (as though it were a duty) smiling a little and now and then considering Lois where she stood at Brother Elisha's knee.

"She's very friendly," Mrs. Jackson said. "She looks like you, Johnnie."

David laughed. "Now why you want to say a thing like that, Ma? That woman ain't never done nothing to you."

Johnnie grinned, embarrassed, and pretended to menace David with his fists.

"Don't you listen to that old, ugly boy," Lorraine said. "He just trying to make you feel bad. Your mother's real good-looking. Tell her I said so."

This embarrassed him even more, but he made a mock bow and said, "Thank you, Sister." And to David: "Maybe now you'll learn to keep your mouth shut."

"Who'll learn to keep whose mouth shut? What kind of talk is that?"

He turned and faced his father, who stood smiling on them as from a height.

"Mrs. Jackson, this is my father," said Roy quickly. "And this is Miss Jackson. You know David."

Lorraine and Mrs. Jackson looked up at the deacon with polite and identical smiles.

"How do you do?" Lorraine said. And from Mrs. Jackson: "I'm very pleased to meet you."

"Praise the Lord," their father said. He smiled. "Don't you let Johnnie talk fresh to you."

"Oh, no, we were just kidding around," David said. There was a short, ugly silence. The deacon said: "It looks like a good day for the outing, praise the Lord. You kids have a good time. Is this your first time with us, Mrs. Jackson?"

"Yes," said Mrs. Jackson. "David came home and told me about it and it's been so long since I've been in the country I just decided I'd take me a day off. And Lorraine's not been feeling too strong, I thought the fresh air would do her some good." She smiled a little painfully as she spoke. Lorraine looked amused.

"Yes, it will, nothing like God's fresh air to help the feeble." At this description of herself as feeble Lorraine looked ready to fall into the Hudson and coughed nastily into her handkerchief. David, impelled by his own perverse demon, looked at Johnnie quickly and murmured, "That's the truth, deacon." The deacon looked at him and smiled and turned to Mrs. Jackson. "We been hoping that your son might join our church someday. Roy brings him out to service every Sunday. Do you like the services, son?" This last was addressed in a hearty voice to David; who, recovering from his amazement at hearing Roy mentioned as his especial pal (for he was Johnnie's friend, it was to be with Johnnie that he came to church!) smiled and said, "Yes sir, I like them alright," and looked at Roy, who considered his father with an expression at once contemptuous, ironic and resigned and at Johnnie, whose face was a mask of rage. He looked sharply at the deacon again; but he, with his arm around Roy, was still talking.

"This boy came to the Lord just about a month ago," he said proudly. "The Lord saved him just like that. Believe me, Sister Jackson, ain't no better fortress for nobody, young or old, than the arms of Jesus. My son'll tell you so, ain't it, Roy?"

They considered Roy with a stiff, cordial curiosity. He muttered murderously, "Yes sir."

"Johnnie tells me you're a preacher," Mrs. Jackson said at last. "I'll come out and hear you sometime with David."

"Don't come out to hear me," he said. "You come out and listen to the Word of God. We're all just vessels in His hand. Do you know the Lord, sister?"

"I try to do His will," Mrs. Jackson said.

He smiled kindly. "We must all grow in grace." He looked at Lorraine. "I'll be expecting to see you too, young lady."

"Yes, we'll be out," Lorraine said. They shook hands. "It's very nice to have met you," she said.

"Goodbye." He looked at David. "Now you be good. I want to see you saved soon." He released Roy and started to walk away. "You kids enjoy yourselves. Johnnie, don't you get into no mischief, you hear me?"

He affected not to have heard; he put his hands in his pants' pockets and pulled out some change and pretended to count it. His hand was clammy and it shook. When his father repeated his admonition, part of the change spilled to the deck and he bent to pick it up. He wanted at once to shout to his father the most dreadful curses that he knew and he wanted to weep. He was aware that they were all intrigued by the tableau presented by his father and himself, that they were all vaguely cognizant of an unnamed and deadly tension. From his knees on the deck he called back (putting into his voice as much asperity, as much fury and hatred as he dared):

"Don't worry about me, Daddy. Roy'll see to it that I behave."

There was a silence after he said this; and he rose to his feet and saw that they were all watching him. David looked pitying and shocked, Roy's head was bowed and he looked apologetic. His father called:

"Excuse yourself, Johnnie, and come here."

"Excuse me," he said, and walked over to his father. He looked up into his father's face with an anger which surprised and even frightened him. But he did not drop his eyes, knowing that his father saw there (and he wanted him to see it) how much he hated him.

"What did you say?" his father asked.

"I said you don't have to worry about me. I don't think I'll get into any mischief." And his voice surprised him, it was more deliberately cold and angry than he had intended and there was a sardonic stress on the word 'mischief.' He knew that his father would then and there have knocked him down if they had not been in the presence of saints and strangers.

"You be careful how you speak to me. Don't you get grown too fast. We get home, I'll pull down those long pants and we'll see who's the man, you hear me?"

Yes we will, he thought and said nothing. He looked with a deliberate casualness about the deck. Then they felt the lurch of the boat as it began to move from the pier. There was an excited raising of voices and "I'll see you later," his father said and turned away.

He stood still, trying to compose himself to return to Mrs. Jackson and Lorraine. But as he turned with his hands in his pants' pockets he saw that David and Roy were coming toward him and he stopped and waited for them.

"It's a bitch," Roy said.

David looked at him, shocked. "That's no language for a saved boy." He put his arm around Johnnie's shoulder. "We're off to Bear Mountain," he cried, "*up* the glorious Hudson"—and he made a brutal gesture with his thumb.

"Now suppose Sylvia saw you do that," said Roy, "what would you say, huh?"

"We needn't worry about her," Johnnie said. "She'll be sitting with the old folks all day long."

"Oh, we'll figure out a way to take care of *them*," said David. He turned to Roy. "Now you the saved one, why don't you talk to Sister Daniels and distract her attention while we talk to the girl? You the baby, anyhow, girl don't want to talk to you."

"I ain't got enough salvation to talk to that hag," Roy said. "I got a Daddy-made salvation. I'm saved when I'm with Daddy." They laughed and Roy added, "And I ain't no baby, either, I got everything my Daddy got."

"And a lot your Daddy don't dream of," David said.

Oh, thought Johnnie, with a sudden, vicious, chilling anger, *he doesn't have to dream about it!*

"Now let's act like we Christians," David said. "If we was real smart now, we'd go over to where she's sitting with all those people and act like we wanted to hear about God. Get on the good side of her mother."

"And suppose *he* comes back?" asked Johnnie.

Gabriel was sitting at the other end of the boat, talking with his wife. "Maybe he'll stay there," David said; there was a note of apology in his voice.

They approached the saints.

"Praise the Lord," they said sedately.

"Well, praise Him," Father James said. "How are you young men today?" He grabbed Roy by the shoulder. "Are you coming along in the Lord?"

"Yes, sir," Roy muttered, "I'm trying." He smiled into Father James's face.

"It's a wonderful thing," Brother Elisha said, "to give up to the Lord in your youth." He looked up at Johnnie and David. "Why don't you boys surrender? Ain't nothing in the world for you, I'll tell you that. He says, 'Remember thy Creator in the days of thy youth when the evil days come not.' "

"Amen," said Sister Daniels. "We're living in the last days, children. Don't think because you're young you got plenty of time. God takes the young as well as the old. You got to hold yourself in readiness all the time lest when He comes He catch you unprepared. Yes sir. Now's the time."

"You boys going to come to service today, ain't you?" asked Sister McCandless. "We're going to have service on the ship, you know." She looked at Father James. "Reckon we'll start as soon as we get a little further up the river, won't we, Father?"

"Yes," Father James said, "we're going to praise God right in the middle of the majestic Hudson." He leaned back and released Roy as he spoke. "Want to see you children there. I want to hear you make a *noise* for the Lord."

"I ain't never seen none of these young men Shout," said Sister Daniels, regarding them with distrust. She looked at David and Johnnie. "Don't believe I've ever even heard you testify."

"We're not saved yet, sister," David told her gently.

"That's alright," Sister Daniels said. "You *could* get up and praise the Lord for your life, health and strength. Praise Him for what you got, He'll give you something more."

"That's the truth," said Brother Elisha. He smiled at Sylvia. "I'm a witness, bless the Lord."

"They going to make a noise yet," said Sister McCandless. "Lord's going to touch everyone of these young men one day and bring them on their knees to the altar. You mark my words, you'll see." And she smiled at them.

"You just stay around the house of God long enough," Father James said. "One of these days the Spirit'll jump on you. I won't never forget the day It jumped on me."

"That *is* the truth," Sister McCandless cried, "so glad It jumped on me one day, hallelujah!"

"Amen," Sister Daniels cried, "amen."

"Looks like we're having a little service right now," Brother Elisha said smiling. Father James laughed heartily and cried, "Well, praise Him anyhow."

"I believe next week the church is going to start a series of revival meetings," Brother Elisha said. "I want to see you boys at every one of them, you hear?" He laughed as he spoke and added as David seemed about to protest, "No, no, brother, don't want no excuses. You *be* there. Get you boys to the altar, then maybe you'll pay more attention in Sunday School."

At this they all laughed and Sylvia said in her mild voice, looking mockingly at Roy, "Maybe we'll even see Brother Roy Shout." Roy grinned.

"Like to see you do some Shouting too," her mother grumbled. "You got to get closer to the Lord." Sylvia smiled and bit her lip; she cast a glance at David.

"Now everybody ain't got the same kind of spirit," Brother Elisha said, coming to Sylvia's aid. "Can't *all* make as much noise as you make," he said, laughing gently, "we all ain't got your energy."

Sister Daniels smiled and frowned at this reference to her size and passion and said, "Don't care, brother, when the Lord moves inside you, you bound to do something. I've seen that girl Shout all night and come back the next night and Shout some more. I don't believe in no dead religion, no sir. The saints of God need a revival."

"Well, we'll work on Sister Sylvia," said Brother Elisha.

Directly before and behind them stretched nothing but the river, they had long ago lost sight of the point of their departure. They steamed beside the Palisades, which rose rough and gigantic from the dirty, broad and blue-green Hudson. Johnnie and David and Roy wandered downstairs to the bottom deck, standing by the rail and leaning over to watch the white, writhing spray which followed the boat. From the river there floated up to their faces a soft, cool breeze. They were quiet for a long time, standing together, watching the river and the mountains and hearing vaguely the hum of activity behind them on the boat. The sky was high and blue, with here and there a spittle-like, changing cloud; the sun was orange and beat with anger on their uncovered heads.

And David muttered finally, "Be funny if they were right."

"If who was right?" asked Roy.

"Elisha and them—"

"There's only one way to find out," said Johnnie.

"Yes," said Roy, "and I ain't homesick for heaven yet."

"You always got to be so smart," David said.

"Oh," said Roy, "you just sore because Sylvia's still up there with Brother Elisha."

"You think they going to be married?" Johnnie asked.

"Don't talk like a fool," David said.

"Well it's a cinch you ain't never going to get to talk to her till you get saved," Johnnie said. He had meant to say 'we.' He looked at David and smiled.

"Might be worth it," David said.

"*What* might be worth it?" Roy asked, grinning.

"Now be nice," David said. He flushed, the dark blood rising beneath the dark skin. "How you expect me to get saved if you going to talk that way? You supposed to be an example."

"Don't look at me, boy," Roy said.

"I want you to talk to Johnnie," Gabriel said to his wife.

"What about?"

"That boy's pride is running away with him. Ask him to tell you what he said to me this morning soon as he got in front of his friends. He's your son, alright."

"What did he say?"

He looked darkly across the river. "You ask him to tell you about it tonight. I wanted to knock him down."

She had watched the scene and knew this. She looked at her husband briefly, feeling a sudden, outraged anger, barely conscious; sighed and turned to look at her youngest child where he sat involved in a complicated and strenuous and apparently joyless game which utilized a red ball, jacks, blocks and a broken shovel.

"I'll talk to him," she said at last. "He'll be alright." She wondered what on earth she would say to him; and what he would say to her. She looked covertly about the boat, but he was nowhere to be seen.

"That proud demon's just eating him up," he said bitterly. He watched the river hurtle past. "Be the best thing in the world if the Lord would take his soul." He had meant to say 'save' his soul.

Now it was noon and all over the boat there was the activity of lunch. Paper bags and huge baskets were opened. There was then revealed splendor: cold pork chops, cold chicken, bananas, apples, oranges, pears, and soda-pop, candy and cold lemonade. All over the boat the chosen of God relaxed; they sat in groups and talked and laughed; some of the more worldly gossiped and some of the more courageous young people dared to walk off together. Beneath them the strong, indifferent river raged within the channel and the screaming spray pursued them. In the engine room children watched the motion of the ship's gears as they rose and fell and chanted. The tremendous bolts of steel seemed almost human, imbued with a relentless force that was not human. There was something monstrous about this machine which bore such enormous weight and cargo.

Sister Daniels threw a paper bag over the side and wiped her mouth with her large handkerchief. "Sylvia, you be careful how you speak to these unsaved boys," she said.

"Yes, I am, Mama."

"Don't like the way that little Jackson boy looks at you. That child's got a demon. You be careful."

"Yes, Mama."

"You got plenty of time to be thinking about boys. Now's the time for you to be thinking about the Lord."

"Yes'm."

"You *mind* now," her mother said.

"Mama, I want to go home!" Lois cried. She crawled into her mother's arms, weeping.

"Why, what's the matter, honey?" She rocked her daughter gently. "Tell Mama what's the matter? Have you got a pain?"

"I want to go home, I want to go home." Lois sobbed.

"A very fine preacher, a man of God and a friend of mine will run the service for us," said Father James.

"Maybe you've heard about him—a Reverend Peters? A real man of God, amen."

"I thought," Gabriel said, smiling, "that perhaps I could bring the message some Sunday night. The Lord called me a long time ago. I used to have my own church down home."

"You don't want to run too fast, Deacon Grimes," Father James said. "You just take your time. You been coming along right well on Young Ministers' Nights." He paused and looked at Gabriel. "Yes, indeed."

"I just thought," Gabriel said humbly, "that I could be used to more advantage in the house of God."

Father James quoted the text which tells us how preferable it is to be a gate-keeper in the house of God than to dwell in the tent of the wicked; and started to add the dictum from Saint Paul about obedience to those above one in the Lord but decided (watching Gabriel's face) that it was not necessary yet.

"You just keep praying," he said kindly. "You get a little closer to God. He'll work wonders. You'll see." He bent closer to his deacon. "And try to get just a little closer to the *people*."

Roy wandered off with a gawky and dazzled girl named Elizabeth. Johnnie and David wandered restlessly up and down the boat alone. They mounted to the topmost deck and leaned over the railing in the deserted stern. Up here the air was sharp and clean. They faced the water, their arms around each other.

"Your old man was kind of rough this morning," David said carefully, watching the mountains pass.

"Yes," Johnnie said. He looked at David's face against the sky. He shivered suddenly in the sharp, cold air and buried his face in David's shoulder. David looked down at him and tightened his hold.

"Who do you love?" he whispered. "Who's your boy?"

"You," he muttered fiercely, "I love you."

"Roy!" Elizabeth giggled, "*Roy Grimes*. If you *ever* say a thing like that *again*."

Now the service was beginning. From all corners of the boat there was the movement of the saints of God. They gathered together their various possessions and moved their chairs from top and bottom decks to the large main hall. It was early afternoon, not quite two o'clock. The sun was high and fell everywhere with a copper light. In the city the heat would have been insupportable; and here, as the saints filed into the huge, high room, once used as a ballroom, to judge from the faded and antique appointments, the air slowly began to be oppressive. The room was the color of black mahogany and coming in from the bright deck, one groped suddenly in darkness; and took one's sense of direction from the elegant grand piano which stood in the front of the room on a little platform.

They sat in small rows with one wide aisle between them, forming, almost unconsciously, a hierarchy. Father James sat in the front next to Sister McCandless. Opposite them sat Gabriel and Deacon Jones and, immediately behind them, Sister Daniels and her daughter. Brother Elisha walked in swiftly, just as they were beginning to be settled. He strode to the piano and knelt down for a second before rising to take his place. There was a quiet stir, the saints adjusted themselves, waiting while Brother Elisha tentatively ran his fingers over the keys. Gabriel looked about impatiently for Roy and Johnnie, who, engaged no doubt in sinful conversation with David, were not yet in service. He looked back to where Mrs. Jackson sat with Lorraine, uncomfortable smiles on their faces, and glanced at his wife, who met his questioning regard quietly, the expression on her face not changing.

Brother Elisha struck the keys and the congregation joined in the song, *Nothing Shall Move Me from the Love of God,* with tambourine and heavy hands and stomping feet. The walls and the floor of the ancient hall trembled and the candelabra wavered in the high ceiling. Outside the river rushed past under the heavy shadow of the Palisades and the copper sun beat down. A few of the strangers who had come along on the outing appeared at the doors and stood watching with an uneasy amusement. The saints sang on, raising their strong voices in praises to Jehovah and seemed unaware of those unsaved who watched and who, some day, the power of the Lord might cause to tremble.

The song ended as Father James rose and faced the congregation, a broad smile on his face. They watched him expectantly, with love. He stood silent for a moment, smiling down upon them. Then he said, and his voice was loud and filled with triumph:

"Well, let us all say, Amen!"

And they cried out obediently, "Well, Amen!"

"Let us all say, praise Him!"

"Praise Him!"

"Let us all say, hallelujah!"

"Hallelujah!"

"Well, glory!" cried Father James. The Holy Ghost touched him and he cried again, "Well, bless Him! Bless His holy name!"

They laughed and shouted after him, their joy so great that they laughed as children and some of them cried as children do; in the fullness and assurance of salvation, in the knowledge that the Lord was in their midst and that each heart, swollen to anguish, yearned only to be filled with His glory. Then, in that moment, each of them might have mounted with wings like eagles far past the sordid persistence of the flesh, the depthless iniquity of the heart, the doom of hours and days and weeks; to be received by the Bridegroom where He waited on high in glory; where all tears were wiped away and death had no power; where the wicked ceased from troubling and the weary soul found rest.

"Saints, let's praise Him," Father James said. "Today, right in the middle of God's great river, under God's great roof, beloved, let us raise our voices in thanksgiving that God has seen fit to save us, amen!"

"Amen! Hallelujah!"

"—and to keep us saved, amen, to keep us, oh glory to God, from the snares of Satan, from the temptation and the lust and the evil of this world!"

"Talk about it!"

"*Preach!*"

"Ain't nothing strange, amen, about worshiping God *wherever* you might be, ain't that right? Church, when you get this mighty salvation you just can't keep it in, hallelujah! you got to talk about it—"

"Amen!"

"You got to live it, amen. When the Holy Ghost touches you, you *move*, bless God!"

"Well, it's so!"

"Want to hear some testimonies today, amen! I want to hear some *singing* today, bless God! Want to see some *Shouting*, bless God, hallelujah!"

"Talk about it!"

"And I don't want to see none of the saints hold back. If the Lord saved you, amen, He give you a witness *every*where you go. Yes! My soul is a witness, bless our God!"

"Glory!"

"If you ain't saved, amen, get up and praise Him anyhow. Give God the glory for sparing your sinful life, *praise* Him for the sunshine and the rain, praise Him for all the works of His hands. Saints, I want to hear some praises today, you hear me? I want you to make this old boat *rock*, hallelujah! I want to *feel* your salvation. Are you saved?"

"Amen!"

"Are you sanctified?"

"Glory?"

"Baptized in fire?"

"Yes! So glad!"

"Testify!"

Now the hall was filled with a rushing wind on which forever rides the Lord, death or healing indifferently in His hands. Under this fury the saints bowed low, crying out "holy!" and tears fell. On the open deck sinners stood and watched, beyond them the fiery sun and the deep river, the black-brown-green, unchanging cliffs. That sun, which covered earth and water now, would one day refuse to shine, the river would cease its rushing and its numberless dead would rise; the cliffs would shiver, crack, fall and where they had been would then be nothing but the unleashed wrath of God.

"Who'll be the first to tell it?" Father James cried. "Stand up and talk about it!"

Brother Elisha screamed, "Have mercy, Jesus!" and rose from the piano stool, his powerful frame possessed. And the Holy Ghost touched him and he cried again, bending nearly double, while his feet beat ageless, dreadful signals on the floor, while his arms moved in the air like wings and his face, distorted, no longer his own face not the face of a young man, but timeless, anguished, grim with ecstasy, turned blindly toward heaven. *Yes, Lord,* they cried, *yes!*

"Dearly beloved . . ."

"Talk about it!"

"Tell it !"

"I want to thank and praise the Lord, amen . . ."

"Amen!"

". . . for being here, I want to thank Him for my life, health, and strength. . . ."

"Amen!"

"Well, glory!"

". . . I want to thank Him, hallelujah, for saving my soul one day. . . ."

"Oh!"

"Glory!"

". . . for causing the light, bless God, to shine in *my* heart one day when I was still a child, amen, I want to thank Him for bringing me to salvation in the days of my *youth*, hallelujah, when I have all my faculties, amen, before Satan had a chance to destroy my body in the world!"

"Talk about it!"

"He saved me, dear ones, from the world and the things of the world. Saved me, amen, from cardplaying . . ."

"Glory!"

". . . saved me from drinking, bless God, saved me from the streets, from the movies and all the filth that is in the world!"

"I *know* it's so!"

"He saved me, beloved, and sanctified me and filled me with the blessed Holy Ghost, *hallelujah!* Give me a new song, amen, which I didn't know before and set my feet on the King's highway. Pray for me beloved, that I will stand in these last and evil days."

"Bless your name, Jesus!"

During his testimony Johnnie and Roy and David had stood quietly beside the door, not daring to enter while he spoke. The moment he sat down they moved quickly, together, to the front of the high hall and knelt down beside their seats to pray. The aspect of each of them underwent always, in this company a striking, even an exciting change; as though their youth, barely begun, were already put away; and the animal, so vividly restless and undiscovered, so tense with power, ready to spring had been already stalked and trapped and offered, a perpetual blood-sacrifice, on the altar of the Lord. Yet their bodies continued to change and grow, preparing them, mysteriously and with ferocious speed, for manhood. No matter how careful their movements, these movements suggested, with a distinctness dreadful for the redeemed to see, the pagan lusting beneath the blood-washed robes. In them was perpetually and perfectly poised the power of revelation against the power of nature; and the saints, considering them with a baleful kind of love, struggled to bring their souls to safety in order, as it were, to steal a march on the flesh while the flesh still slept. A kind of storm, infernal, blew over the congregation as they passed; someone cried, "Bless them, Lord!" and immediately, honey-colored Sister Russell, while they knelt in prayer, rose to her feet to testify.

From the moment that they closed their eyes and covered their faces they were isolated from the joy that moved everything beside them. Yet this same isolation served only to make the glory of the saints more real, the pulse of conviction, however faint, beat in and the glory of God then held an undertone of abject terror. Roy was the first to rise, sitting very straight in his seat and allowing his face to reveal nothing; just as Sister Russell ended her testimony and sat down, sobbing, her head thrown back and both hands raised to heaven. Immediately Sister Daniels raised her strong, harsh voice and hit her tambourine, singing. Brother Elisha turned on the piano stool and hit the keys. Johnnie and David rose from their knees and as they rose the congregation rose, clapping their hands singing. The three boys did not sing; they stood together, carefully ignoring one another, their feet steady on the slightly tilting floor but their bodies moving back and forth as the music grew more savage. And someone cried aloud, a timeless sound of wailing; fire splashed the open deck and filled the doors and bathed the sinners standing there; fire filled the great hall and splashed the faces of the saints and a wind, unearthly, moved about their heads. Their hands were arched before them, moving, and their eyes were raised to heaven. Sweat stained the deacon's collar and soaked the tight headbands of the women. Was it true then? and had there indeed been born one day in Bethlehem a Saviour who was Christ the Lord? who had died for them—for *them!*—the spat-upon and beaten with rods, who had worn a crown of thorns and seen His blood run down like rain; and who had lain in the grave three days and vanquished death and hell and risen again in glory—*was it for them?*

Lord, I want to go, show me the way!

For unto us a child is born, unto us a son is given—and His name shall be called Wonderful, the mighty God, the everlasting Father, the Prince of Peace. Yes, and He was coming back one day, the King of glory; He would crack the face of heaven and descend to judge the nations and gather up His people and take them to their rest.

Take me by my hand and lead me on!

Somewhere in the back a woman cried out and began the Shout. They looked carefully about, still not looking at one another, and saw, as from a great distance and through intolerable heat, such heat as might have been faced by the Hebrew children when cast bound into the fiery furnace, that one of the saints was dancing under the arm of the Lord. She danced out into the aisle, beautiful with a beauty unbearable, graceful with grace that poured from heaven. Her face was lifted up, her eyes were closed and the feet which moved so surely now were not her own. One by one the power of God moved others and—as it had been written—the Holy Ghost descended from heaven with a Shout. Sylvia raised her hands, the tears poured down her face, and in a moment, she too moved out into the aisle, Shouting. Is it true then? the saints rejoiced, Roy beat the tambourine. David, grave and shaken, clapped his hands and his body moved insistently in the rhythm of the dancers. Johnnie stood beside him, hot and faint and repeating yet again his struggle, summoning in panic all his forces, to save him from this frenzy. And yet daily he recognized that he was black with sin, that the secrets of his heart were a stench in God's nostrils. *Though your sins be as scarlet they shall be white as snow. Come, let us reason together, saith the Lord.*

Now there was a violent discord on the piano and Brother Elisha leapt to his feet, dancing. Johnnie watched the spinning body and listened in terror and anguish, to the bestial sobs. Of the men it was only Elisha who danced and the women moved toward him and he moved toward the women. Johnnie felt blow over him an icy wind, all his muscles tightened, as though they furiously resisted some imminent bloody act, as the body of Isaac must have revolted when he saw his father's knife, and, sick and nearly sobbing, he closed his eyes. It was Satan, surely, who stood so foully at his shoulder; and what, but the blood of Jesus, should ever set him free? He thought of the many times he had stood in the congregation of the righteous—and yet he was not saved. He remained among the vast army of the doomed, whose lives—as he had been told, as he now, with such heart-sickness, began to discover for himself—were swamped with wretchedness and whose end was wrath and weeping. Then, for he felt himself falling, he opened his eyes and watched the rejoicing of the saints. His eyes found his father where he stood clapping his hands, glittering with sweat and overwhelming. Then Lois began to shout. For the first time he looked at Roy; their eyes met in brief, wry wonder and Roy imperceptibly shrugged. He watched his mother standing over Lois, her own face obscurely troubled. The light from the door was on her face, the entire room was filled with this strange light. There was no sound now except the sound of Roy's tambourine and the heavy rhythm of the saints; the sound of heavy feet and hands and the sound of weeping. Perhaps centuries past the children of Israel led by Miriam had made just such a noise as they came out of the wilderness. *For unto us is born this day a Saviour who is Christ the Lord.*

Yet, in the copper sunlight Johnnie felt suddenly, not the presence of the Lord, but the presence of David; which seemed to reach out to him, hand reaching out to hand in the fury of flood-time, to drag him to the bottom of the water or to carry him safe to shore. From the corner of his eye he watched his friend, who held him with such power; and felt, for that moment, such a depth of love, such nameless and terrible joy and pain, that he might have fallen, in the face of that company, weeping at David's feet.

Once at Bear Mountain they faced the very great problem of carrying Sylvia sufficiently far from her mother's sight to present her with her birthday present. This problem, difficult enough, was made even more difficult by the continual presence of Brother Elisha; who, inspired by the afternoon's service and by Sylvia's renewal of her faith, remained by her side to bear witness to the goodness and power of the Lord. Sylvia listened with her habitual rapt and painful smile. Her mother, on the one side and Brother Elisha on the other, seemed almost to be taking turns in advising her on her conduct as a saint of God. They began to despair, as the sun moved visibly westward, of ever giving her the gold-plated butterfly which rested uncomfortably in David's waistcoat pocket.

Of course, as Johnnie once suggested, there was really no reason they could not go up to her, surrounded as she was, and give her the jewel and get it over with—the more particularly as David evinced a desire to explore the wonders of Bear Mountain until this mission should have been fulfilled. Sister Daniels could scarcely object to an innocuous memento from three young men, all of whom attended church devoutly and one of whom professed salvation. But this was far from satisfactory for David, who did not wish to hear Sylvia's "thank-you's" in the constricting presence of the saints. Therefore they waited, wandering about the sloping park, lingering near the lake and the skating rink and watching Sylvia.

"God, why don't they go off somewhere and sleep? or pray?" cried David finally. He glared at the nearby rise where Sylvia and her mother sat talking with Brother Elisha. The sun was in their faces and struck from Sylvia's hair as she restlessly moved her head, small blue-black sparks.

Johnnie swallowed his jealousy at seeing how Sylvia filled his comrade's mind; he said, half-angrily, "I still don't see why we don't just go over and give it to her."

Roy looked at him. "Boy, you sound like you ain't got good sense," he said.

Johnnie, frowning, fell into silence. He glanced sidewise at David's puckered face (his eyes were still on Sylvia) and abruptly turned and started walking off.

"Where you going, boy?" David called.

"I'll be back," he said. And he prayed that David would follow him.

But David was determined to catch Sylvia alone and remained where he was with Roy. "Well, make it snappy," he said; and sprawled, full length, on the grass.

As soon as he was alone his pace slackened; he leaned his forehead against the bark of a tree, shaking and burning as in the teeth of a fever. The bark of the tree was rough and cold and though it offered no other comfort he stood there quietly for a long time, seeing beyond him—but it brought no peace—the high clear sky where the sun in fading glory traveled; and the deep earth covered with vivid banners, grass, flower, thorn and vine, thrusting upward forever the brutal trees. At his back he heard the voices of the children and the saints. He knew that he must return, that he must be on hand should David at last outwit Sister Daniels and present her daughter with the golden butterfly. But he did not want to go back, now he realized that he had no interest in the birthday present, no interest whatever in Sylvia—that he had had no interest all along. He shifted his stance, he turned from the tree as he turned his mind from the abyss which suddenly yawned, that abyss, depthless and terrifying, which he had encountered already in dreams. And he slowly began to walk, away from the saints and the voices of the children, his hands in his pockets, struggling to ignore the question which now screamed and screamed in his mind's bright haunted house.

It happened quite simply. Eventually Sister Daniels felt the need to visit the ladies' room, which was a long ways off. Brother Elisha remained where he was while Roy and David, like two beasts crouching in the underbrush, watched him and waited their opportunity. Then he also rose and wandered off to get a cold lemonade for Sylvia. She sat quietly alone on the green rise, her hands clasped around her knees, dreaming.

They walked over to her, in terror that Sister Daniels would suddenly reappear. Sylvia smiled as she saw them coming and waved to them merrily. Roy grinned and threw himself on his belly on the ground beside her. David remained standing, fumbling in his waist-coat pocket.

"We got something for you," Roy said.

David produced the butterfly. "Happy birthday, Sylvia," he said. He stretched out his hand, the butterfly glinted oddly in the sun, and he realized with surprise that his hand was shaking. She grinned widely, in amazement and delight, and took the pin from him.

"It's from Johnnie, too," he said. "I—we—hope you like it—"

She held the small gold pin in her palm and stared down at it; her face was hidden. After a moment she murmured, "I'm so surprised." She looked up, her eyes shining, almost wet. "Oh, it's wonderful," she said. "I never expected anything. I don't know what to say. It's marvelous, it's wonderful." She pinned the butterfly carefully to her light blue dress. She coughed slightly. "Thank you," she said.

"Your mother won't mind, will she?" Roy asked. "I mean—" he stammered awkwardly under Sylvia's sudden gaze—"we didn't know, we didn't want to get you in any trouble—"

"No," David said. He had not moved; he stood watching Sylvia. Sylvia looked away from Roy and up at David, his eyes met hers and she smiled. He smiled back, suddenly robbed of speech. She looked away again over the path her mother had taken and frowned slightly. "No," she said, "no, she won't mind."

Then there was silence. David shifted uncomfortably from one foot to the other. Roy lay contentedly face down on the grass. The breeze from the river, which lay below them and out of sight, grew subtly more insistent for they had passed the heat of the day; and the sun, moving always westward, fired and polished the tips of trees. Sylvia sighed and shifted on the ground.

"Why isn't Johnnie here?" she suddenly asked.

"He went off somewhere," Roy said. "He said he'd be right back." He looked at Sylvia and smiled. She was looking at David.

"You must want to grow real tall," she said mockingly. "Why don't you sit down?"

David grinned and sad down cross-legged next to Sylvia. "Well, the ladies like 'em tall." He lay on his back and stared up at the sky. "It's a fine day," he said.

She said, "Yes," and looked down at him; he had closed his eyes and was bathing his face in the slowly waning sun. Abruptly, she asked him:

"Why don't you get saved? You around the church all the time and you not saved yet? Why don't you?"

He opened his eyes in amazement. Never before had Sylvia mentioned salvation to him, except as a kind of joke. One of the things he most liked about her was the fact that she never preached to him. Now he smiled uncertainly and stared at her.

"I'm not joking," she said sharply. "I'm perfectly serious. Roy's saved—at least he *says* so—" and she smiled darkly, in the fashion of the old folks, at Roy—"and anyway, you ought to be thinking about your soul."

"Well, I don't know," David said. "I *think* about it. It's—well, I don't know if I can—well, live it—"

"All you got to do is make up your mind. If you really want to be saved, He'll save you. Yes, and He'll keep you too." She did not sound at all hysterical or transfigured. She spoke very quietly and with great earnestness and frowned as she spoke. David, taken off guard, said nothing. He looked embarrassed and pained and surprised. "Well, I don't know," he finally repeated.

"Do you ever pray?" she asked. "I mean, *really* pray?"

David laughed, beginning to recover himself. "It's not fair," he said, "you oughtn't to catch me all unprepared like that. Now I don't know what to say." But as he looked at her earnest face he sobered. "Well, I try to be decent. I don't bother nobody." He picked up a grass blade and stared at it. "I don't know," he said at last. "I do my best."

"*Do* you?" she asked.

He laughed again, defeated. "Girl," he said, "you *are* a killer."

She laughed too. "You black-eyed demon," she said, "if I don't see you at revival services I'll never speak to you again." He looked up quickly, in some surprise, and she said, still smiling, "Don't look at me like that. I mean it."

"All right, sister," he said. Then: "If I come out can I walk you home?"

"I got my mother to walk me home—"

"Well, let your mother walk home with Brother Elisha," he said, grinning, "Let the old folks stay together."

"Loose him, Satan!" she cried, laughing, "loose the boy!"

"The brother needs prayer," Roy said.

"Amen," said Sylvia. She looked down again at David. "I want to see you at church. Don't you forget it."

"All right," he said. "I'll be there."

The boat whistles blew at six o'clock, punctuating their holiday; blew, fretful and insistent, through the abruptly dispirited park and skaters left the skating rink; boats were rowed in furiously from the lake. Children were called from the swings and the seesaw and the merry-go-round and forced to leave behind the ball which had been lost in the forest and the torn kite which dangled from the top of a tree. ("Hush now," said their parents, "we'll get you another one—come along." *"Tomorrow?"*—"Come along, honey, it's time to go!") The old folks rose from the benches, from the grass, gathered together the empty lunch-basket, the half-read newspaper, the Bible which was carried everywhere; and they started down the hillside, an army in disorder. David walked with Sylvia and Sister Daniels and Brother Elisha, listening to their conversation (good Lord, thought Johnnie, don't they ever mention anything but sin?) and carrying Sylvia's lunchbasket. He seemed interested in what they were saying; every now and then he looked at Sylvia and grinned and she grinned back. Once, as Sylvia stumbled, he put his hand on her elbow to steady her and held her arm perhaps a moment too long. Brother Elisha, on the far side of Sister Daniels, noticed this and a frown passed over his face. He kept talking, staring now and then hard at Sylvia and trying, with a certain almost humorous helplessness, to discover what was in her mind. Sister Daniels talked of nothing but the service on the boat and of the forthcoming revival. She scarcely seemed to notice David's presence, though once she spoke to him, making some remark about the need, on his part, of much prayer. Gabriel carried the sleeping baby in his arms, striding beside his wife and Lois—who stumbled perpetually and held tightly to her mother's hand. Roy was somewhere in the back, joking with Elizabeth. At a turn in the road the boat and the dock appeared below them, a dead gray-white in the sun.

Johnnie walked down the slope alone, watching David and Sylvia ahead of him. When he had come back, both Roy and David had disappeared and Sylvia sat again in the company of her mother and Brother Elisha; and if he had not seen the gold butterfly on her dress he would have been aware of no change. She thanked him for his share in it and told him that Roy and David were at the skating rink.

But when at last he found them they were far in the middle of the lake in a rowboat. He was afraid of water, he could not row. He stood on the bank and watched them. After a long while they saw him and waved and started to bring the boat in so that he could join them. But the day was ruined for him; by the time they brought the boat in, the hour, for which they had hired it, was over; David went in search of his mother for more money but when he came back it was time to leave. Then he walked with Sylvia.

All during the trip home David seemed preoccupied. When he finally sought out Johnnie he found him sitting by himself on the top deck, shivering a little in the night air. He sat down beside him. After a moment Johnnie moved and put his head on David's shoulder. David put his arms around him. But now where there had been peace there was only panic and where there had been safety, danger, like a flower, opened.

The Narrator's Focus

1. POINT OF VIEW

As soon as we ask the question "who is telling the story?" we have become involved in the technical problem of *point of view,* figuratively the mind through which a writer has chosen to present his story. That is, he selects his narrator and then decides where to place him within the fictional framework. For whoever is responsible for telling the story must be given a position from which he can properly satisfy authorial purpose.

There are several different points of view available to the short story writer. Let us look briefly at a few of the possibilities.

There is of course the first-person narrator, the "I" of the fiction. When a writer decides upon this particular point of view, he is faced with further choice. Is the "I" to be a major character, a central actor comparable to Joseph Conrad's captain in "The Secret Sharer" or Cassill's young musician in "The Biggest Band"? Again, is he to be a somewhat ambivalent performer—now an active agent, now a seemingly peripheral minor character—like the narrator of Delmore Schwartz's "In Dreams Begin Responsibilities"? Or is he to function solely as an observer, one who—like the celebrated barber of Ring Lardner's "Haircut"—reports without personal commitment what he sees and hears?

Whatever role is conceived for the "I," the first-person point of view has certain narrative advantages. It may not only clarify the narrator's personality but also promote a near-intimacy between him and the reader, as in Updike's "A & P." This first-person mode of address heightens the credibility of the account because we tend to believe eye-witness reports more readily than hearsay. We can, for example, better understand the struggle between the doctor and the little girl in Williams' "Use of Force" because the doctor himself reports details of the conflict and his own reactions to the "final unreasoning assault" with which he "overpowered the child's neck and jaws." In this same instance the use of a first-person point of view amplifies the irony of the situation. Directly and yet without self-perception the doctor reveals the nature of the child's disease but he also isolates his own more terrifying malady. His is a moral illness—"a blind fury," an instinctive delight in the use of force for its own sake.

While the first-person point of view has definite advantages, it is nonetheless the most restrictive focus of narrative; whatever the "I" has not himself seen or heard cannot logically enter the story as a direct "scene." The effect of relating matters at second-hand—that is, as coming to the narrator from other witnesses—often suffers by contrast. The process of retelling dilutes the authority of personal experience: readers cannot escape the illusion of an imposed distance; an additional narrating presence almost inevitably causes a loss of immediacy, a dulling of the vivid associations established by the primary speaker. For this reason, most first-person storytellers—except for bold exceptions like Conrad—prefer the safe consistency of the single speaker to the risks inherent in recruiting secondary voices.

Radically opposed to this limited field of vision, in so far as it is the most widely embracing, is what we call the omniscient point of view. When a writer chooses this comprehensive "angle of vision," he is permitted to speak directly in his own voice as well as in that of his characters. That is to say, he describes all their actions and thoughts. Then going one step further, he comments in his own person upon them; this accession of authority is comparable to the license appropriated by an editorial writer. We find such omniscience practiced in much of the fiction of the eighteenth and nineteenth centuries, in the efforts of such writers as Fielding, Dickens, and Thackeray. Closer at hand, we find it as well in Melville's "The Bell-Tower."

The omniscient point of view is no longer a fashionable narrative technique. It offers intimacy but, as E. M. Forster says, "at the expense of illusion and nobility. It is like standing a man a drink so that he may not criticize your opinions. . . . To take your reader into your confidence about the universe is a dangerous thing." Far more popular today is a less expansive technique, one favored by Henry James, for example. Quite simply this is a third-person restricted point of view which focuses upon one or more main characters through whose presence, actions, and mind, we are made to see and understand the fictional crisis. Thus in "The Liar" we come to appreciate the personalities of Colonel and Mrs. Capadose only as their relationship is made clear to Oliver Lyon. Similarly, in F. Scott Fitzgerald's brief story "The Lost Decade" the tragedy of Louis Trimble is seen through the eyes of Orrison Brown and finally—if implicitly—clarified by his terse "Jesus. . . . Drunk for ten years."

Unlike Fitzgerald in this story, many an author achieves his end while standing slightly apart, eschewing intrusion into the minds of his characters. Instead he may affect an indeterminate, wholly external point of view; that is, he may offer setting and dialogue dramatically and with a minimum of exposition. There is no overt awareness of the writer; there is simply an unseen presence who narrates and describes several characters, their actions and their consequences. We are not aware of Faulkner as Faulkner in "Dry September." Yet we know what the barber thinks and says; we know about the behavior of Butch, of Plunkett, of Minnie Cooper, of Willie Mayes. Only in the last sentence of the short story is there a hint of Faulkner himself as a moral voice which, unrelated to any character in the story, cannot any longer be still. "The dark world seemed to lie stricken beneath the cold moon and the endless stars."

The Secret Sharer
Joseph Conrad

On my right hand there were lines of fishing stakes resembling a
mysterious system of half-submerged bamboo fences, incomprehensible in its division of the domain of tropical fishes, and crazy of
aspect as if abandoned forever by some nomad tribe of fishermen
now gone to the other end of the ocean; for there was no sign of
human habitation as far as the eye could reach. To the left a group
of barren islets, suggesting ruins of stone walls, towers, and block-
houses, had its foundations set in a blue sea that itself looked solid,
so still and stable did it lie below my feet; even the track of light
from the westering sun shone smoothly, without that animated
glitter which tells of an imperceptible ripple. And when I turned my
head to take a parting glance at the tug which had just left us anchored outside the bar, I saw the straight line of the flat shore joined
to the stable sea, edge to edge, with a perfect and unmarked closeness, in one leveled floor half brown, half blue under the enormous

dome of the sky. Corresponding in their significance to the islets of the sea, two small clumps of trees, one on each side of the only fault in the impeccable joint, marked the mouth of the river Meinam we had just left on the first preparatory stage of our homeward journey; and, far back on the inland level, a larger and loftier mass, the grove surrounding the great Paknam pagoda, was the only thing on which the eye could rest from the vain task of exploring the monotonous sweep of the horizon. Here and there gleams as of a few scattered pieces of silver marked the windings of the great river; and on the nearest of them, just within the bar, the tug steaming right into the land became lost to my sight, hull and funnel and masts, as though the impassive earth had swallowed her up without an effort, without a tremor. My eye followed the light cloud of her smoke, now here, now there, above the plain, according to the devious curves of the stream, but always fainter and farther away, till I lost it at last behind the miter-shaped hill of the great pagoda. And then I was left alone with my ship, anchored at the head of the Gulf of Siam.

She floated at the starting point of a long journey, very still in an immense stillness, the shadows of her spars flung far to the eastward by the setting sun. At that moment I was alone on her decks. There was not a sound in her—and around us nothing moved, nothing lived, not a canoe on the water, not a bird in the air, not a cloud in the sky. In this breathless pause at the threshold of a long passage we seemed to be measuring our fitness for a long and arduous enterprise, the appointed task of both our existences to be carried out, far from all human eyes, with only sky and sea for spectators and for judges.

There must have been some glare in the air to interfere with one's sight, because it was only just before the sun left us that my roaming eyes made out beyond the highest ridge of the principal islet of the group something which did away with the solemnity of perfect solitude. The tide of darkness flowed on swiftly; and with tropical suddenness a swarm of stars came out above the shadowy earth, while I lingered yet, my hand resting lightly on my ship's rail as if on the shoulder of a trusted friend. But, with all that multitude of celestial bodies staring down at one, the comfort of quiet communion with her was gone for good. And there were also disturbing sounds by this time—voices, footsteps forward; the steward flitted along the main deck, a busily ministering spirit; a hand bell tinkled urgently under the poop deck. . . .

I found my two officers waiting for me near the supper table, in the lighted cuddy. We sat down at once, and as I helped the chief mate, I said:

"Are you aware that there is a ship anchored inside the islands? I saw her mastheads above the ridge as the sun went down."

He raised sharply his simple face, overcharged by a terrible growth of whisker, and emitted his usual ejaculations: "Bless my soul, sir! You don't say so!"

My second mate was a round-cheeked, silent young man, grave beyond his years, I thought; but as our eyes happened to meet I detected a slight quiver on his lips. I looked down at once. It was not my part to encourage sneering on board my ship. It must be said, too, that I knew very little of my officers. In consequence of certain events of no particular significance, except to myself, I had been appointed to the command only a fortnight before. Neither did I know much of the hands forward. All these people had been together for eighteen months or so, and my position was that of the only stranger on board. I mention this because it has some bearing on what is to follow. But what I felt most was my being a stranger to the ship; and if all the truth must be told, I was somewhat of a stranger to myself. The youngest man on board (barring the second mate), and untried as yet by a position of the fullest responsibility, I was willing to take the adequacy of the others for granted. They had simply to be equal to their tasks; but I wondered how far I should turn out faithful to that ideal conception of one's own personality every man sets up for himself secretly.

Meantime the chief mate, with an almost visible effect of collaboration on the part of his round eyes and frightful whiskers, was trying to evolve a theory of the anchored ship. His dominant trait was to take all things into earnest consideration. He was of a painstaking turn of mind. As he used to say, he "liked to account to himself" for practically everything that came in his way, down to a miserable scorpion he had found in his cabin a week before. The why and the wherefore of that scorpion—how it got on board and came to select his room rather than the pantry (which was a dark place and more what a scorpion would be partial to), and how on earth it managed to drown itself in the inkwell of his writing desk—had exercised him infinitely. The ship within the islands was much more easily accounted for; and just as we were about to rise from the table he made his pronouncement. She was, he doubted not, a ship from home lately arrived. Probably she drew too much water to cross the bar except at the top of spring tides. Therefore she went into that natural harbor to wait for a few days in preference to remaining in an open roadstead.

"That's so," confirmed the second mate, suddenly, in his slightly hoarse voice. "She draws over twenty feet. She's the Liverpool ship *Sephora* with a cargo of coal. Hundred and twenty-three days from Cardiff."

We looked at him in surprise.

"The tugboat skipper told me when he came on board for your letters, sir," explained the young man. "He expects to take her up the river the day after tomorrow."

After thus overwhelming us with the extent of his information he slipped out of the cabin. The mate observed regretfully that he "could not account for that young fellow's whims." What prevented him telling us all about it at once, he wanted to know.

I detained him as he was making a move. For the last two days the crew had had plenty of hard work, and the night before they had very little sleep. I felt painfully that I—a stranger—was doing something unusual when I directed him to let all hands turn in without setting an anchor watch. I proposed to keep on deck myself till one o'clock or thereabouts. I would get the second mate to relieve me at that hour.

"He will turn out the cook and the steward at four," I concluded, "and then give you a call. Of course at the slightest sign of any sort of wind we'll have the hands up and make a start at once."

He concealed his astonishment. "Very well, sir." Outside the cuddy he put his head in the second mate's door to inform him of my unheard-of caprice to take a five hours' anchor watch on myself. I heard the other raise his voice incredulously: "What? The captain himself?" Then a few more murmurs, a door closed, then another. A few moments later I went on deck.

My strangeness, which had made me sleepless, had prompted that unconventional arrangement, as if I had expected in those solitary hours of the night to get on terms with the ship of which I knew nothing, manned by men of whom I knew very little more. Fast alongside a wharf, littered like any ship in port with a tangle of unrelated things, invaded by unrelated shore people, I had hardly seen her yet properly. Now, as she lay cleared for sea, the stretch of her main deck seemed to me very fine under the stars. Very fine, very roomy for her size, and very inviting. I descended the poop and paced the waist, my mind picturing to myself the coming passage through the Malay Archipelago, down the Indian Ocean, and up the Atlantic. All its phases were familiar enough to me, every characteristic, all the alternatives which were likely to face me on the high seas—everything! . . . except the novel responsibility of command. But I took heart from the reasonable thought that the ship was like other ships, the men like other men, and that the sea was not likely to keep any special surprises expressly for my discomfiture.

Arrived at that comforting conclusion, I bethought myself of a cigar and went below to get it. All was still down there. Everybody at the after end of the ship was sleeping profoundly. I came out again on the quarter-deck, agreeably at ease in my sleeping suit on that warm breathless night, barefooted, a glowing cigar in my teeth, and, going forward, I was met by the profound silence of the fore end of the ship. Only as I passed the door of the forecastle I heard a deep, quiet, trustful sigh of some sleeper inside. And suddenly I rejoiced in the great security of the sea as compared with the unrest of the land, in my choice of that untempted life presenting no disquieting problems, invested with an elementary moral beauty by the absolute straight-forwardness of its appeal and by the singleness of its purpose.

The riding light in the fore-rigging burned with a clear, untroubled, as if symbolic, flame, confident and bright in the mysterious shades of the night. Passing on my way aft along the other side of the ship, I observed that the rope side ladder put over, no doubt, for the master of the tug when he came to fetch away our letters, had not been hauled in as it should have been. I became annoyed at this, for exactitude in small matters is the very soul of discipline. Then I reflected that I had myself peremptorily dismissed my officers from duty, and by my own act had prevented the anchor watch being formally set and things properly attended to. I asked myself whether it was wise ever to interfere with the established routine of duties even from the kindest of motives. My action might have made me appear eccentric. Goodness only knew how that absurdly whiskered mate would "account" for my conduct, and what the whole ship thought of that informality of their new captain. I was vexed with myself.

Not from compunction certainly, but, as it were mechanically, I proceeded to get the ladder in myself. Now a side ladder of that sort is a light affair and comes in easily, yet my vigorous tug, which should have brought it flying on board, merely recoiled upon my body in a totally unexpected jerk. What the devil! ... I was so astounded by the immovableness of that ladder that I remained stock-still, trying to account for it to myself like that imbecile mate of mine. In the end, of course, I put my head over the rail.

The side of the ship made an opaque belt of shadow on the darkling glassy shimmer of the sea. But I saw at once something elongated and pale floating very close to the ladder. Before I could form a guess a faint flash of phosphorescent light, which seemed to issue suddenly from the naked body of a man, flickered in the sleeping water with the elusive, silent play of summer lightning in a night sky. With a gasp I saw revealed to my stare a pair of feet, the long legs, a broad livid back immersed right up to the neck in a greenish cadaverous glow. One hand, awash, clutched the bottom rung of the ladder. He was complete but for the head. A headless corpse! The cigar dropped out of my gaping mouth with a tiny plop and a short hiss quite audible in the absolute stillness of all things under heaven. At that I suppose he raised up his face, a dimly pale oval in the shadow of the ship's side. But even then I could only barely make out down there the shape of his blackhaired head. However, it was enough for the horrid, frost-bound sensation which had gripped me about the chest to pass off. The moment of vain exclamations was past, too. I only climbed on the spare spar and leaned over the rail as far as I could, to bring my eyes nearer to that mystery floating alongside.

As he hung by the ladder, like a resting swimmer, the sea lightning played about his limbs at every stir; and he appeared in it ghastly, silvery, fishlike. He remained as mute as a fish, too. He made no motion to get out of the water, either. It was inconceivable that he should not attempt to come on board, and strangely troubling to suspect that perhaps he did not want to. And my first words were prompted by just that troubled incertitude.

"What's the matter?" I asked in my ordinary tone; speaking down to the face upturned exactly under mine.

"Cramp," it answered, no louder. Then slightly anxious, "I say, no need to call anyone."

"I was not going to," I said.

"Are you alone on deck?"

"Yes."

I had somehow the impression that he was on the point of letting go the ladder to swim away beyond my ken—mysterious as he came. But, for the moment, this being appearing as if he had risen from the bottom of the sea (it was certainly the nearest land to the ship) wanted only to know the time. I told him. And he, down there, tentatively:

"I suppose your captain's turned in?"

"I am sure he isn't," I said.

He seemed to struggle with himself, for I heard something like the low, bitter murmur of doubt. "What's the good?" His next words came out with a hestitating effort.

"Look here, my man. Could you call him out quietly?"

I thought the time had come to declare myself.

"*I* am the captain."

I heard a "By Jove!" whispered at the level of the water. The phosphorescence flashed in the swirl of the water all about his limbs, his other hand seized the ladder.

"My name's Leggatt."

The voice was calm and resolute. A good voice. The self-possession of that man had somehow induced a corresponding state in myself. It was very quietly that I remarked:

"You must be a good swimmer."

"Yes. I've been in the water practically since nine o'clock. The question for me now is whether I am to let go this ladder and go on swimming till I sink from exhaustion, or—to come on board here."

I felt this was no mere formula of desperate speech, but a real alternative in the view of a strong soul. I should have gathered from this that he was young; indeed, it is only the young who are ever confronted by such clear issues. But at the time it was pure intuition on my part. A mysterious communication was established already between us two—in the face of that silent, darkened tropical sea. I was young, too; young enough to make no comment. The man in the water began suddenly to climb the ladder, and I hastened away from the rail to fetch some clothes.

Before entering the cabin I stood still, listening in the lobby at the foot of the stairs. A faint snore came through the closed door of the chief mate's room. The second mate's door was on the hook, but the darkness in there was absolutely soundless. He, too, was young and could sleep like a stone. Remained the steward, but he was not likely to wake up before he was called. I got a sleeping suit out of my room and, coming back on deck, saw the naked man from the sea sitting on the main hatch, glimmering white in the darkness, his elbows on his knees and his head in his hands. In a moment he had concealed his damp body in a sleeping suit of the same gray-stripe pattern as the one I was wearing and followed me like my double on the poop. Together we moved right aft, barefooted, silent.

"What is it?" I asked in a deadened voice, taking the lighted lamp out of the binnacle, and raising it to his face.

"An ugly business."

He had rather regular features; a good mouth; light eyes under somewhat heavy, dark eyebrows; a smooth, square forehead; no growth on his cheeks, a small, brown mustache, and a well-shaped, round chin. His expression was concentrated, meditative, under the inspecting light of the lamp I held up to his face; such as a man thinking hard in solitude might wear. My sleeping suit was just right for his size. A well-knit young fellow of twenty-five at most. He caught his lower lip with the edge of white, even teeth.

"Yes," I said, replacing the lamp in the binnacle. The warm, heavy tropical night closed upon his head again.

"There's a ship over there," he murmured.

"Yes, I know. The *Sephora*. Did you know of us?"

"Hadn't the slightest idea. I am the mate of her—"He paused and corrected himself. "I should say I *was*."

"Aha! Something wrong?"

"Yes. Very wrong indeed. I've killed a man."

"What do you mean? Just now?"

"No, on the passage. Weeks ago. Thirty-nine south. When I say a man—"

"Fit of temper," I suggested, confidently.

The shadowy, dark head, like mine, seemed to nod imperceptibly above the ghostly gray of my sleeping suit. It was, in the night, as though I had been faced by my own reflection in the depths of a somber and immense mirror.

"A pretty thing to have to own up to for a *Conway* boy," murmured my double, distinctly.

"You're a *Conway* boy?"

"I am," he said, as if startled. Then, slowly . . . "Perhaps you too—"

It was so; but being a couple of years older I had left before he joined. After a quick interchange of dates a silence fell; and I thought suddenly of my absurd mate with his terrific whiskers and the "Bless my soul—you don't say so" type of intellect. My double gave me an inkling of his thoughts by saying:

"My father's a parson in Norfolk. Do you see me before a judge and jury on that charge? For myself I can't see the necessity. There are fellows that an angel from heaven— And I am not that. He was one of those creatures that are just simmering all the time with a silly sort of wickedness. Miserable devils that have no business to live at all. He wouldn't do his duty and wouldn't let anybody else do theirs. But what's the good of talking! You know well enough the sort of ill-conditioned snarling cur—"

He appealed to me as if our experiences had been as identical as our clothes. And I knew well enough the pestiferous danger of such a character where there are no means of legal repression. And I knew well enough also that my double there was no homicidal ruffian. I did not think of asking him for details, and he told me the story roughly in brusque, disconnected sentences. I needed no more. I saw it all going on as though I were myself inside that other sleeping suit.

"It happened while we were setting a reefed foresail, at dusk. Reefed foresail! You understand the sort of weather. The only sail we had left to keep the ship running; so you may guess what it had been like for days. Anxious sort of job, that. He gave me some of his cursed insolence at the sheet. I tell you I was overdone with this terrific weather that seemed to have no end to it. Terrific, I tell you—and a deep ship. I believe the fellow himself was half crazed with funk. It was no time for gentlemanly reproof, so I turned round and felled him like an ox. He up and at me. We closed just as an awful sea made for the ship. All hands saw it coming and took to the rigging, but I had him by the throat, and went on shaking him like a rat, the men above us yelling, 'Look out! look out!' Then a crash as if the sky had fallen on my head. They say that for over ten minutes hardly anything was to be seen of the ship—just the three masts and a bit of the forecastle head and of the poop all awash driving along in a smother of foam. It was a miracle that they found us, jammed together behind the forebits. It's clear that I meant business, because I was holding him by the throat still when they picked us up. He was black in the face. It was too much for them. It seems they rushed us aft together, gripped as we were, screaming 'Murder!' like a lot of lunatics, and broke into the cuddy. And the ship running for her life, touch and go all the time, any minute her last in a sea fit to turn your hair gray only a-looking at it. I understand that the skipper, too, started raving like the rest of them. The man had been deprived of sleep for more than a week, and to have this sprung on him at the height of a furious gale nearly drove him out of his mind. I wonder they didn't fling me overboard after getting the carcass of their precious shipmate out of my fingers. They had rather a job to separate us, I've been told. A sufficiently fierce story to make an old judge and a respectable jury sit up a bit. The first thing I heard when I came to myself was the maddening howling of that endless gale, and on that the voice of the old man. He was hanging on to my bunk, staring into my face out of his sou'wester.

" 'Mr. Leggatt, you have killed a man. You can act no longer as chief mate of this ship.' "

His care to subdue his voice made it sound monotonous. He rested a hand on the end of the skylight to steady himself with, and all that time did not stir a limb, so far as I could see. "Nice little tale for a quiet tea party," he concluded in the same tone.

One of my hands, too, rested on the end of the skylight; neither did I stir a limb, so far as I knew. We stood less than a foot from each other. It occurred to me that if old "Bless my soul—you don't say so" were to put his head up the companion and catch sight of us, he would think he was seeing double, or imagine himself come upon a scene of weird witchcraft; the strange captain having a quiet confabulation by the wheel with his own gray ghost. I became very much concerned to prevent anything of the sort. I heard the other's soothing undertone.

"My father's a parson in Norfolk," it said. Evidently he had forgotten he had told me this important fact before. Truly a nice little tale.

"You had better slip down into my stateroom now," I said, moving off stealthily. My double followed my movements; our bare feet made no sound; I let him in, closed the door with care, and, after giving a call to the second mate, returned on deck for my relief.

"Not much sign of any wind yet," I remarked when he approached.

"No, sir. Not much," he assented, sleepily, in his hoarse voice, with just enough deference, no more, and barely suppressing a yawn.

"Well, that's all you have to look out for. You have got your orders.

"Yes, sir."

I paced a turn or two on the poop and saw him take up his position face forward with his elbow in the ratlines of the mizzen-rigging before I went below. The mate's faint snoring was still going on peacefully. The cuddy lamp was burning over the table on which stood a vase with flowers, a polite attention from the ship's provision merchant—the last flowers we should see for the next three months at the very least. Two bunches of bananas hung from the beam symmetrically, one on each side of the rudder casing. Everything was as before in the ship—except that two of her captain's sleeping suits were simultaneously in use, one motionless in the cuddy, the other keeping very still in the captain's stateroom.

It must be explained here that my cabin had the form of the capital letter L, the door being within the angle and opening into the short part of the letter. A couch was to the left, the bed-place to the right; my writing desk and the chronometers' table faced the door. But anyone opening it, unless he stepped right inside, had no view of what I call the long (or vertical) part of the letter. It contained some lockers surmounted by a bookcase; and a few clothes, a thick jacket or two, caps, oilskin coat, and such like, hung on hooks. There was at the bottom of that part a door opening into my bathroom, which could be entered also directly from the saloon. But that way was never used.

The mysterious arrival had discovered the advantage of this particular shape. Entering my room, lighted strongly by a big bulkhead lamp swung on gimbals above my writing desk, I did not see him anywhere till he stepped out quietly from behind the coats hung in the recessed part.

"I heard somebody moving about, and went in there at once," he whispered.

I, too, spoke under my breath.

"Nobody is likely to come in here without knocking and getting permission."

He nodded. His face was thin and the sunburn faded, as though he had been ill. And no wonder. He had been, I heard presently, kept under arrest in his cabin for nearly seven weeks. But there was nothing sickly in his eyes or in his expression. He was not a bit like me, really; yet, as we stood leaning over my bed-place, whispering side by side, with our dark heads together and our backs to the door, anybody bold enough to open it stealthily would have been treated to the uncanny sight of a double captain busy talking in whispers with his other self.

"But all this doesn't tell me how you came to hang on to our side ladder," I inquired, in the hardly audible murmurs we used, after he had told me something more of the proceedings on board the *Sephora* once the bad weather was over.

"When we sighted Java Head I had had time to think all those matters out several times over. I had six weeks of doing nothing else, and with only an hour or so every evening for a tramp on the quarter deck."

He whispered, his arms folded on the side of my bed-place, staring through the open port. And I could imagine perfectly the manner of this thinking out—a stubborn if not a steadfast operation; something of which I should have been perfectly incapable.

"I reckoned it would be dark before we closed with the land," he continued, so low that I had to strain my hearing, near as we were to each other, shoulder touching shoulder almost. "So I asked to speak to the old man. He always seemed very sick when he came to see me—as if he could not look me in the face. You know, that foresail saved the ship. She was too deep to have run long under bare poles. And it was I that managed to set it for him. Anyway, he came. When I had him in my cabin—he stood by the door looking at me as if I had the halter around my neck already—I asked him right away to leave my cabin door unlocked at night while the ship was going through Sundra Straits. There would be the Java coast within two or three miles, off Angier Point. I wanted nothing more. I've had a prize for swimming my second year in the *Conway*."

"I can believe it," I breathed out.

"God only knows why they locked me in every night. To see some of their faces you'd have thought they were afraid I'd go about at night strangling people. Am I a murdering brute? Do I look it? By Jove! if I had been he wouldn't have trusted himself like that into my room. You'll say I might have chucked him aside and bolted out, there and then—it was dark already. Well, no. And for the same reason I wouldn't think of trying to smash the door. There would have been a rush to stop me at the noise, and I did not mean to get into a confounded scrimmage. Somebody else might have got killed—for I would not have broken out only to get chucked back, and I did not want any more of that work. He refused, looking more sick than ever. He was afraid of the men, and also of that old second mate of his who had been sailing with him for years—a gray-headed old humbug; and his steward, too, had been with him devil knows how long —seventeen years or more—a dogmatic sort of loafer who hated me like poison, just because I was the chief mate. No chief mate ever made more than one voyage in the *Sephora,* you know. Those two old chaps ran the ship. Devil only knows what the skipper wasn't afraid of (all his nerve went to pieces altogether in that hellish spell of bad weather we had)—of what the law would do to him—of his wife, perhaps. Oh, yes! she's on board. Though I don't think she would have meddled. She would have been only too glad to have me out of the ship in any way. The 'brand of Cain' business, don't you see. That's all right. I was ready enough to go off wandering on the face of the earth—and that was price enough to pay for an Abel of that sort. Anyhow, he wouldn't listen to me. 'This thing must take its course. I represent the law here.' He was shaking like a leaf. 'So you won't?' 'No!' 'Then I hope you will be able to sleep on that,' I said, and turned my back on him. 'I wonder that *you* can,' cries he, and locks the door.

"Well, after that, I couldn't. Not very well. That was three weeks ago. We have had a slow passage through the Java Sea; drifted about Carimata for ten days. When we anchored here they thought, I suppose, it was all right. The nearest land (and that's five miles) is the ship's destination; the consul would soon set about catching me; and there would have been no object in bolting to these islets there. I don't suppose there's a drop of water on them. I don't know how it was, but tonight that steward, after bringing me my supper, went out to let me eat it, and left the door unlocked. And I ate it—all there was, too. After I had finished I strolled out on the quarter-deck. I don't know that I meant to do anything. A breath of fresh air was all I wanted, I believe. Then a sudden temptation came over me. I kicked off my slippers and was in the water before I had made up my mind fairly. Somebody heard the splash and they raised an awful hullabaloo. 'He's gone! Lower the boats! He's committed suicide! No, he's swimming.' Certainly I was swimming. It's not so easy for a swimmer like me to commit suicide by drowning. I landed on the nearest islet before the boat left the ship's side. I heard them pulling about in the dark, hailing, and so on, but after a bit they gave up. Everything quieted down and the anchorage became as still as death. I sat down on a stone and began to think. I felt certain they would start searching for me at daylight. There was no place to hide on those stony things—and if there had been, what would have been the good? But now I was clear of that ship, I was not going back. So after a while I took off all my clothes, tied them up in a bundle with a stone inside, and dropped them in the deep water on the outer side of that islet. That was suicide enough for me. Let them think what they liked, but I didn't mean to drown myself. I meant to swim till I sank—but that's not the same thing. I struck out for another of these little islands, and it was from that one that I first saw your riding light. Something to swim for. I went on easily, and on the way I came upon a flat rock a foot or two above water. In the daytime, I dare say, you might make it out with a glass from your poop. I scrambled up on it and rested myself for a bit. Then I made another start. That last spell must have been over a mile."

His whisper was getting fainter and fainter, and all the time he stared straight out through the porthole, in which there was not even a star to be seen. I had not interrupted him. There was something that made comment impossible in his narrative, or perhaps in himself; a sort of feeling, a quality, which I can't find a name for. And when he ceased, all I found was a futile whisper: "So you swam for our light?"

"Yes—straight for it. It was something to swim for. I couldn't see any stars low down because the coast was in the way, and I couldn't see the land, either. The water was like glass. One might have been swimming in a confounded thousand-feet deep cistern with no place for scrambling out anywhere; but what I didn't like was the notion of swimming round and round like a crazed bullock before I gave out; and as I didn't mean to go back . . . No. Do you see me being hauled back, stark naked, off one of these little islands by the scruff of the neck and fighting like a wild beast? Somebody would have got killed for certain, and I did not want any of that. So I went on. Then your ladder—"

"Why didn't you hail the ship?" I asked, a little louder.

He touched my shoulder lightly. Lazy footsteps came right over our heads and stopped. The second mate had crossed from the other side of the poop and might have been hanging over the rail, for all we knew.

"He couldn't hear us talking—could he?" My double breathed into my very ear, anxiously.

His anxiety was an answer, a sufficient answer, to the question I had put to him. An answer containing all the difficulty of that situation. I closed the porthole quietly, to make sure. A louder word might have been overheard.

"Who's that?" he whispered then.

"My second mate. But I don't know much more of the fellow than you do."

And I told him a little about myself. I had been appointed to take charge while I least expected anything of the sort, not quite a fortnight ago. I didn't know either the ship or the people. Hadn't had the time in port to look about me or size anybody up. And as to the crew, all they knew was that I was appointed to take the ship home. For the rest, I was almost as much of a stranger on board as himself, I said. And at the moment I felt it most acutely. I felt that it would take very little to make me a suspect person in the eyes of the ship's company.

He had turned about meantime; and we, the two strangers in the ship, faced each other in identical attitudes.

"Your ladder—" he murmured, after a silence. "Who'd have thought of finding a ladder hanging over at night in a ship anchored out here! I felt just then a very unpleasant faintness. After the life I've been leading for nine weeks, anybody would have got out of condition. I wasn't capable of swimming round as far as your rudder chains. And, lo and behold! there was a ladder to get hold of. After I gripped it I said to myself, 'What's the good?' When I saw a man's head looking over I thought I would swim away presently and leave him shouting—in whatever language it was. I didn't mind being looked at. I—I liked it. And then you speaking to me so quietly—as if you expected me—made me hold on a little longer. It had been a confounded lonely time—I don't mean while swimming. I was glad to talk a little to somebody that didn't belong to the *Sephora*. As to asking for the captain, that was a mere impulse. It could have been no use, with all the ship knowing about me and the other people pretty certain to be round here in the morning. I don't know—I wanted to be seen, to talk with somebody, before I went on. I don't know what I would have said. . . . 'Fine night, isn't it?' or something of the sort."

"Do you think they will be round here presently?" I asked with some incredulity.

"Quite likely," he said, faintly.

He looked extremely haggard all of a sudden. His head rolled on his shoulders.

"H'm. We shall see then. Meantime get into that bed," I whispered. "Want help? There."

It was a rather high bed-place with a set of drawers underneath. This amazing swimmer really needed the lift I gave him by seizing his leg. He tumbled in, rolled over on his back, and flung one arm a- cross his eyes. And then, with his face nearly hidden, he must have looked exactly as I used to look in that bed. I gazed upon my other self for a while before drawing across carefully the two green serge curtains which ran on a brass rod. I thought for a moment of pinning them together for greater safety, but I sat down on the couch, and once there I felt unwilling to rise and hunt for a pin. I would do it in a moment. I was extremely tired, in a peculiarly intimate way, by the strain of stealthiness, by the effort of whispering and the general secrecy of this excitement. It was three o'clock by now and I had been on my feet since nine, but I was not sleepy; I could not have gone to sleep. I sat there, fagged out, looking at the curtains, trying to clear my mind of the confused sensation of being in two places at once, and greatly bothered by an exasperating knocking in my head. It was a relief to discover suddenly that it was not in my head at all, but on the outside of the door. Before I could collect myself the words "Come in" were out of my mouth, and the steward entered with a tray, bringing in my morning coffee. I had slept, after all, and I was so frightened that I shouted. "This way! I am here, steward," as though he had been miles away. He put down the tray on the table next the couch and only then said, very quietly, "I can see you are here, sir." I felt him give me a keen look, but I dared not meet his eyes just then. He must have wondered why I had drawn the curtains of my bed before going to sleep on the couch. He went out, hooking the door open as usual.

I heard the crew washing decks above me. I knew I would have been told at once if there had been any wind. Calm, I thought, and I was doubly vexed. Indeed, I felt dual more than ever. The steward reappeared suddenly in the doorway. I jumped up from the couch so quickly that he gave a start.

"What do you want here?"

"Close your port, sir—they are washing decks."

"It is closed," I said, reddening.

"Very well, sir." But he did not move from the doorway and returned my stare in an extraordinary, equivocal manner for a time. Then his eyes wavered, all his expression changed, and in a voice unusually gentle, almost coaxingly:

"May I come in to take the empty cup away, sir?"

"Of course!" I turned my back on him while he popped in and out. Then I unhooked and closed the door and even pushed the bolt. This sort of thing could not go on very long. The cabin was as hot as an oven, too. I took a peep at my double, and discovered that he had not moved, his arm was still over his eyes; but his chest heaved; his hair was wet; his chin glistened with perspiration. I reached over him and opened the port.

"I must show myself on deck," I reflected.

Of course, theoretically, I could do what I liked, with no one to say nay to me within the whole circle of the horizon; but to lock my cabin door and take the key away I did not dare. Directly I put my head out of the companion I saw the group of my two officers, the second mate barefooted, the chief mate in long india-rubber boots, near the break of the poop, and the steward halfway down the poop ladder talking to them eagerly. He happened to catch sight of me and dived, the second ran down on the main deck shouting some order or other, and the chief mate came to meet me, touching his cap.

There was a sort of curiosity in his eye that I did not like. I don't know whether the steward had told them that I was "queer" only, or downright drunk, but I know the man meant to have a good look at me. I watched him coming with a smile which, as he got into point-

THE NARRATOR'S FOCUS 296

blank range, took effect and froze his very whiskers. I did not give him time to open his lips.

"Square the yards by lifts and braces before the hands go to breakfast."

It was the first particular order I had given on board that ship; and I stayed on deck to see it executed, too. I had felt the need of asserting myself without loss of time. That sneering young cub got taken down a peg or two on that occasion, and I also seized the opportunity of having a good look at the face of every foremast man as they filed past me to go to the after braces. At breakfast time, eating nothing myself, I presided with such frigid dignity that the two mates were only too glad to escape from the cabin as soon as decency permitted; and all the time the dual working of my mind distracted me almost to the point of insanity. I was constantly watching myself, my secret self, as dependent on my actions as my own personality, sleeping in that bed, behind that door which faced me as I sat at the head of the table. It was very much like being mad, only it was worse because one was aware of it.

I had to shake him for a solid minute, but when at last he opened his eyes it was in the full possession of his senses, with an inquiring look.

"All's well so far," I whispered. "Now you must vanish into the bathroom."

He did so, as noiseless as a ghost, and I then rang for the steward, and facing him boldly, directed him to tidy up my stateroom while I was having my bath—"and be quick about it." As my tone admitted of no excuses, he said, "Yes, sir," and ran off to fetch his dustpan and brushes. I took a bath and did most of my dressing, splashing, and whistling softly for the steward's edification, while the secret sharer of my life stood drawn up bolt upright in that little space, his face looking very sunken in daylight, his eyelids lowered under the stern, dark line of his eyebrows drawn together by a slight frown.

When I left him there to go back to my room the steward was finishing dusting. I sent for the mate and engaged him in some insignificant conversation. It was, as it were, trifling with the terrific character of his whiskers; but my object was to give him an opportunity for a good look at my cabin. And then I could at last shut, with a clear conscience, the door of my stateroom and get my double back into the recessed part. There was nothing else for it. He had to sit still on a small folding stool, half smothered by the heavy coats hanging there. We listened to the steward going into the bathroom out of the saloon, filling the water bottles there, scrubbing the bath, setting things to rights, whisk, bang, clatter—out again into the saloon—turn the key—click. Such was my scheme for keeping my second self invisible. Nothing better could be contrived under the circumstances. And there we sat; I at my writing desk ready to appear busy with some papers, he behind me, out of sight of the door. It would not have been prudent to talk in daytime; and I could not have stood the excitement of that queer sense of whispering to myself. Now and then, glancing over my shoulder, I saw him far back there, sitting rigidly on the low stool, his bare feet close together, his arms folded, his head hanging on his breast—and perfectly still. Anybody would have taken him for me.

I was fascinated by it myself. Every moment I had to glance over my shoulder. I was looking at him when a voice outside the door said:

"Beg pardon, sir."

"Well!" . . . I kept my eyes on him, and so, when the voice outside the door announced, "There's a ship's boat coming our way, sir," I saw him give a start—the first movement he had made for hours. But he did not raise his bowed head.

"All right. Get the ladder over."

I hesitated. Should I whisper something to him? But what? His immobility seemed to have been never disturbed. What could I tell him he did not know already? . . . Finally I went on deck.

II

The skipper of the *Sephora* had a thin red whisker all round his face, and the sort of complexion that goes with hair of that color; also the particular, rather smeary shade of blue in the eyes. He was not exactly a showy figure; his shoulders were high, his stature but middling—one leg slightly more bandy than the other. He shook hands, looking vaguely around. A spiritless tenacity was his main characteristic, I judged. I behaved with a politeness which seemed to disconcert him. Perhaps he was shy. He mumbled to me as if he were ashamed of what he was saying; gave his name (it was something like Archbold—but at this distance of years I hardly am sure), his ship's name, and a few other particulars of that sort, in the manner of a criminal making a reluctant and doleful confession. He had had terrible weather on the passage out—terrible—terrible—wife aboard, too.

By this time we were seated in the cabin and the steward brought in a tray with a bottle and glasses. "Thanks! No." Never took liquor. Would have some water, though. He drank two tumblerfuls. Terrible thirsty work. Ever since daylight had been exploring the islands round his ship.

"What was that for—fun?" I asked, with an appearance of polite interest.

"No!" He sighed. "Painful duty."

As he persisted in his mumbling and I wanted my double to hear every word, I hit upon the notion of informing him that I regretted to say I was hard of hearing.

"Such a young man, too!" he nodded, keeping his smeary blue, unintelligent eyes fastened upon me. What was the cause of it—some disease? he inquired, without the least sympathy and as if he thought that, if so, I'd got no more than I deserved.

"Yes; disease," I admitted in a cheerful tone which seemed to shock him. But my point was gained, because he had to raise his voice to give me his tale. It is not worth while to record that version. It was just over two months since all this had happened, and he had thought so much about it that he seemed completely muddled as to its bearings, but still immensely impressed.

"What would you think of such a thing happening on board your own ship? I've had the *Sephora* for these fifteen years. I am a well-known shipmaster."

He was densely distressed—and perhaps I should have sympathized with him if I had been able to detach my mental vision from the unsuspected sharer of my cabin as though he were my second self. There he was on the other side of the bulkhead, four or five feet from us, no more, as we sat in the saloon. I looked politely at Captain Archbold (if that was his name), but it was the other I saw, in a gray sleeping suit, seated on a low stool, his bare feet close together, his arms folded, and every word said between us falling into the ears of his dark head bowed on his chest.

"I have been at sea now, man and boy, for seven-and-thirty years, and I've never heard of such a thing happening in an English ship. And that it should be my ship. Wife on board, too."

I was hardly listening to him.

"Don't you think," I said, "that the heavy sea which, you told me, came aboard just then might have killed the man? I have seen the sheer weight of a sea kill a man very neatly, by simply breaking his neck."

"Good God!" he uttered, impressively, fixing his smeary blue eyes on me. "The sea! No man killed by the sea ever looked like that." He seemed positively scandalized at my suggestion. And as I gazed at him, certainly not prepared for anything original on his part, he advanced his head close to mine and thrust his tongue out at me so suddenly that I couldn't help starting back.

After scoring over my calmness in this graphic way he nodded wisely. If I had seen the sight, he assured me, I would never forget it as long as I lived. The weather was too bad to give the corpse a proper sea burial. So next day at dawn they took it up on the poop, covering its face with a bit of bunting; he read a short prayer, and then, just as it was, in its oilskins and long boots, they launched it amongst those mountainous seas that seemed ready every moment to swallow up the ship herself and the terrified lives on board of her.

"That reefed foresail saved you," I threw in.

"Under God—it did," he exclaimed fervently. "It was by a special mercy, I firmly believe, that it stood some of those hurricane squalls."

"It was the setting of that sail which—" I began.

"God's own hand in it," he interrupted me. "Nothing less could have done it. I don't mind telling you that I hardly dared give the order. It seemed impossible that we could touch anything without losing it, and then our last hope would have been gone."

The terror of that gale was on him yet. I let him go on for a bit, then said, casually—as if returning to a minor subject:

"You were very anxious to give up your mate to the shore people, I believe?"

He was. To the law. His obscure tenacity on that point had in it something incomprehensible and a little awful; something, as it were, mystical, quite apart from his anxiety that he should not be suspected of "countenancing any doings of that sort." Seven-and-thirty virtuous years at sea, of which over twenty of immaculate command, and the last fifteen in the *Sephora,* seemed to have laid him under some piti-less obligation.

"And you know," he went on, groping shamefacedly amongst his feelings, "I did not engage that young fellow. His people had some interest with my owners. I was in a way forced to take him on. He looked very smart, very gentlemanly, and all that. But do you know —I never liked him, somehow. I am a plain man. You see, he wasn't exactly the sort for the chief mate of a ship like the *Sephora.*"

I had become so connected in thoughts and impressions with the secret sharer of my cabin that I felt as if I, personally, were being given to understand that I, too, was not the sort that would have done for the chief mate of a ship like the *Sephora.* I had no doubt of it in my mind.

"Not at all the style of man. You understand," he insisted super-fluously, looking hard at me.

I smiled urbanely. He seemed at a loss for a while.

"I suppose I must report a suicide."

"Beg pardon?"

"Sui-cide! That's what I'll have to write to my owners directly I get in."

"Unless you manage to recover him before tomorrow," I assented, dispassionately. . . . "I mean, alive."

He mumbled something which I really did not catch, and I turned my ear to him in a puzzled manner. He fairly bawled:

"The land—I say, the mainland is at least seven miles off my anchorage."

"About that."

My lack of excitement, of curiosity, of surprise, of any sort of pro-nounced interest, began to arouse his distrust. But except for the felicitous pretense of deafness I had not tried to pretend anything. I had felt utterly incapable of playing the part of ignorance properly, and therefore was afraid to try. It is also certain that he had brought

some ready-made suspicions with him, and that he viewed my politeness as a strange and unnatural phenomenon. And yet how else
could I have received him? Not heartily! That was impossible for
psychological reasons, which I need not state here. My only object
was to keep off his inquiries. Surlily? Yes, but surliness might have
provoked a point-blank question. From its novelty to him and from
its nature, punctilious courtesy was the manner best calculated to
restrain the man. But there was the danger of his breaking through
my defense bluntly. I could not, I think, have met him by a direct
lie, also for psychological (not moral) reasons. If he had only known
how afraid I was of his putting my feeling of identity with the other
to the test! But, strangely enough—(I thought of it only afterward)
—I believe that he was not a little disconcerted by the reverse side
of that weird situation, by something in me that reminded him of
the man he was seeking—suggested a mysterious similitude to the
young fellow he had distrusted and disliked from the first.

However that might have been, the silence was not very prolonged. He took another oblique step.

"I reckon I had no more than a two-mile pull to your ship. Not
a bit more."

"And quite enough, too, in this awful heat," I said.

Another pause full of mistrust followed. Necessity, they say, is
mother of invention, but fear, too, is not barren of ingenious suggestions. And I was afraid he would ask me point-blank for news of my
other self.

"Nice little saloon, isn't it?" I remarked, as if noticing for the first
time the way his eyes roamed from one closed door to the other. "And
very well fitted out, too. Here, for instance," I continued, reaching
over the back of my seat negligently and flinging the door open, "is
my bathroom."

He made an eager movement, but hardly gave it a glance. I got
up, shut the door of the bathroom, and invited him to have a look
round, as if I were very proud of my accommodation. He had to rise
and be shown round, but he went through the business without any
raptures whatever.

"And now we'll have a look at my stateroom," I declared, in a voice as loud as I dared to make it, crossing the cabin to the star-board side with purposely heavy steps.

He followed me in and gazed around. My intelligent double had vanished. I played my part.

"Very convenient—isn't it?"

"Very nice. Very com..." He didn't finish, and went out brusquely as if to escape from some unrighteous wiles of mine. But it was not to be. I had been too frightened not to feel vengeful; I felt I had him on the run, and I meant to keep him on the run. My polite insistence must have had something menacing in it, because he gave in suddenly. And I did not let him off a single item; mate's room, pantry, storerooms, the very sail locker which was also under the poop—he had to look into them all. When at last I showed him out on the quarter-deck he drew a long, spiritless sigh, and mumbled dismally that he must really be going back to his ship now. I desired my mate, who had joined us, to see to the captain's boat.

The man of whiskers gave a blast on the whistle which he used to wear hanging round his neck, and yelled, "*Sephora* away!" My dou-ble down there in my cabin must have heard, and certainly could not feel more relieved than I. Four fellows came running out from some-where forward and went over the side, while my own men, appearing on deck too, lined the rail. I escorted my visitor to the gangway cere-moniously, and nearly overdid it. He was a tenacious beast. On the very ladder he lingered, and in that unique, guiltily consciousness manner of sticking to the point:

"I say... you... you don't think that—"

I covered his voice loudly:

"Certainly not.... I am delighted. Good-by."

I had an idea of what he meant to say, and just saved myself by the privilege of defective hearing. He was too shaken generally to insist, but my mate, close witness of that parting, looked mystified and his face took on a thoughtful cast. As I did not want to appear as if I wished to avoid all communication with my officers, he had the opportunity to address me.

"Seems a very nice man. His boat's crew told our chaps a very extraordinary story, if what I am told by the steward is true. I suppose you had it from the captain, sir?"

"Yes. I had a story from the captain."

"A very horrible affair—isn't it, sir?"

"It is."

"Beats all these tales we hear about murders in Yankee ships."

"I don't think it beats them. I don't think it resembles them in the least."

"Bless my soul—you don't say so! But of course I've no acquaintance whatever with American ships, not I, so I couldn't go against your knowledge. It's horrible enough for me....But the queerest part is that those fellows seemed to have some idea the man was hidden aboard here. They had really. Did you ever hear of such a thing?"

"Preposterous—isn't it?"

We were walking to and fro athwart the quarter-deck. No one of the crew forward could be seen (the day was Sunday), and the mate pursued:

"There was some little dispute about it. Our chaps took offense. 'As if we would harbor a thing like that,' they said. 'Wouldn't you like to look for him in our coal hole?' Quite a tiff. But they made it up in the end. I suppose he did drown himself. Don't you, sir?"

"I don't suppose anything."

"You have no doubt in the matter, sir?"

"None whatever."

I left him suddenly. I felt I was producing a bad impression, but with my double down there it was most trying to be on deck. And it was almost as trying to be below. Altogether a nerve-trying situation. But on the whole I felt less torn in two when I was with him. There was no one in the whole ship whom I dared take into my confidence. Since the hands had got to know his story, it would have been impossible to pass him off for anyone else, and an accidental discovery was to be dreaded now more than ever....

The steward being engaged in laying the table for dinner, we could talk only with our eyes when I first went down. Later in the afternoon we had a cautious try at whispering. The Sunday quietness of the ship was against us; the stillness of air and water around her was against us; the elements, the men were against us—everything was against us in our secret partnership; time itself—for this could not go on forever. The very trust in Providence was, I suppose, denied to his guilt. Shall I confess that this thought cast me down very much? And as to the chapter of accidents which counts for so much in the book of success, I could only hope that it was closed. For what favorable accident could be expected?

"Did you hear everything?" were my first words as soon as we took up our position side by side, leaning over my bed-place.

He had. And the proof of it was his earnest whisper, "The man told you he hardly dared to give the order."

I understood the reference to be to that saving foresail.

"Yes. He was afraid of it being lost in the setting."

"I assure you he never gave the order. He may think he did, but he never gave it. He stood there with me on the break of the poop after the maintopsail blew away, and whimpered about our last hope—positively whimpered about it and nothing else—and the night coming on! To hear one's skipper go on like that in such weather was enough to drive any fellow out of his mind. It worked me up into a sort of desperation. I just took it into my own hands and went away from him, boiling, and—. But what's the use telling you? *You* know! ... Do you think that if I had not been pretty fierce with them I should have got the men to do anything? Not it! The bosun perhaps? Perhaps! It wasn't a heavy sea—it was a sea gone mad! I suppose the end of the world will be something like that; and a man may have the heart to see it coming once and be done with it—but to have to face it day after day—I don't blame anybody. I was precious little better than the rest. Only—I was an officer of that old coal-wagon, anyhow—"

"I quite understand," I conveyed that sincere assurance into his ear. He was out of breath with whispering; I could hear him pant slightly. It was all very simple. The same strung-up force which had given twenty-four men a chance, at least, for their lives, had, in a sort of recoil, crushed an unworthy mutinous existence.

But I had no leisure to weigh the merits of the matter—footsteps in the saloon, a heavy knock. "There's enough wind to get under way with, sir." Here was the call of a new claim upon my thoughts and even upon my feelings.

"Turn the hands up," I cried through the door. "I'll be on deck directly."

I was going out to make the acquaintance of my ship. Before I left the cabin our eyes met—the eyes of the only two strangers on board. I pointed to the recessed part where the little campstool awaited him and laid my finger on my lips. He made a gesture—somewhat vague—a little mysterious, accompanied by a faint smile, as if of regret.

This is not the place to enlarge upon the sensations of a man who feels for the first time a ship move under his feet to his own independent word. In my case they were not unalloyed. I was not wholly alone with my command; for there was that stranger in my cabin. Or rather, I was not completely and wholly with her. Part of me was absent. That mental feeling of being in two places at once affected me physically as if the mood of secrecy had penetrated my very soul. Before an hour had elapsed since the ship had begun to move, having occasion to ask the mate (he stood by my side) to take a compass bearing of the Pagoda, I caught myself reaching up to his ear in whispers. I say I caught myself, but enough had escaped to startle the man. I can't describe it otherwise than by saying that he shied. A grave, preoccupied manner, as though he were in possession of some perplexing intelligence, did not leave him henceforth. A little later I moved away from the rail to look at the compass with such a stealthy gait that the helmsman noticed it—and I could not help noticing the unusual roundness of his eyes. These are trifling instances, though it's to no commander's advantage to be suspected of ludicrous eccentricities. But I was also more seriously affected. There are to a seaman certain words, gestures, that should in given conditions come as naturally, as instinctively as the winking of a menaced eye. A certain order should spring on to his lips without thinking; a certain sign should get itself made, so to speak, without reflection. But all unconscious alertness had abandoned me. I had to make an effort of will to recall myself back (from the cabin) to the conditions of the moment. I felt that I was appearing an irresolute commander to those people who were watching me more or less critically.

And, besides, there were the scares. On the second day out, for instance, coming off the deck in the afternoon (I had straw slippers on my bare feet) I stopped at the open pantry door and spoke to the steward. He was doing something there with his back to me. At the sound of my voice he nearly jumped out of his skin, as the saying is, and incidentally broke a cup.

"What on earth's the matter with you?" I asked astonished.

He was extremely confused. "Beg pardon, sir. I made sure you were in your cabin."

"You see I wasn't."

"No, sir. I could have sworn I had heard you moving in there not a moment ago. It's most extraordinary... very sorry, sir."

I passed on with an inward shudder. I was so identified with my secret double that I did not even mention the fact in those scanty, fearful whispers we exchanged. I suppose he had made some slight noise of some kind or other. It would have been miraculous if he hadn't at one time or another. And yet, haggard as he appeared, he looked always perfectly self-controlled, more than calm—almost invulnerable. On my suggestion he remained almost entirely in the bathroom, which, upon the whole, was the safest place. There could be really no shadow of an excuse for anyone ever wanting to go in there, once the steward had done with it. It was a very tiny place. Sometimes he reclined on the floor, his legs bent, his head sustained on one elbow. At others I would find him on the campstool, sitting in his gray sleeping suit and with his cropped dark hair like a patient, unmoved convict. At night I would smuggle him into my bed-place, and we would whisper together, with the regular footfalls of the officer of the watch passing and repassing over our heads. It was an infinitely miserable time. It was lucky that some tins of fine preserves were stowed in a locker in my stateroom; hard bread I could always get hold of; and so he lived on stewed chicken, paté de foie gras, asparagus, cooked oysters, sardines—on all sorts of abominable sham delicacies out of tins. My early morning coffee he always drank; and it was all I dared do for him in that respect.

Every day there was the horrible maneuvering to go through so that my room and then the bathroom should be done in the usual way. I came to hate the sight of the steward, to abhor the voice of that harmless man. I felt that it was he who would bring on the disaster of discovery. It hung like a sword over our heads.

The fourth day out, I think (we were then working down the east side of the Gulf of Siam, tack for tack, in light winds and smooth water)—the fourth day, I say, of this miserable juggling with the unavoidable, as we sat at our evening meal, that man, whose slightest movement I dreaded, after putting down the dishes ran upon deck busily. This could not be dangerous. Presently he came down again; and then it appeared that he had remembered a coat of mine which I had thrown over a rail to dry after having been wetted in a shower which had passed over the ship in the afternoon. Sitting stolidly at the head of the table I became terrified at the sight of the garment on his arm. Of course he made for my door. There was no time to lose.

"Steward," I thundered. My nerves were so shaken that I could not govern my voice and conceal my agitation. This was the sort of thing that made my terrifically whiskered mate tap his forehead with his forefinger. I had detected him using that gesture while talking on deck with a confidential air to the carpenter. It was too far to hear a word, but I had no doubt that this pantomime could only refer to the strange new captain.

"Yes, sir," the pale-faced steward turned resignedly to me. It was this maddening course of being shouted at, checked without rhyme or reason, arbitrarily chased out of my cabin, suddenly called into it, sent flying out of his pantry on incomprehensible errands, that accounted for the growing wretchedness of his expression.

"Where are you going with that coat?"

"To your room, sir."

"Is there another shower coming?"

"I'm sure I don't know, sir. Shall I go up again and see, sir?"

"No, Never mind."

My object was attained, as of course my other self in there would have heard everything that passed. During this interlude my two officers never raised their eyes off their respective plates; but the lip of that confounded cub, the second mate, quivered visibly.

I expected the steward to hook my coat on and come out at once. He was very slow about it; but I dominated by nervousness sufficiently not to shout after him. Suddenly I became aware (it could be heard plainly enough) that the fellow for some reason or other was opening the door of the bathroom. It was the end. The place was literally not big enough to swing a cat in. My voice died in my throat and I went stony all over. I expected to hear a yell of surprise and terror, and made a movement, but had not the strength to get on my legs. Everything remained still. Had my second self taken the poor wretch by the throat? I don't know what I would have done next moment if I had not seen the steward come out of my room, close the door, and then stand quietly by the sideboard.

Saved, I thought. But, no! Lost! Gone! He was gone!

I laid my knife and fork down and leaned back in my chair. My head swam. After a while, when sufficiently recovered to speak in a steady voice, I instructed my mate to put the ship round at eight o'clock himself.

"I won't come on deck," I went on. "I think I'll turn in, and unless the wind shifts I don't want to be disturbed before midnight. I feel a bit seedy."

"You did look middling bad a little while ago," the chief mate remarked without showing any great concern.

They both went out, and I stared at the steward clearing the table. There was nothing to be read on that wretched man's face. But why did he avoid my eyes I asked myself. Then I thought I should like to hear the sound of his voice.

"Steward!"

"Sir!" Startled as usual.

"Where did you hang up that coat?"

"In the bathroom, sir." The usual anxious tone. "It's not quite dry yet, sir."

For some time longer I sat in the cuddy. Had my double vanished as he had come? But of his coming there was an explanation, whereas his disappearance would be inexplicable. . . . I went slowly into my dark room, shut the door, lighted the lamp, and for a time dared not turn round. When at last I did I saw him standing bolt upright in the narrow recessed part. It would not be true to say I had a shock, but an irresistible doubt of his bodily existence flitted through my mind. Can it be, I asked myself, that he is not visible to other eyes than mine? It was like being haunted. Motionless, with a grave face, he raised his hands slightly at me in a gesture which meant clearly, "Heavens! what a narrow escape!" Narrow indeed. I think I had come creeping quietly as near insanity as any man who has not actually gone over the border. That gesture restrained me, so to speak.

The mate with the terrific whiskers was now putting the ship on the other tack. In the moment of profound silence which follows upon the hands going to their stations I heard on the poop his raised voice: "Hard alee!" and the distant shout of the order repeated on the main-deck. The sails, in that light breeze, made but a faint fluttering noise. It ceased. The ship was coming round slowly; I held my breath in the renewed stillness of expectation; one wouldn't have thought that there was a single living soul on her decks. A sudden brisk shout, "Mainsail haul!" broke the spell, and in the noisy cries and rush overhead of the men running away with the main brace we two, down in my cabin, came together in our usual position by the bed-place.

He did not wait for my question. "I heard him fumbling here and just managed to squat myself down in the bath," he whispered to me. "The fellow only opened the door and put his arm in to hang the coat up. All the same—"

"I never thought of that," I whispered back, even more appalled than before at the closeness of the shave, and marveling at that something unyielding in his character which was carrying him through so finely. There was no agitation in his whisper. Whoever was being driven distracted, it was not he. He was sane. And the proof of his sanity was continued when he took up the whispering again.

"It would never do for me to come to life again."

It was something that a ghost might have said. But what he was alluding to was his old captain's reluctant admission of the theory of suicide. It would obviously serve his turn—if I had understood at all the view which seemed to govern the unalterable purpose of his action.

"You must maroon me as soon as ever you can get amongst these islands off the Cambodje shore," he went on.

"Maroon you! We are not living in a boy's adventure tale," I protested. His scornful whispering took me up.

"We aren't indeed! There's nothing of a boy's tale in this. But there's nothing else for it. I want no more. You don't suppose I am afraid of what can be done to me? Prison or gallows or whatever they may please. But you don't see me coming back to explain such things to an old fellow in a wig and twelve respectable tradesmen, do you? What can they know whether I am guilty or not—or of *what* I am guilty, either? That's my affair. What does the Bible say? 'Driven off the face of the earth.' Very well. I am off the face of the earth now. As I came at night so I shall go."

"Impossible!" I murmured. "You can't."

"Can't? . . . Not naked like a soul on the Day of Judgment. I shall freeze on to this sleeping suit. The Last Day is not yet—and . . . you have understood thoroughly. Didn't you?"

I felt suddenly ashamed of myself. I may say truly that I understood—and my hesitation in letting that man swim away from my ship's side had been a mere sham sentiment, a sort of cowardice.

"It can't be done now till next night," I breathed out. "The ship is on the offshore tack and the wind may fail us."

"As long as I know that you understand," he whispered. "But of course you do. It's a great satisfaction to have got somebody to understand. You seem to have been there on purpose." And in the same whisper, as if we two whenever we talked had to say things to each other which were not fit for the world to hear, he added, "It's very wonderful."

We remained side by side talking in our secret way—but sometimes silent or just exchanging a whispered word or two at long intervals.

And as usual he stared through the port. A breath of wind came now and again into our faces. The ship might have been moored in dock, so gently and on an even keel she slipped through the water, that did not murmur even at our passage, shadowy and silent like a phantom sea.

At midnight I went on deck, and to my mate's great surprise put the ship round on the other tack. His terrible whiskers flitted round me in silent criticism. I certainly should not have done it if it had been only a question of getting out of that sleepy gulf as quickly as possible. I believe he told the second mate, who relieved him, that it was a great want of judgment. The other only yawned. That intolerable cub shuffled about so sleepily and lolled against the rails in such a slack, improper fashion that I came down on him sharply.

"Aren't you properly awake yet?"

"Yes, sir! I am awake."

"Well, then, be good enough to hold yourself as if you were. And keep a lookout. If there's any current we'll be closing with some islands before daylight."

The east side of the gulf is fringed with islands, some solitary, others in groups. On the blue background of the high coast they seem to float on silvery patches of calm water, arid and gray, or dark green and rounded like clumps of evergreen bushes, with the larger ones, a mile or two long, showing the outlines of ridges, ribs of gray rock under the dark mantle of matted leafage. Unknown to trade, to travel, almost to geography, the manner of life they harbor is an unsolved secret. There must be villages—settlements of fishermen at least—on the largest of them, and some communication with the world is probably kept up by native craft. But all that forenoon, as we headed for them, fanned along by the faintest of breezes, I saw no sign of man or canoe in the field of the telescope I kept on pointing at the scattered group.

At noon I gave no orders for a change of course, and the mate's whiskers became much concerned and seemed to be offering themselves unduly to my notice. At last I said:

"I am going to stand right in. Quite in—as far as I can take her."

The stare of extreme surprise imparted an air of ferocity also to his eyes, and he looked truly terrific for a moment.

"We're not doing well in the middle of the gulf," I continued, casually. "I am going to look for the land breezes tonight."

"Bless my soul! Do you mean, sir, in the dark amongst the lot of all them islands and reefs and shoals?"

"Well—if there are any regular land breezes at all on this coast one must get close inshore to find them, mustn't one?"

"Bless my soul!" he exclaimed again under his breath. All that afternoon he wore a dreamy, contemplative appearance which in him was a mark of perplexity. After dinner I went into my stateroom as if I meant to take some rest. There we two bent our dark heads over a half-unrolled chart lying on my bed.

"There," I said. "It's got to be Koh-ring. I've been looking at it ever since sunrise. It has got two hills and a low point. It must be inhabited. And on the coast opposite there is what looks like the mouth of a biggish river—with some town, no doubt, not far up. It's the best chance for you that I can see."

"Anything. Koh-ring let it be."

He looked thoughtfully at the chart as if surveying chances and distances from a lofty height—and following with his eyes his own figure wandering on the blank land of Cochin-China, and then passing off that piece of paper clean out of sight into uncharted regions. And it was as if the ship had two captains to plan her course for her. I had been so worried and restless running up and down that I had not had the patience to dress that day. I had remained in my sleeping suit, with straw slippers and a soft floppy hat. The closeness of the heat in the gulf had been most oppressive, and the crew were used to see me wandering in that airy attire.

"She will clear the south point as she heads now," I whispered into his ear. "Goodness only knows when, though, but certainly after dark. I'll edge her in to half a mile, as far as I may be able to judge in the dark—"

"Be careful," he murmured, warningly—and I realized suddenly that all my future, the only future for which I was fit, would perhaps go irretrievably to pieces in any mishap to my first command.

I could not stop a moment longer in the room. I motioned him to get out of sight and made my way on the poop. That unplayful cub had the watch. I walked up and down for a while thinking things out, then beckoned him over.

"Send a couple of hands to open the two quarter-deck ports," I said, mildly.

He actually had the impudence, or else so forgot himself in his wonder at such an incomprehensible order, as to repeat:

"Open the quarter-deck ports! What for, sir?"

"The only reason you need concern yourself about is because I tell you to do so. Have them open wide and fastened properly."

He reddened and went off, but I believe made some jeering remark to the carpenter as to the sensible practice of ventilating a ship's quarter-deck. I know he popped into the mate's cabin to impart the fact to him because the whiskers came on deck, as it were by chance, and stole glances at me from below—for signs of lunacy or drunkenness, I suppose.

A little before supper, feeling more restless than ever, I rejoined, for a moment, my second self. And to find him sitting so quietly was surprising, like something against nature, inhuman.

I developed my plan in a hurried whisper.

"I shall stand in as close as I dare and then put her round. I shall presently find means to smuggle you out of here into the sail locker, which communicates with the lobby. But there is an opening, a sort of square for hauling the sails out which gives straight on the quarter-deck and which is never closed in fine weather, so as to give air to the sails. When the ship's way is deadened in stays and all the hands are aft at the main braces you shall have a clear road to slip out and get overboard through the open quarter-deck port. I've had them both fastened up. Use a rope's end to lower yourself into the water so as to avoid a splash—you know. It could be heard and cause some beastly complication."

He kept silent for a while, then whispered, "I understand."

"I won't be there to see you go," I began with an effort. "The rest ... I only hope I have understood, too."

"You have. From first to last," and for the first time there seemed to be a faltering, something strained in his whisper. He caught hold of my arm, but the ringing of the supper bell made me start. He didn't, though; he only released his grip.

After supper I didn't come below again till well past eight o'clock. The faint, steady breeze was loaded with dew; and the wet, darkened sails held all there was of propelling power in it. The night, clear and starry, sparkled darkly, and the opaque, lightless patches shifting slowly against the low stars were the drifting islets. On the port bow there was a big one more distant and shadowily imposing by the great space of sky it eclipsed.

On opening the door I had a back view of my very own self looking at a chart. He had come out of the recess and was standing near the table.

"Quite dark enough," I whispered.

He stepped back and leaned against my bed with a level, quiet glance. I sat on the couch. We had nothing to say to each other. Over our heads the officer of the watch moved here and there. Then I heard him move quickly. I knew what that meant. He was making for the companion; and presently his voice was outside my door.

"We are drawing in pretty fast, sir. Land looks rather close."

"Very well," I answered. "I am coming on deck directly."

I waited till he was gone out of the cuddy, then rose. My double moved too. The time had come to exchange our last whispers, for neither of us was ever to hear each other's natural voice.

"Look here!" I opened a drawer and took out three sovereigns. "Take this, anyhow. I've got six and I'd give you the lot, only I must keep a little money to buy some fruit and vegetables for the crew from native boats as we go through Sunda straits."

He shook his head.

"Take it," I urged him, whispering desperately. "No one can tell what—"

He smiled and slapped meaningly the only pocket of the sleeping jacket. It was not safe, certainly. But I produced a large old silk handkerchief of mine, and tying the three pieces of gold in a corner, pressed it on him. He was touched, I suppose, because he took it at last and tied it quickly round his waist under the jacket, on his bare skin.

Our eyes met; several seconds elapsed, till, our glances still mingled, I extended my hand and turned the lamp out. Then I passed through the cuddy, leaving the door of my room wide open.... "Steward!"

He was still lingering in the pantry in the greatness of his zeal, giving a rub-up to a plated cruet stand the last thing before going to bed. Being careful not to wake up the mate, whose room was opposite, I spoke in an undertone.

He looked round anxiously. "Sir!"

"Can you get me a little hot water from the galley?"

"I am afraid, sir, the galley fire's been out for some time now."

"Go and see."

He fled up the stairs.

"Now," I whispered, loudly, into the saloon—too loudly, perhaps, but I was afraid I couldn't make a sound. He was by my side in an instant—the double captain slipped past the stairs—through the tiny dark passage—a sliding door. We were in the sail locker, scrambling on our knees over the sails. A sudden thought struck me. I saw myself wandering barefooted, bareheaded, the sun beating on my dark poll. I snatched off my floppy hat and tried hurriedly in the dark to ram it on my other self. He dodged and fended off silently. I wonder what he thought had come to me before he understood and suddenly desisted. Our hands met gropingly, lingered united in a steady, motionless clasp for a second. . . . No word was breathed by either of us when they separated.

I was standing quietly by the pantry door when the steward returned.

"Sorry, sir. Kettle barely warm. Shall I light the spirit lamp?"

"Never mind."

I came out on deck slowly. It was now a matter of conscience to shave the land as close as possible—for now he must go overboard whenever the ship was put in stays. Must! There could be no going back for him. After a moment I walked over to leeward and my heart flew into my mouth at the nearness of the land on the bow. Under any other circumstances I would not have held on a minute longer. The second mate had followed me anxiously.

I looked on till I felt I could command my voice.

"She will weather," I said then in a quiet tone.

"Are you going to try that, sir?" he stammered out incredulously.

I took no notice of him and raised my tone just enough to be heard by the helmsman.

"Keep her good full."

"Good full, sir."

The wind fanned my cheek, the sails slept, the world was silent. The strain of watching the dark loom of the land grow bigger and denser was too much for me. I had shut my eyes—because the ship must go closer. She must! The stillness was intolerable. Were we standing still?

When I opened my eyes the second view started my heart with a thump. The black southern hill of Koh-ring seemed to hang right over the ship like a towering fragment of the everlasting night. On that enormous mass of blackness there was not a gleam to be seen, not a sound to be heard. It was gliding irresistibly toward us and yet seemed already within reach of the hand. I saw the vague figures of the watch grouped in the waist, gazing in awed silence.

"Are you going on, sir?" inquired an unsteady voice at my elbow. I ignored it. I had to go on.

"Keep her full. Don't check her way. That won't do now," I said warningly.

"I can't see the sails very well," the helmsman answered me, in strange, quavering tones.

Was she close enough? Already she was, I won't say in the shadow of the land, but in the very blackness of it, already swallowed up as it were, gone too close to be recalled, gone from me altogether.

"Give the mate a call," I said to the young man who stood at my elbow as still as death. "And turn all hands up."

My tone had a borrowed loudness reverberated from the height of the land. Several voices cried out together: "We are all on deck, sir."

Then stillness again, with the great shadow gliding closer, towering higher, without a light, without a sound. Such a hush had fallen on the ship that she might have been a bark of the dead floating in slowly under the very gate of Erebus.

"My God! Where are we?"

It was the mate moaning at my elbow. He was thunderstruck, and as it were deprived of the moral support of his whiskers. He clapped his hands and absolutely cried out, "Lost!"

"Be quiet," I said sternly.

He lowered his tone, but I saw the shadowy gesture of his despair. "What are we doing here?"

"Looking for the land wind."

He made as if to tear his hair, and addressed me recklessly.

"She will never get out. You have done it, sir. I knew it'd end in something like this. She will never weather, and you are too close now to stay. She'll drift ashore before she's round. O my God!"

I caught his arm as he was raising it to batter his poor devoted head, and shook it violently.

"She's ashore already," he wailed, trying to tear himself away. "Is she? ... Keep good full there!"

"Good full, sir," cried the helmsman in a frightened, thin, childlike voice.

I hadn't let go the mate's arm and went on shaking it. "Ready about, do you hear? You go forward"—shake—"and stop there"—shake—"and hold your noise"—shake—"and see these head sheets properly overhauled"—shake, shake—shake.

And all the time I dared not look toward the land lest my heart should fail me. I released my grip at last and he ran forward as if fleeing for dear life.

I wondered what my double there in the sail locker thought of this commotion. He was able to hear everything—and perhaps he was able to understand why, on my conscience, it had to be thus close—no less. My first order. "Hard alee!" re-echoed ominously under the towering shadow of Koh-ring as if I had shouted in a mountain gorge. And then I watched the land intently. In that smooth water and light wind it was impossible to feel the ship coming-to. No! I could not feel her. And my second self was making now ready to slip out and lower himself overboard. Perhaps he was gone already ... ?

The great black mass brooding over our very mastheads began to pivot away from the ship's side silently. And now I forgot the secret stranger ready to depart, and remembered only that I was a total stranger to the ship. I did not know her. Would she do it? How was she to be handled?

I swung the mainyard and waited helplessly. She was perhaps stopped, and her very fate hung in the balance, with the black mass of Koh-ring like the gate of the everlasting night towering over her taffrail. What would she do now? Had she way on her yet? I stepped to the side swiftly, and on the shadowy water I could see nothing except a faint phosphorescent flash revealing the glassy smoothness of the sleeping surface. It was impossible to tell—and I had not learned yet the feel of my ship. Was she moving? What I needed was something easily seen, a piece of paper, which I could throw overboard and watch. I had nothing on me. To run down for it I didn't dare. There was no time. All at once my strained, yearning stare distinguished a white object floating within a yard of the ship's side. White on the black water. A phosphorescent flash passed under it. What was that thing? . . . I recognized my own floppy hat. It must have fallen off his head . . . and he didn't bother. Now I had what I wanted—the saving mark for my eyes. But I hardly thought of my other self, now gone from the ship, to be hidden forever from all friendly faces, to be a fugitive and a vagabond on the earth, with no brand of the curse on his sane forehead to stay a slaying hand . . . too proud to explain.

And I watched the hat—the expression of my sudden pity for his mere flesh. It had been meant to save his homeless head from the dangers of the sun. And now—behold—it was saving the ship, by serving me for a mark to help out the ignorance of my strangeness. Ha! It was drifting forward, warning me just in time that the ship had gathered sternway.

"Shift the helm," I said in a low voice to the seaman standing still like a statue.

The man's eyes glistened wildly in the binnacle light as he jumped round to the other side and spun round the wheel.

I walked to the break of the poop. On the overshadowed deck all hands stood by the forebraces waiting for my order. The stars ahead seemed to be gliding from right to left. And all was so still in the world that I heard the quiet remark "She's round," passed in a tone of intense relief between two seamen.

"Let go and haul."

The foreyards ran round with a great noise, amidst cheery cries. And now the frightful whiskers made themselves heard giving various orders. Already the ship was drawing ahead. And I was alone with her. Nothing! no one in the world should stand now between us, throwing a shadow on the way of silent knowledge and mute affection, the perfect communion of a seaman with his first command.

Walking to the taffrail, I was in time to make out, on the very edge of a darkness thrown by a towering black mass like the very gateway of Erebus—yes, I was in time to catch an evanescent glimpse of my white hat left behind to mark the spot where the secret sharer of my cabin and of my thoughts, as though he were my second self, had lowered himself into the water to take his punishment: a free man, a proud swimmer striking out for a new destiny.

COMMENTARY
by Joseph Conrad

In his preface to the collection called *The Shorter Tales of Joseph Conrad*, the author speaks of his reputation as a writer of sea tales and of the various pieces which appear in this particular volume. "The Secret Sharer" is one of those pieces and what he has to say in general terms of the other "Tales" applies with equal relevance to it.

. . . Though I have been often classed as a writer of the sea I have always felt that I had no specialty in that or any other specific subject. It is true that I have found a full text of life on the sea, long before I thought of writing a line or even felt the faintest stirring towards self-expression by means of the printed word. Sea life had been my life. It had been my own self-sufficient, self-satisfying possession. When the change came over the spirit of my dream (Calderon said that "Life is a Dream") my past had, by the very force of my work, become one of the sources of what I may call, for want of a better word, my inspiration—of the inner force which sets the pen in motion. I would add here "for better or worse," if those words did not sound horribly ungrateful after so many proofs of sympathy from the public for which this particular Preface is destined.

As a matter of fact I have written of the sea very little if the pages were counted. It has been the scene, but very seldom the aim, of my endeavour. It is too late after all those years to try to keep back the truth; so I will confess here that when I launched my first paper boats in the days of my literary childhood, I aimed at an element as restless, as dangerous, as changeable as the sea, and even more vast;—the unappeasable ocean of human life. I trust this grandiloquent image will be accepted with an indulgent smile of the kind that is accorded to the lofty ambitions of well-meaning beginners. Much time has passed since, and I can assure my readers that I have never felt more humble than I do to-day while I sit tracing these words, and that I see now, more clearly than ever before, that indeed those were but paper boats, freighted with a grown-up child's dreams and launched innocently upon that terrible sea that, unlike the honest salt water of my early life, knows no hope of changing horizons but lies within the circle of an Eternal Shadow.

Approaching the problem of selection for this book in the full consciousness of my feelings, my concern was to give it some sort of unity, or in other words, its own character. Looking over the directive impulses of my writing life I discovered my guide in the one that had prompted me so often to deal with men whose existence was, so to speak, cast upon the waters. Thus the characteristic trait of the stories included in this volume consists in the central figure of each being a seaman presented either in the relations of his professional life with his own kind, or in contact with landsmen and women, and embroiled in the affairs of that larger part of mankind which dwells on solid earth.

It would have been misleading to label those productions as sea tales. They deal with feelings of universal import, such, for instance, as the sustaining and inspiring sense of youth, or the support given by a stolid courage which confronts the unmeasurable force of an elemental fury simply as a thing that has got to be met and lived through with professional constancy. Of course, there is something more than mere ideas in those stories. I modestly hope that there are human beings in them, and also the articulate appeal of their humanity so strangely constructed from inertia and restlessness, from weakness and from strength and many other interesting contradictions which affect their conduct, and in a certain sense are meant to give a colouring to the actual events of the tale, and even to the response which is expected from the reader. To call them "studies of seamen" would have been pretentious and even misleading, in view of the obscurity of the individuals and the private character of the incidents. "Shorter Tales" is yet the best title I can think of for this collection. It commends itself to me by its non-committal character, which will neither raise false hopes nor awaken blind antagonisms.

. . . . .

... As I have said before in another preface, they are all authentic because they are the product of twenty years of life—my own life. Deliberate invention had little to do with their existence—if they do exist. In each there lurks more than one intention. The facts gleaned from hearsay or experience in the various parts of the globe were but opportunities offered to the writer. What he has done with them is matter for a verdict which must be left to the individual consciences of the readers.*

Conrad was particularly pleased with "The Secret Sharer," which appeared first in a volume called 'Twixt Land and Sea (1912). In a letter to Edward Garnett dated 5 November 1912, he indicated his pleasure in it. "Thanks for your letter on the 3 tales—very much of sorts. I daresay Freya is pretty rotten. On the other hand the Secret Sharer between you and me, is *it*. Eh? No damned tricks with girls there. Eh? Every word fits and there's not a single uncertain note. Luck my boy. Pure luck. I knew you would spot the thing at sight. But I repeat: mere luck."**

The Lost Decade
F. Scott Fitzgerald

All sorts of people came into the offices of the news-weekly and Orrison Brown had all sorts of relations with them. Outside of office hours he was "one of the editors"—during work time he was simply a curly-haired man who a year before had edited the Dartmouth *Jack-O-Lantern* and was now only too glad to take the undesirable

*Preface to "The Shorter Tales," in *Last Essays* (Garden City, N.Y., 1926), pp. 142–44.

**Letters from Joseph Conrad, 1895–1924, ed. Edward Garnett (Indianapolis, 1928), p. 243.

assignments around the office, from straightening out illegible copy to playing call boy without the title.

He had seen this visitor go into the editor's office—a pale, tall man of forty with blond statuesque hair and a manner that was neither shy nor timid, nor otherworldly like a monk, but something of all three. The name on his card, Louis Trimble, evoked some vague memory, but having nothing to start on, Orrison did not puzzle over it—until a buzzer sounded on his desk, and previous experience warned him that Mr. Trimble was to be his first course at lunch.

"Mr. Trimble—Mr. Brown," said the Source of all luncheon money. "Orrison—Mr. Trimble's been away a long time. Or he feels it's a long time—almost twelve years. Some people would consider themselves lucky to've missed the last decade."

"That's so," said Orrison.

"I can't lunch today," continued his chief. "Take him to Voisin or 21 or anywhere he'd like. Mr. Trimble feels there're lots of things he hasn't seen."

Trimble demurred politely.

"Oh, I can get around."

"I know it, old boy. Nobody knew this place like you did once— and if Brown tries to explain the horseless carriage just send him back here to me. And you'll be back yourself by four, won't you?"

Orrison got his hat.

"You've been away ten years?" he asked while they went down in the elevator.

"They'd begun the Empire State Building," said Trimble. "What does that add up to?"

"About 1928. But as the chief said, you've been lucky to miss a lot." As a feeler he added, "Probably had more interesting things to look at."

"Can't say I have."

They reached the street and the way Trimble's face tightened at the roar of traffic made Orrison take one more guess.

"You've been out of civilization?"

"In a sense." The words were spoken in such a measured way that Orrison concluded this man wouldn't talk unless he wanted to—and simultaneously wondered if he could have possibly spent the thirties in a prison or an insane asylum.

"This is the famous 21," he said. "Do you think you'd rather eat somewhere else?"

Trimble paused, looking carefully at the brownstone house.

"I can remember when the name 21 got to be famous," he said, "about the same year as Moriarity's." Then he continued almost apologetically, "I thought we might walk up Fifth Avenue about five minutes and eat wherever we happened to be. Some place with young people to look at."

Orrison gave him a quick glance and once again thought of bars and gray walls and bars; he wondered if his duties included introducing Mr. Trimble to complaisant girls. But Mr. Trimble didn't look as if that was in his mind—the dominant expression was of absolute and deep-seated curiosity and Orrison attempted to connect the name with Admiral Byrd's hideout at the South Pole or flyers lost in Brazilian jungles. He was, or he had been, quite a fellow— that was obvious. But the only definite clue to his environment— and to Orrison the clue that led nowhere—was his countryman's obedience to the traffic lights and his predilection for walking on the side next to the shops and not the street. Once he stopped and gazed into a haberdasher's window.

"Crêpe ties," he said. "I haven't seen one since I left college."

"Where'd you go?"

"Massachusetts Tech."

"Great place."

"I'm going to take a look at it next week. Let's eat somewhere along here—" They were in the upper Fifties "—you choose."

There was a good restaurant with a little awning just around the corner.

"What do you want to see most?" Orrison asked, as they sat down.

Trimble considered.

"Well—the back of people's heads," he suggested. "Their necks— how their heads are joined to their bodies. I'd like to hear what those two little girls are saying to their father. Not exactly what they're saying but whether the words float or submerge, how their mouths shut when they've finished speaking. Just a matter of rhythm—Cole

Porter came back to the States in 1928 because he felt that there were new rhythms around."

Orrison was sure he had his clue now, and with nice delicacy did not pursue it by a millimeter—even suppressing a sudden desire to say there was a fine concert in Carnegie Hall tonight.

"The weight of spoons," said Trimble, "so light. A little bowl with a stick attached. The cast in that waiter's eye. I knew him once but he wouldn't remember me."

But as they left the restaurant the same waiter looked at Trimble rather puzzled as if he almost knew him. When they were outside Orrison laughed:

"After ten years people will forget."

"Oh, I had dinner there last May—" He broke off in an abrupt manner.

It was kind of nutsy, Orrison decided—and changed himself suddenly into a guide.

"From here you get a good candid focus on Rockefeller Center," he pointed out with spirit "—and the Chrysler Building and the Armistead Building, the daddy of all the new ones."

"The Armistead Building," Trimble rubber-necked obediently. "Yes—I designed it."

Orrison shook his head cheerfully—he was used to going out with all kinds of people. But that stuff about having been in the restaurant last May . . .

He paused by the brass entablature in the cornerstone of the building. "Erected 1928," it said.

Trimble nodded.

"But I was taken drunk that year—every-which-way drunk. So I never saw it before now."

"Oh." Orrison hesitated. "Like to go in now?"

"I've been in it—lots of times. But I've never seen it. And now it isn't what I want to see. I wouldn't ever be able to see it now. I simply want to see how people walk and what their clothes and shoes and hats are made of. And their eyes and hands. Would you mind shaking hands with me?"

"Not at all, sir."

"Thanks. Thanks. That's very kind. I suppose it looks strange—but people will think we're saying good-bye. I'm going to walk up the avenue for awhile, so we *will* say good-bye. Tell your office I'll be in at four."

Orrison looked after him when he started out, half expecting him to turn into a bar. But there was nothing about him that suggested or ever had suggested drink.

"Jesus," he said to himself. "Drunk for ten years."

He felt suddenly of the texture of his own coat and then he reached out and pressed his thumb against the granite of the building by his side.

In Dreams Begin Responsibilities
Delmore Schwartz

I

I think it is the year 1909. I feel as if I were in a moving-picture theater, the long arm of light crossing the darkness and spinning, my eyes fixed upon the screen. It is a silent picture, as if an old Biograph one, in which the actors are dressed in ridiculously old-fashioned clothes, and one flash succeeds another with sudden jumps, and the actors, too, seem to jump about, walking too fast. The shots are full of rays and dots, as if it had been raining when the picture was photographed. The light is bad.

It is Sunday afternoon, June 12th, 1909, and my father is walking down the quiet streets of Brooklyn on his way to visit my mother. His clothes are newly pressed, and his tie is too tight in his high collar. He jingles the coins in his pocket, thinking of the witty things he will say. I feel as if I had by now relaxed entirely in the soft darkness of the theater; the organist peals out the obvious approximate emotions on which the audience rocks unknowingly. I am

Cf. *"In dreams begins responsibility."*—Old Play. From *Responsibilities* (1914) in *The Collected Poems of W. B. Yeats* (N.Y., 1940), p. 114.

anonymous. I have forgotten myself: it is always so when one goes to a movie, it is, as they say, a drug.

My father walks from street to street of trees, lawns and houses, once in a while coming to an avenue on which a streetcar skates and yaws, progressing slowly. The motorman, who has a handle-bar mustache, helps a young lady wearing a hat like a feathered bowl onto the car. He leisurely makes change and rings his bell as the passengers mount the car. It is obviously Sunday, for everyone is wearing Sunday clothes and the streetcar's noises emphasize the quiet of the holiday (Brooklyn is said to be the city of churches). The shops are closed and their shades drawn but for an occasional stationery store or drugstore with great green balls in the window.

My father has chosen to take this long walk because he likes to walk and think. He thinks about himself in the future and so arrives at the place he is to visit in a mild state of exaltation. He pays no attention to the houses he is passing, in which the Sunday dinner is being eaten, nor to the many trees which line each street, now coming to their full green and the time when they will enclose the whole street in leafy shadow. An occasional carriage passes, the horses' hooves falling like stones in the quiet afternoon, and once in a while an automobile, looking like an enormous upholstered sofa, puffs and passes.

My father thinks of my mother, of how lady-like she is, and of the pride which will be his when he introduces her to his family. They are not yet engaged and he is not yet sure that he loves my mother, so that, once in a while, he becomes panicky about the bond already established. But then he reassures himself by thinking of the big men he admires who are married: William Randolph Hearst and William Howard Taft, who has just become the President of the United States.

My father arrives at my mother's house. He has come too early and so is suddenly embarrassed. My aunt, my mother's younger sister, answers the loud bell with her napkin in her hand, for the family is still at dinner. As my father enters, my grandfather rises from the table and shakes hands with him. My mother has run upstairs to tidy herself. My grandmother asks my father if he has had dinner and tells him that my mother will be down soon. My grandfather opens the conversation by remarking about the mild June weather. My father sits uncomfortably near the table, holding his hat in his hand. My grandmother tells my aunt to take my father's hat. My uncle, twelve years old, runs into the house, his hair tousled. He shouts a greeting to my father, who has often given him nickels, and then runs upstairs, as my grandmother shouts after him. It is evident that the respect in which my father is held in this house is tempered by a good deal of mirth. He is impressive, but also very awkward.

II

Finally my mother comes downstairs and my father, being at the moment engaged in conversation with my grandfather, is made uneasy by her entrance, for he does not know whether to greet my mother or to continue the conversation. He gets up from his chair clumsily and says "Hello" gruffly. My grandfather watches this, examining their congruence, such as it is, with a critical eye, and meanwhile rubbing his bearded cheek roughly, as he always does when he reasons. He is worried; he is afraid my father will not make a good husband for his oldest daughter. At this point something happens to the film, just as my father says something funny to my mother: I am awakened to myself and my unhappiness just as my interest has become most intense. The audience begins to clap impatiently. Then the trouble is attended to, but the film has been returned to a portion just shown, and once more I see my grandfather rubbing his bearded cheek, pondering my father's character. It is difficult to get back into the picture once more and forget myself, but as my mother giggles at my father's words, the darkness drowns me.

My father and mother depart from the house, my father shaking hands with my grandfather once more, out of some unknown uneasiness. I stir uneasily also, slouched in the hard chair of the theater. Where is the older uncle, my mother's older brother? He is studying in his bedroom upstairs, studying for his final examinations at the College of the City of New York, having been dead of double pneumonia for the last twenty-one years. My mother and father walk down the same quiet streets once more. My mother is holding my father's arm and telling him of the novel she has been reading and my father utters judgments of the characters as the plot is made clear to him. This is a habit which he very much enjoys, for he feels the utmost superiority and confidence when he is approving or condemning the behavior of other people. At times he feels moved to utter a brief "Ugh," whenever the story becomes what he would call sugary. This tribute is the assertion of his manliness. My mother feels satisfied by the interest she has awakened; and she is showing my father how intelligent she is and how interesting.

They reach the avenue, and the streetcar leisurely arrives. They are going to Coney Island this afternoon, although my mother really considers such pleasures inferior. She has made up her mind to indulge only in a walk on the boardwalk and a pleasant dinner, avoiding the riotous amusements as being beneath the dignity of so dignified a couple.

My father tells my mother how much money he has made in the week just past, exaggerating an amount which need not have been exaggerated. But my father has always felt that actualities somehow fall short, no matter how fine they are. Suddenly I begin to weep. The determined old lady who sits next to me in the theater is annoyed and looks at me with an angry face, and being intimidated, I stop. I drag out my handkerchief and dry my face, licking the drop which has fallen near my lips. Meanwhile I have missed something, for here are my father and mother alighting from the streetcar at the last stop, Coney Island.

III

They walk toward the boardwalk and my mother commands my father to inhale the pungent air from the sea. They both breathe in deeply, both of them laughing as they do so. They have in common a great interest in health, although my father is strong and husky, and my mother is frail. They are both full of theories about what is good to eat and not good to eat, and sometimes have heated discussions about it, the whole matter ending in my father's announcement, made with a scornful bluster, that you have to die sooner or later anyway. On the boardwalk's flagpole, the American flag is pulsing in an intermittent wind from the sea.

My father and mother go to the rail of the boardwalk and look down on the beach where a good many bathers are casually walking about. A few are in the surf. A peanut whistle pierces the air with its pleasant and active whine, and my father goes to buy peanuts. My mother remains at the rail and stares at the ocean. The ocean seems merry to her; it pointedly sparkles and again and again the pony waves are released. She notices the children digging in the wet sand, and the bathing costumes of the girls who are her own age. My father returns with the peanuts. Overhead the sun's lightning strikes and strikes, but neither of them are at all aware of it. The boardwalk is full of people dressed in their Sunday clothes and casually strolling. The tide does not reach as far as the boardwalk, and the strollers would feel no danger if it did. My father and mother lean on the rail of the boardwalk and absently stare at the ocean. The ocean is becoming rough; the waves come in slowly, tugging strength from far back. The moment before they somersault, the moment when they arch their backs so beautifully, showing white veins in the green and black, that moment is intolerable. They finally crack, dashing fiercely upon the sand, actually driving, full force downward, against it, bouncing upward and forward, and at last petering out into a small stream of bubbles which slides up the beach and then is recalled. The sun overhead does not disturb my father and my mother. They gaze idly at the ocean, scarcely interested in its harshness. But I stare at the terrible sun which breaks up sight, and the fatal merciless passionate ocean. I forget my parents. I stare fascinated, and finally, shocked by their indifference, I burst out weeping once more. The old lady next to me pats my shoulder and says: "There, there, young man, all of this is only a movie, only a movie," but I look up once more at the terrifying sun and the terrifying ocean, and being unable to control my tears I get up and go to the men's room, stumbling over the feet of the other people seated in my row.

IV

When I return, feeling as if I had just awakened in the morning sick for lack of sleep, several hours have apparently passed and my parents are riding on the merry-go-round. My father is on a black horse, my mother on a white one, and they seem to be making an eternal circuit for the single purpose of snatching the nickel rings which are attached to an arm of one of the posts. A hand-organ is playing; it is inseparable from the ceaseless circling of the merry-go-round.

For a moment it seems that they will never get off the carousel, for it will never stop, and I feel as if I were looking down from the fiftieth story of a building. But at length they do get off; even the hand-organ has ceased for a moment. There is a sudden and sweet stillness, as if the achievement of so much motion. My mother has acquired only two rings, my father, however, ten of them, although it was my mother who really wanted them.

They walk on along the boardwalk as the afternoon descends by imperceptible degrees into the incredible violet of dusk. Everything fades into a relaxed glow, even the ceaseless murmuring from the beach. They look for a place to have dinner. My father suggests the best restaurant on the boardwalk and my mother demurs, according to her principles of economy and housewifeliness.

However they do go to the best place, asking for a table near the window so that they can look out upon the boardwalk and the mobile ocean. My father feels omnipotent as he places a quarter in the waiter's hand in asking for a table. The place is crowded and here too there is music, this time from a kind of string trio. My father orders with a fine confidence.

As their dinner goes on, my father tells of his plans for the future and my mother shows with expressive face how interested she is, and how impressed. My father becomes exultant, lifted up by the waltz that is being played and his own future begins to intoxicate him. My father tells my mother that he is going to expand his business, for there is a great deal of money to be made. He wants to settle down. After all, he is twenty-nine, he has lived by himself since his thirteenth year, he is making more and more money, and he is envious of his friends when he visits them in the security of their homes, surrounded, it seems, by the calm domestic pleasures, and by delightful children, and then as the waltz reaches the moment when the dancers will swing madly, then, then with awful daring, then he asks my mother to marry him, although awkwardly enough and puzzled as to how he had arrived at the question, and she, to make the whole business worse, begins to cry, and my father looks nervously about, not knowing at all what to do now, and my mother says: "It's all I've wanted from the first moment I saw you," sobbing, and he finds all of this very difficult, scarcely to his taste, scarcely as he thought it would be, on his long walks over Brooklyn Bridge in the revery of a fine cigar, and it was then, at that point, that I stood up in the theater and shouted: "Don't do it! It's not too late to change your minds, both of you. Nothing good will come of it, only remorse, hatred, scandal, and two children whose characters are monstrous." The whole audience turned to look at me, annoyed, the usher came hurrying down the aisle flashing his searchlight, and the old lady next to me tugged me down into my seat, saying: "Be quiet. You'll be put out, and you paid thirty-five cents to come in." And so I shut my eyes because I could not bear to see what was happening. I sat there quietly.

V

But after a while I begin to take brief glimpses and at length I watch again with thirsty interest, like a child who tries to maintain his sulk when he is offered a bribe of candy. My parents are now having their pictures taken in a photographer's booth along the boardwalk. The place is shadowed in the mauve light which is apparently necessary. The camera is set to the side on its tripod and looks like a Martian man. The photographer is instructing my parents in how to pose. My father has his arm over my mother's shoulder, and both of them smile emphatically. The photographer brings my mother a bouquet of flowers to hold in her hand, but she holds it at the wrong angle. Then the photographer covers himself with the black cloth which drapes the camera and all that one sees of him is one protruding arm and his hand with which he holds tightly to the rubber ball which he squeezes when the picture is taken. But he is not satisfied with their appearance. He feels that somehow there is something wrong in their pose. Again and again he comes out from his hiding place with new directions. Each suggestion merely makes matters worse. My father is becoming impatient. They try a seated pose. The photographer explains that he has his pride, he wants to make beautiful pictures, he is not merely interested in all of this for the money. My father says: "Hurry up, will you? We haven't got all night." But the photographer only scurries about apologetically, issuing new directions. The photographer charms me, and I approve of him with all my heart, for I know exactly how he feels, and as he criticizes each revised pose according to some obscure idea of rightness, I become quite hopeful. But then my father says angrily: "Come on, you've had enough time, we're not going to wait any longer." And the photographer, sighing unhappily, goes back into the black covering and holds out his hand, saying, "One, two, three, Now!" and the picture is taken, with my father's smile turned to a grimace and my mother's bright and false. It takes a few minutes for the picture to be developed and as my parents sit in the curious light they become depressed.

VI

They have passed a fortune-teller's booth and my mother wishes to go in, but my father does not. They begin to argue about it. My mother becomes stubborn, my father once more impatient. What my father would like to do now is walk off and leave my mother there, but he knows that that would never do. My mother refuses to budge. She is near tears, but she feels an uncontrollable desire to hear what the palm-reader will say. My father consents angrily and they both go into the booth which is, in a way, like the photographer's, since it is draped in black cloth and its light is colored and shadowed. The place is too warm, and my father keeps saying that this is all nonsense, pointing to the crystal ball on the table. The fortune-teller, a short, fat woman garbed in robes supposedly exotic, comes into the room and greets them, speaking with an accent, but suddenly my father feels that the whole thing is intolerable; he tugs at my mother's arm but my mother refuses to budge. And then, in terrible anger, my father lets go of my mother's arm and strides out, leaving my mother stunned. She makes a movement as if to go after him, but the fortune-teller holds her and begs her not to do so, and

I in my seat in the darkness am shocked and horrified. I feel as if I were walking a tight-rope one hundred feet over a circus audience and suddenly the rope is showing signs of breaking, and I get up from my seat and begin to shout once more the first words I can think of to communicate my terrible fear, and once more the usher comes hurrying down the aisle flashing his searchlight, and the old lady pleads with me, and the shocked audience has turned to stare at me, and I keep shouting: "What are they doing? Don't they know what they are doing? Why doesn't my mother go after my father and beg him not to be angry? If she does not do that, what will she do? Doesn't my father know what he is doing?" But the usher has seized my arm, and is dragging me away, and as he does so, he says: "What are *you* doing? Don't you know you can't do things like this, you can't do whatever you want to do, even if other people aren't about? You will be sorry if you do not do what you should do. You can't carry on like this, it is not right, you will find that out soon enough, everything you do matters so much," and as he said that, dragging me through the lobby of the theater, into the cold light, I woke up into the bleak winter morning of my twenty-first birthday, the window-sill shining with its lip of snow, and the morning already begun.

2. STREAM-OF-CONSCIOUSNESS

Stream-of-consciousness is closely related to point of view and indeed in a short story like Virginia Woolf's "String Quartet" it is the point of view. In this work all the external forces—the music itself, scraps of nearby conversation—are revealed to the reader through the mind and feelings of the central character. The focus is her consciousness as she passes through a series of mental and emotional experiences at the concert. When stream-of-consciousness functions as a point of view, the plot development depends not upon physical, outward activity but upon the various ways in which that activity affects the inner being of the central character. It is a difficult point of view to maintain: first, because the author must reproduce the seeming disorder of spontaneous human thought and feeling without calling attention to the artistic order which he has imposed upon the reproduction itself; and second, because it demands the sacrifice of the artist's own conscious personality—sometimes to the point of total annihilation. To use the language of James Joyce, the artist successfully employing stream-of-consciousness is one who, "like the God of the creation, remains within or behind or beyond or above his handiwork, invisible, refined out of existence, indifferent, paring his fingernails."

The String Quartet
Virginia Woolf

Well, here we are, and if you cast your eye over the room you will
see that Tubes and trams and omnibuses, private carriages not a few,
even, I venture to believe, landaus with bays in them, have been busy
at it, weaving threads from one end of London to the other. Yet I
begin to have my doubts—

If indeed it's true, as they're saying, that Regent Street is up, and
the Treaty signed, and the weather not cold for the time of year, and
even at that rent not a flat to be had, and the worst of influenza its
after effects; if I bethink me of having forgotten to write about the
leak in the larder, and left my glove in the train; if the ties of blood
require me, leaning forward, to accept cordially the hand which is
perhaps offered hesitatingly—

"Seven years since we met!"

"The last time in Venice."

"And where are you living now?"

"Well, the late afternoon suits me the best, though, if it weren't
asking too much——"

"But I knew you at once!"

"Still, the war made a break——"

If the mind's shot through by such little arrows, and—for human
society compels it—no sooner is one launched than another presses
forward; if this engenders heat and in addition they've turned on the
electric light; if saying one thing does, in so many cases, leave behind
it a need to improve and revise, stirring besides regrets, pleasures,
vanities, and desires—if it's all the facts I mean, and the hats, the fur
boas, the gentlemen's swallow-tail coats, and pearl tie-pins that come
to the surface—what chance is there?

Of what? It becomes every minute more difficult to say why, in
spite of everything, I sit here believing I can't now say what, or even
remember the last time it happened.

"Did you see the procession?"

"The King looked cold."

"No, no, no. But what was it?"

"She's bought a house at Malmesbury."

"How lucky to find one!"

On the contrary, it seems to me pretty sure that she, whoever she may be, is damned, since it's all a matter of flats and hats and sea gulls, or so it seems to be for a hundred people sitting here well dressed, walled in, furred, replete. Not that I can boast, since I too sit passive on a gilt chair, only turning the earth above a buried memory, as we all do, for there are signs, if I'm not mistaken, that we're all recalling something, furtively seeking something. Why fidget? Why so anxious about the sit of cloaks; and gloves—whether to button or unbutton? Then watch that elderly face against the dark canvas, a moment ago urbane and flushed; now taciturn and sad, as if in shadow. Was it the sound of the second violin tuning in the ante-room? Here they come; four black figures, carrying instruments, and seat themselves facing the white squares under the downpour of light; rest the tips of their bows on the music stand; with a simultaneous movement lift them; lightly poise them, and, looking across at the player opposite, the first violin counts one, two three——

Flourish, spring, burgeon, burst! The pear tree on the top of the mountain. Fountains jet; drops descend. But the waters of the Rhone flow swift and deep, race under the arches, and sweep the trailing water leaves, washing shadows over the silver fish, the spotted fish rushed down by the swift waters, now swept into an eddy where— it's difficult this—conglomeration of fish all in a pool; leaping, splashing, scraping sharp fins; and such a boil of current that the yellow pebbles are churned round and round, round and round— free now, rushing downwards, or even somehow ascending in exquisite spirals into the air; curled like thin shavings from under a plane; up and up.... How lovely goodness is in those who, stepping lightly, go smiling through the world! Also in jolly old fishwives, squatted under arches, obscene old women, how deeply they laugh and shake and rollick, when they walk, from side to side, hum, hah!

"That's an early Mozart, of course——"

"But the tune, like all his tunes, makes one despair—I mean hope. What do I mean? That's the worst of music! I want to dance, laugh, eat pink cakes, yellow cakes, drink thin, sharp wine. Or an indecent story, now—I could relish that. The older one grows the more one likes indecency. Hah, hah! I'm laughing. What at? You said nothing, nor did the old gentleman opposite.... But suppose—suppose—Hush!"

The melancholy river bears us on. When the moon comes through the trailing willow boughs, I see your face, I hear your voice and the bird singing as we pass the osier bed. What are you whispering? Sorrow, sorrow. Joy, joy. Woven together, like reeds in moonlight. Woven together, inextricably commingled, bound in pain and strewn in sorrow—crash!

The boat sinks. Rising, the figures ascend, but now leaf thin, tapering to a dusky wraith, which, fiery tipped, draws its twofold passion from my heart. For me it sings, unseals my sorrow, thaws compassion, floods with love the sunless world, nor, ceasing, abates its tenderness but deftly, subtly, weaves in and out until in this pattern, this consummation, the cleft ones unify; soar, sob, sink to rest, sorrow and joy.

Why then grieve? Ask what? Remain unsatisfied? I say all's been settled; yes; laid to rest under a coverlet of rose leaves, falling. Falling. Ah, but they cease. One rose leaf, falling from an enormous height, like a little parachute dropped from an invisible balloon, turns, flutters waveringly. It won't reach us.

"No, no. I noticed nothing. That's the worst of music—these silly dreams. The second violin was late, you say?"

"There's old Mrs. Munro, feeling her way out—blinder each year, poor woman—on this slippery floor."

Eyeless old age, grey-headed Sphinx. . . . There she stands on the pavement, beckoning, so sternly, the red omnibus.

"How lovely! How well they play! How—how—how!"

The tongue is but a clapper. Simplicity itself. The feathers in the hat next me are bright and pleasing as a child's rattle. The leaf on the plane-tree flashes green through the chink in the curtain. Very strange, very exciting.

"How—how—how!" Hush!

These are the lovers on the grass.

"If, madam, you will take my hand——"

"Sir, I would trust you with my heart. Moreover, we have left our bodies in the banqueting hall. Those on the turf are the shadows of our souls."

"Then these are the embraces of our souls." The lemons nod assent. The swan pushes from the bank and floats dreaming into mid stream.

"But to return. He followed me down the corridor, and, as we turned the corner, trod on the lace of my petticoat. What could I do but cry 'Ah!' and stop to finger it? At which he drew his sword, made passes as if he were stabbing something to death, and cried, 'Mad! Mad! Mad!' Whereupon I screamed, and the Prince, who was writing in the large vellum book in the oriel window, came out in his velvet skull-cap and furred slippers, snatched a rapier from the wall—the King of Spain's gift, you know—on which I escaped, flinging on this cloak to hide the ravages to my skirt—to hide . . . But listen! the horns!"

The gentleman replies so fast to the lady, and she runs up the scale with such witty exchange of compliment now culminating in a sob of passion, that the words are indistinguishable though the meaning is plain enough—love, laughter, flight, pursuit, celestial bliss—all floated out on the gayest ripple of tender endearment—until the sound of the silver horns, at first far distant, gradually sounds more and more distinctly, as if seneschals were saluting the dawn or proclaiming ominously the escape of the lovers. . . . The green garden, moonlit pool, lemons, lovers, and fish are all dissolved in the opal sky, across which, as the horns are joined by trumpets and supported by clarions there rise white arches firmly planted on marble pillars. . . . Tramp and trumpeting. Clang and clangour. Firm establishment. Fast foundations. March of myriads. Confusion and chaos trod to earth. But this city to which we travel has neither stone nor marble; hangs enduring; stands unshakable; nor does a face, nor does a flag greet or welcome. Leave then to perish your hope; droop in the desert my joy; naked advance. Bare are the pillars; auspicious to none; casting no shade; resplendent; severe. Back then I fall, eager no more, desiring only to go, find the street, mark the buildings, greet the applewoman, say to the maid who opens the door: A starry night.

"Good night, good night. You go this way?"

"Alas. I go that." .

COMMENTARY
by the Editors

Like the shifting thoughts and impressions of its narrator, "The String Quartet" is a kaleidoscope of moods and images. Its structure, indeed, has the appearance of a narrative but an elusive one, as delicate and multitextured as a dream or fantasy. There is resonance and substance beneath the gossamer surface, however, a connection with experience —albeit a negative one—that symbolizes the way in which an individual views herself and reality. More precisely, through the technique of stream-of-consciousness, Mrs. Woolf defines an introspective personality who transfigures events of the moment into romantic yearnings. In a narrative sense, as this character drifts from one imagined scene or episode to another, she reveals a breaking-away from the seeming order of conscious reality. But the depiction of conscious reality, Mrs. Woolf maintained for her artistic purposes, merely limits human awareness unless it is refined by imagination. Her aim, hence, was to enlarge those limits, to expand perception beyond conventional notions of logic. "Life," she wrote in explanation of her fictional concern, "is not a series of gig lamps symmetrically arranged; life is a luminous halo, a semi-transparent envelope surrounding us from the beginning of consciousness to the end. Is it not the task of the novelist to convey this varying, this unknown and uncircumscribed spirit, whatever aberration or complexity it may display, with as little mixture of the alien and external as possible?"

Mrs. Woolf attempts to achieve this goal by juxtaposing the tangible present and a vividly imagined past. Deliberately she has framed her narrator in a pattern of contrasts which set her apart from the other concert-goers and yet—with the persistence of a musical refrain—make her an almost contemptuous eavesdropper. Thus the author shows how the sensitive individual may be caught between two existences, with the banalities of the now activating remembrance of a precious past, whether it is her own or a borrowing from history. There is a conflict, then, determined by the restless, unordered flow of thoughts and images which promotes a tension between people, between past and present, between illusion and reality. On this level, the struggle is for being and awareness, and it is a wholly internalized one confined within the mind of the narrator.

But on another, perhaps simpler, level, she is the protagonist, the person of sensibility and romantic visions who seeks the real truth and beauty of existence. So conceived, she is opposed by a social order or blunted, imperceptive individuals who are dominated by their material interests. Unlike the narrator, they cannot or will not fuse the present with the past and are doomed to the tragedy of incompleteness.

Mrs. Woolf is obviously uninterested in external events for their own sake. But she is not uninterested in the effects of external events upon an individual's state of mind. It is precisely for this reason that her internal point of view succeeds. Choosing to depict character through the identification of outer symbols and the individual personality, she employs an associational process, a controlled semblance of uncontrolled impressions. In that way she demonstrates how—for her, at least—the "unknown and uncircumscribed spirit"—enriches immediate existence. Symbolically and inherently, the music is an important detail. As a narrative property, however, it is important not for itself but as a technique for stimulating and managing the stream of associations. The sparse physical details of the concert hall and the people in it are likewise important only for peripheral reasons. Their inane conversations, their idle attendance, merely highlight the distinctions between the solid citizen—the formal music-lover—and the person of imagination who vibrates, as it were, meaningfully in tune with the music.

Examined now with the perspective afforded by the narrator's inner vision and desires, the introductory lines of "The String Quartet" provide something more than a casual narrative statement:

> Well, here we are, and if you cast your eye over the room you will see that tubes and trams and omnibuses, private carriages not a few, even I venture to believe, landaus with bays in them, have been busy at it, weaving threads from one end of London to the other. Yet I begin to have my doubts—

These people, the narrator seems to say, have come here for a shared cause, a fondness for music. And if this is indeed a communal experience, it should also be a binding one. Were this true, we speculate on behalf of the narrator, they would all be gathered together in a kind of vast psychic interchange of personalities, mingling their pasts and experiences within a framework of recollection set in motion by the music. But she doubts that they have come here to surrender themselves to the flow of associations which make memory and imagining as relevant as the flat reality of the present moment.

Her doubts are justified, for the disjunction between illusion and reality is progressively manifest as the story moves toward its conclusion. This union of the narrator with her neighbors is not even a temporary one, for these unimaginative people refuse to retreat from their outer selves or to merge with each other beyond the social trivia of chitchat. Only the first-person "I" achieves this ideal state, and even for her it cannot last beyond the closing notes of the concert. When the music dies, she can no longer sustain the fullness of an inseparable past and present; she is left now only with the incompleteness of an impoverished reality. For the average person, the entertainment is over; it is time to say good-night, casually and without regret. Having never experienced the totality that he might have grasped, he has lost nothing. The narrator alone, deprived of the unifying flux of time past, is aware of her loss and she goes her way sadly.

Content and Purpose

1. THEME AND INTENTION

Up to this point we have been discussing such interrelated qualities of fiction as structure, order, and emotion. Now we must concern ourselves with abstract content as another ingredient which contributes to the fictional whole. The short story writer not only records some aspect of experience but he usually interprets and evaluates it. This interpretation and evaluation become his theme, which is to say, the controlling, the underlying concept of his fiction.

It would be wrong, however, to approach theme as an exclusively intellectual matter. Although a writer thinks about "the stuff of experience," he also reacts to it emotionally. There is therefore a complex of feeling and thought, a special crystallization of an author's ideas set forth in terms which may owe as much to the senses as to reason. Theme could not function artistically without the support of feeling (mood and tone) or a narrative superstructure (plot, character, and setting). Thematically, hence, "Hubert and Minnie" can be said to deal with a problem of futility in human relationships when two individuals seek love as though it were for one partner, at least, an exercise in self-absorption. To let it go at that, however, would be to reduce a poignant, serio-comic situation to the banality of quasi-philosophic statement. What gives the theme its narrative attractiveness is the coloration afforded by Huxley's thoughtfully emotive view of the affair: his sly, almost playful, irony tempers an implicit tragedy and serves as a critical commentary which brings the mind as well as feelings into play.

According to Katherine Anne Porter, theme is the essence of the storyteller's art, although she is careful to relate it organically to the ultimate design of the fictional work. She argued

... a short story needed *first* a *theme,* and then a point of view, a certain knowledge of human nature and strong feeling about it, and style—that is to say, his own special way of telling a thing that makes it precisely his own and no one else's. ... The greater the theme and the better the style, the better the story you might say.

You might say, and it would be nice to think you would. Especially if you are an author and write short stories. Now listen carefully: except in emergencies, when you are trying to manufacture a quick trick and need some easy money, you don't really need a plot. If you have one, all well and good, if you know what it means and what to do with it. If you are aiming to take up the writing *trade,* you need very different equipment from that which you will need for the *art,* or even just the *profession* of writing. ...

First, have faith in your theme; then get so well acquainted with your characters that they live and grow in your imagination exactly as you saw them in the flesh; and finally, tell their story with all the truth and tenderness and severity you are capable of; and if you have any character of your own, you will have a style of your own; it grows, as your ideas grow, and as your knowledge of your craft increases.

You will discover after a great while that you are probably a writer. You may even make some money at it.*

Much more succinctly, Frank O'Connor sees theme not as the all-

*"No Plot, My Dear, No Story" [1942], reprinted from *The Days Before* (New York, 1952), pp. 134–36.

embracing essence of the short story but as its undeniable source of initiation. All his stories, he said, begin with "just notes of themes. If somebody tells me a good story, I'll write it down in my four lines; that is the secret of the theme. If you make the subject of a story twelve or fourteen lines, that's a treatment. You've already committed yourself to the sort of character, the sort of surroundings, and the moment you've committed yourself, the story is already written. It has ceased to be fluid, you can't design it any longer, you can't model it. So I always confine myself to my four lines. If it won't go into four that means you haven't reduced it to its ultimate simplicity, reduced it to the fable."*

We can never know with certainty whether theme is basic to all the other elements which go into the making of a short story or whether it is but one part of that process known critically as *intention*. We do know, however, that every writer as he confronts the unique task of composition will achieve his own brand of certainty. The term *intention* presents its own difficulties and complications. As it appears here (to paraphrase John Crowe Ransom in *The New Criticism*), intention is the total meaning of the completed work and it contributes specific or particularized details which were not necessarily part of the initial conception. Intention, in short, is evident only in the finished effort and need not have been systematized or ordered by the author at the time he began to give his vision a rational form.

Throughout this volume we have urged that the meaning of any serious work of fiction stems from complexity, from the interplay of its dominant qualities. And we have urged with equal insistence that this same meaning must be summed up as the author's achievement, his realized intention. As a practical demonstration of this premise, we have analyzed Doris Lessing's story "The Nuisance." In our interpretation we have attempted to show how a variety of fictional elements have been fitted together so that each part is dependent upon every other one. Like an intricate mosaic, then, each unit contributes its particular shape to the shape of the whole until we cease

*From an interview originally published in the *Paris Review,* Autumn-Winter, 1957, reprinted here from *Writers at Work,* ed. Malcolm Cowley (New York, 1958).

to be aware of single elements and reflect only upon their combined totality, the accomplished intention. Toward this end, therefore, we do pay attention to theme, character, plot, setting, and mood. But what impresses us finally is the integrated massive effect of these parts.

Hubert and Minnie

Aldous Huxley

For Hubert Lapell this first love-affair was extremely important.
"Important" was the word he had used himself when he was writing
about it in his diary. It was an event in his life, a real event for a
change. It marked, he felt, a genuine turning-point in his spiritual
development.

"Voltaire," he wrote in his diary—and he wrote it a second time
in one of his letters to Minnie—"Voltaire said that one died twice:
once with the death of the whole body and once before, with the
death of one's capacity to love. And in the same way one is born
twice, the second time being on the occasion when one first falls in
love. One is born, then, into a new world—a world of intenser feelings, heightened values, more penetrating insights." And so on.

In point of actual fact Hubert found this new world a little disappointing. The intenser feelings proved to be rather mild; not by
any means up to literary standards.

> *"I tell thee I am mad*
> *In Cressid's love. Thou answer'st: she is fair;*
> *Pour'st in the open ulcer of my heart*
> *Her eyes, her hair, her cheek, her gait, her voice. . . . "*

No, it certainly wasn't quite that. In his diary, in his letters to Minnie, he painted, it is true, a series of brilliant and romantic landscapes of the new world. But they were composite imaginary landscapes in the manner of Salvator Rosa—richer, wilder, more picturesquely clear-obscure than the real thing. Hubert would seize with avidity on the least velleity of an unhappiness, a physical desire, a spiritual yearning, to work it up in his letters and journals into something substantially romantic. There were times, generally very late at night, when he succeeded in persuading himself that he was indeed the wildest, unhappiest, most passionate of lovers. But in the daytime he went about his business nourishing something like a grievance against love. The thing was a bit of a fraud; yes, really, he decided, rather a fraud. All the same, he supposed it was important.

For Minnie, however, love was no fraud at all. Almost from the first moment she had adored him. A common friend had brought him to one of her Wednesday evenings. "This is Mr Lapell; but he's too young to be called anything but Hubert." That was how he had been introduced. And, laughing, she had taken his hand and called him Hubert at once. He too had laughed, rather nervously. "My name's Minnie," she said. But he had been too shy to call her anything at all that evening. His brown hair was tufty and untidy, like a little boy's, and he had shy grey eyes that never looked at you for more than a glimpse at a time, but turned away almost at once, as though they were afraid. Quickly he glanced at you, eagerly—then away again; and his musical voice, with its sudden emphases, its quick modulations from high to low, seemed always to address itself to a ghost floating low down and a little to one side of the person to whom he was talking. Above the brows was a forehead beautifully domed, with a pensive wrinkle running up from between the eyes. In repose his full-lipped mouth pouted a little, as though he were expressing some chronic discontent with the world. And, of course, thought Minnie, the world wasn't beautiful enough for his idealism.

"But after all," he had said earnestly that first evening, "one has the world of thought to live in. That, at any rate, is simple and clear and beautiful. One can always live apart from the brutal scramble."

And from the depths of the arm-chair in which, fragile, tired, and in these rather "artistic" surroundings almost incongruously elegant, she was sitting, Helen Glamber laughed her clear little laugh. "I think, on the contrary," she said (Minnie remembered every incident of that first evening), "I think one ought to rush about and know thousands of people, and eat and drink enormously, and make love incessantly, and shout and laugh and knock people over the head." And having vented these Rabelaisian sentiments, Mrs Glamber dropped back with a sigh of fatigue, covering her eyes with a thin white hand; for she had a splitting headache, and the light hurt her.

"Really!" Minnie protested, laughing. She would have felt rather shocked if any one else had said that; but Helen Glamber was allowed to say anything.

Hubert reaffirmed his quietism. Elegant, weary, infinitely fragile, Mrs Glamber lay back in her arm-chair, listening. Or perhaps, under her covering hand, she was trying to go to sleep.

She had adored him at first sight. Now that she looked back she could see that it had been at first sight. Adored him protectively, maternally—for he was only twenty and very young, in spite of the wrinkle between his brows, and the long words and the undergraduate's newly discovered knowledge; only twenty, and she was nearly twenty-nine. And she had fallen in love with his beauty, too. Ah, passionately.

Hubert, perceiving it later, was surprised and exceedingly flattered. This had never happened to him before. He enjoyed being worshipped, and since Minnie had fallen so violently in love with him, it seemed the most natural thing in the world for him to be in love with Minnie. True, if she had not started by adoring him, it would never have occurred to Hubert to fall in love with her. At their first meeting he had found her certainly very nice, but not particularly exciting. Afterwards, the manifest expression of her adoration had made him find her more interesting, and in the end he had fallen in love himself. But perhaps it was not to be wondered at if he found the process a little disappointing.

But still, he reflected on those secret occasions when he had to admit to himself that something was wrong with this passion, love without possession could never, surely, in the nature of things, be quite the genuine article. In his diary he recorded aptly those two quatrains of John Donne:

"So must pure lovers' souls descend
To affections and to faculties,
Which sense may reach and apprehend,
Else a great prince in prison lies.

To our bodies turn we then, that so
Weak men on love revealed my look;
Love's mysteries in souls do grow,
But yet the body is his book."

At their next meeting he recited them to Minnie. The conversation which followed, compounded as it was of philosophy and personal confidences, was exquisite. It really, Hubert felt, came up to literary standards.

The next morning Minnie rang up her friend Helen Glamber and asked if she might come to tea that afternoon. She had several things to talk to her about. Mrs Glamber sighed as she hung up the receiver. "Minnie's coming to tea," she called, turning towards the open door.

From across the passage her husband's voice came back to her. "Good Lord!" it said in a tone of far-away horror, of absent-minded resignation; for John Glamber was deep in his work and there was only a little of him left, so to speak, above the surface to react to the bad news.

Helen Glamber sighed again, and propping herself more comfortably against her pillows she reached for her book. She knew that far-away voice and what it meant. It meant that he wouldn't answer if she went on with the conversation; only say "h'm" or "m'yes." And if she persisted after that, it meant that he'd say, plaintively, heart-breakingly, "Darling, you *must* let me get on with my work."

And at that moment she would so much have liked to talk a little. Instead, she went on reading at the point where she had broken off to answer Minnie's telephone call.

"By this time the flames had enveloped the gynaeceum. Nineteen times did the heroic Patriarch of Alexandria venture into the blazing fabric, from which he succeeded in rescuing all but two of its lovely occupants, twenty-seven in number, all of whom he caused to be transported at once to his own private apartments...."

It was one of those instructive books John liked her to read. History, mystery, lesson, and law. But at the moment she didn't feel much like history. She felt like talking. And that was out of the question; absolutely out of it.

She put down her book and began to file her nails and think of poor Minnie. Yes, poor Minnie. Why was it that one couldn't help saying Good Lord! heart-feltly, when one heard she was coming to tea? And why did one never have the heart to refuse to let her come to tea? She was pathetic, but pathetic in such a boring way. There are some people you like being kind to, people you want to help and befriend. People that look at you with the eyes of sick monkeys. Your heart breaks when you see them. But poor Minnie had none of the charms of a sick monkey. She was just a great big healthy young woman of twenty-eight who ought to have been married and the mother of children, and who wasn't. She would have made such a good wife, such an admirably solicitous and careful mother. But it just happened that none of the men she knew had ever wanted to marry her. And why should they want to? When she came into a room, the light seemed to grow perceptibly dimmer, the electric tension slackened off. She brought no life with her; she absorbed what there was, she was like so much blotting-paper. No wonder nobody wanted to marry her. And yet, of course, it was the only thing. Particularly as she was always falling in love herself. The only thing.

"John!" Mrs Glamber suddenly called. "Is it really true about ferrets?"

"Ferrets?" the voice from across the passage repeated with a remote irritation. "Is what true about ferrets?"

"That the females die if they're not mated."

"How on earth should I know?"

"But you generally know everything."

"But, my darling, really..." The voice was plaintive, full of reproach.

Mrs Glamber clapped her hand over her mouth and only took it off again to blow a kiss. "All right," she said very quickly. "All right. Really. I'm sorry. I won't do it again. Really." She blew another kiss towards the door.

"But ferrets..." repeated the voice.

"Sh—sh, sh—sh."

"Why ferrets?"

"Darling," said Mrs Glamber almost sternly, "you really must go on with your work."

Minnie came to tea. She put the case—hypothetically at first, as though it were the case of a third person; then, gaining courage, she put it personally. It was her own case. Out of the depths of her untroubled, pagan innocence, Helen Glamber brutally advised her. "If you want to go to bed with the young man," she said, "go to bed with him. The thing has no importance in itself. At least not much. It's only important because it makes possible more secret confidences, because it strengthens affection, makes the man in a way dependent on you. And then, of course, it's the natural thing. I'm all for nature except when it comes to painting one's face. They say that ferrets..." But Minnie noticed that she never finished the sentence. Appalled and fascinated, shocked and yet convinced, she listened.

"My darling," said Mrs Glamber that evening when her husband came home—for he hadn't been able to face Minnie; he had gone to the Club for tea— "who was it that invented religion, and sin, and all that? And why?"

John laughed. "It was invented by Adam," he said, "for various little transcendental reasons which you would probably find it difficult to appreciate. But also for the very practical purpose of keeping Eve in order."

"Well, if you call complicating people's lives keeping them in order, then I dare say you're right." Mrs Glamber shook her head. "I find it all too obscure. At sixteen, yes. But one really ought to have grown out of that sort of thing by twenty. And at thirty—the woman's nearly thirty, you know—well, really . . ."

In the end, Minnie wrote to Hubert telling him that she had made up her mind. Hubert was staying in Hertfordshire with his friend Watchett. It was a big house, the food was good, one was very comfortable; and old Mr Watchett, moreover, had a very sound library. In the impenetrable shade of the Wellingtonias Hubert and Ted Watchett played croquet and discussed the best methods of cultivating the Me. You could do a good deal, they decided, with art—books, you know, and pictures and music. "Listen to Stravinsky's *Sacre*," said Ted Watchett, "and you're for ever excused from going to Tibet or the Gold Coast or any of those awful places. And then there's Dostoievsky instead of murder, and D. H. Lawrence as a substitute for sex."

"All the same," said Hubert, "one must have a *certain* amount of actual non-imaginative experience." He spoke earnestly, abstractedly; but Minnie's letter was in his pocket. *"Gnosce teipsum.* You can't really know yourself without coming into collision with events, can you?"

Next day, Ted's cousin, Phoebe, arrived. She had red hair and a milky skin, and was more or less on the musical comedy stage. "One foot on and one foot off," she explained. "The splits." And there and then she did them, the splits, on the drawing-room carpet. "It's quite easy," she said, laughing, and jumped up again with an easy grace that fairly took one's breath away. Ted didn't like her. "Tiresome girl," he said. "So silly, too. Consciously silly, silly on purpose, which makes it worse." And, it was true, she did like boasting about the amount of champagne she could put away without getting buffy, and the number of times she had exceeded the generous allowance and been "blind to the world." She liked talking about her admirers in terms which might make you suppose that they were all her accepted lovers. But then she had the justification of her vitality and her shining red hair.

"Vitality," Hubert wrote in his diary (he contemplated a distant date, after, or preferably before, his death, when these confessions and aphorisms would be published), "vitality can make claims on the world almost as imperiously as can beauty. Sometimes beauty and vitality meet in one person."

It was Hubert who arranged that they should stay at the mill. One of his friends had once been there with a reading party, and found the place comfortable, secluded, and admirably quiet. Quiet, that is to say, with the special quietness peculiar to mills. For the silence there was not the silence of night on a mountain; it was a silence made of continuous thunder. At nine o'clock every morning the mill-wheel began to turn, and its roaring never stopped all day. For the first moments the noise was terrifying, was almost unbearable. Then, after a little, one grew accustomed to it. The thunder became, by reason of its very unintermittence, a perfect silence, wonderfully rich and profound.

At the back of the mill was a little garden hemmed in on three sides by the house, the outhouses, and a high brick wall, and open on the fourth towards the water. Looking over the parapet, Minnie watched it sliding past. It was like a brown snake with arrowy markings on its back; and it crawled, it glided, it slid along for ever. She sat there, waiting: her train, from London, had brought her here soon after lunch; Hubert, coming across country from the Watchetts, would hardly arrive before six. The water flowed beneath her eyes like time, like destiny, smoothly towards some new and violent event.

The immense noise that in this garden was silence enveloped her. Inured, her mind moved in it as though in its native element. From beyond the parapet came the coolness and the weedy smell of water. But if she turned back towards the garden, she breathed at once the hot perfume of sunlight beating on flowers and ripening fruit. In the afternoon sunlight all the world was ripe. The old red house lay there, ripe, like a dropped plum; the walls were riper than the fruits of the nectarine trees so tenderly and neatly crucified on their warm bricks. And that richer silence of unremitting thunder seemed, as it were, the powdery bloom on a day that had come to exquisite maturity and was hanging, round as a peach and juicy with life and happiness, waiting in the sunshine for the bite of eager teeth.

At the heart of this fruit-ripe world Minnie waited. The water flowed towards the wheel; smoothly, smoothly—then it fell, it broke itself to pieces on the turning wheel. And time was sliding onwards, quietly towards an event that would shatter all the smoothness of her life.

"If you really want to go to bed with the young man, go to bed with him." She could hear Helen's clear, shrill voice saying impossible, brutal things. If any one else had said them, she would have run out of the room. But in Helen's mouth they seemed, somehow, so simple, so innocuous, and so true. And yet all that other people had said or implied—at home, at school, among the people she was used to meeting—seemed equally true.

But then, of course, there was love. Hubert had written a Shakespearean sonnet which began:

> *"Love hallows all whereon 'tis truly placed,*
> *Turns dross to gold with one touch of his dart,*
> *Makes matter mind, extremest passion chaste,*
> *And builds a temple in the lustful heart."*

She thought that very beautiful. And very true. It seemed to throw a bridge between Helen and the other people. Love, true love, made all the difference. It justified. Love—how much, how much she loved!

Time passed and the light grew richer as the sun declined out of the height of the sky. The day grew more and more deliciously ripe, swelling with unheard-of sweetness. Over its sun-flushed cheeks the thundery silence of the mill-wheel spread the softest, peachiest of blooms. Minnie sat on the parapet, waiting. Sometimes she looked down at the sliding water, sometimes she turned her eyes towards the garden. Time flowed, but she was now no more afraid of that shattering event that thundered there, in the future. The ripe sweetness of the afternoon seemed to enter into her spirit, filling it to the brim. There was no more room for doubts, or fearful anticipations, or regrets. She was happy. Tenderly, with a tenderness she could not have expressed in words, only with the gentlest of light kisses, with fingers caressingly drawn through the ruffled hair, she thought of Hubert, her Hubert.

Hubert, Hubert.... And suddenly, startlingly, he was standing there at her side.

"Oh," she said, and for a moment she stared at him with round brown eyes, in which there was nothing but astonishment. Then the expression changed. "Hubert," she said softly.

Hubert took her hand and dropped it again; looked at her for an instant, then turned away. Leaning on the parapet, he stared down into the sliding water; his face was unsmiling. For a long time both were silent. Minnie remained where she was, sitting quite still, her eyes fixed on the young man's averted face. She was happy, happy, happy. The long day ripened and ripened, perfection after perfection.

"Minnie," said the young man suddenly, and with a loud abruptness, as though he had been a long time deciding himself to speak and had at last succeeded in bringing out the prepared and pent-up words, "I feel I've behaved very badly towards you. I never ought to have asked you to come here. It was wrong. I'm sorry."

"But I came because I wanted to," Minnie exclaimed.

Hubert glanced at her, then turned away his eyes and went on addressing a ghost that floated, it seemed, just above the face of the sliding water. "It was too much to ask. I shouldn't have done it. For a man it's different. But for a woman . . ."

"But, I tell you, I wanted to."

"It's too much."

"It's nothing," said Minnie, "because I love you." And leaning forward, she ran her fingers through his hair. Ah, tenderness that no words could express! "You silly boy," she whispered. "Did you think I didn't love you enough for that?"

Hubert did not look up. The water slid and slid away before his eyes; Minnie's fingers played in his hair, ran caressingly over the nape of his neck. He felt suddenly a positive hatred for this woman. Idiot! Why couldn't she take a hint? He didn't want her. And why on earth had he ever imagined that he did? All the way in the train he had been asking himself that question. Why? Why? And the question had asked itself still more urgently just now as, standing at the garden door, he had looked out between the apple tree and watched her, unobserved, through a long minute—watched her sitting there on the parapet, turing her vague brown eyes now at the water, now towards the garden, and smiling to herself with an expression that had seemed to him so dim and vacuous that he could almost have fancied her an imbecile.

And with Phoebe yesterday he had stood on the crest of the bare chalk down. Like a sea at their feet stretched the plain, and above the dim horizon towered heroic clouds. Fingers of the wind lifted the red locks of her hair. She stood as though poised, ready to leap off into the boisterous air. "How I should like to fly!" she said. "There's something particularly attractive about airmen, I always think." And she had gone running down the hill.

But Minnie, with her dull hair, her apple-red cheeks, and big, slow body, was like a peasant girl. How had he ever persuaded himself that he wanted her? And what made it much worse, of course, was that she adored him, embarrassingly, tiresomely, like a too affectionate spaniel that insists on tumbling about at your feet and licking your hand just when you want to sit quietly and concentrate on serious things.

Hubert moved away, out of reach of her caressing hand. He lifted towards her for a moment a pair of eyes that had become, as it were, opaque with a cold anger; then dropped them again.

"The sacrifice is too great," he said in a voice that sounded to him like somebody else's voice. He found it very difficult to say this sort of thing convincingly. "I can't ask it of you," the actor pursued. "I won't."

"But it isn't a sacrifice," Minnie protested. "It's a joy, it's happiness. Oh, can't you understand?"

Hubert did not answer. Motionless, his elbows on the parapet, he stared down into the water. Minnie looked at him, perplexed only, at first; but all at once she was seized with a nameless agonizing doubt that grew and grew within her, as the silence prolonged itself, like some dreadful cancer of the spirit, until it had eaten away all her happiness, until there was nothing left in her mind but doubt and apprehension.

"What is it?" she said at last. "Why are you so strange? What is it, Hubert? What is it?"

Leaning anxiously forward, she laid her two hands on either side of his averted face and turned it towards her. Blank and opaque with anger were the eyes. "What is it?" she repeated. "Hubert, what is it?"

Hubert disengaged himself. "It's no good," he said in a smothered voice. "No good at all. It was a mistake. I'm sorry. I think I'd better go away. The trap's still at the door."

And without waiting for her to say anything, without explaining himself any further, he turned and walked quickly away, almost ran, towards the house. Well, thank goodness, he said to himself, he was out of that. He hadn't done it very well, or handsomely, or courage-ously; but, at any rate, he was out of it. Poor Minnie! He felt sorry for her; but after all, what could he do about it? Poor Minnie! Still, it rather flattered his vanity to think that she would be mourning over him. And in any case, he reassured his conscience, she couldn't really mind very much. But on the other hand, his vanity reminded him, she did adore him. Oh, she absolutely worshipped...

The door closed behind him. Minnie was alone again in the garden. Ripe, ripe it lay there in the late sunshine. Half of it was in shadow now; but the rest of it, in the coloured evening light, seemed to have come to the final and absolute perfection of maturity. Bloomy with thundery silence, the choicest fruit of all time hung there, de-liciously sweet, to the core; hung flushed and beautiful on the brink of darkness.

Minnie sat there quite still, wondering what had happened. Had he gone, had he really gone? The door closed behind him with a bang, and almost as though the sound were a signal prearranged, a man walked out from the mill on to the dam and closed the sluice. And all at once the wheel was still. Apocalyptically there was silence; the silence of soundlessness took the place of that other silence that was uninterrupted sound. Gulfs opened endlessly out around her; she was alone. Across the void of soundlessness a belated bee trailed its thin buzzing; the sparrows chirped, and from across the water came the sound of voices and far-away laughter. And as though woken from a sleep, Minnie looked up and listened, fearfully, turn-ing her head from side to side.

The Rocking-Horse Winner
D. H. Lawrence

There was a woman who was beautiful, who started with all the advantages, yet she had no luck. She married for love, and the love turned to dust. She had bonny children, yet she felt they had been thrust upon her, and she could not love them. They looked at her coldly, as if they were finding fault with her. And hurriedly she felt she must cover up some fault in herself. Yet what it was that she must cover up she never knew. Nevertheless, when her children were present, she always felt the centre of her heart go hard. This troubled her, and in her manner she was all the more gentle and anxious for her children, as if she loved them very much. Only she herself knew that at the centre of her heart was a hard little place that could not feel love, no, not for anybody. Everybody else said of her:"She is such a good mother. She adores her children." Only she herself, and her children themselves, knew it was not so. They read it in each other's eyes.

There were a boy and two little girls. They lived in a pleasant house, with a garden, and they had discreet servants, and felt themselves superior to anyone in the neighbourhood.

Although they lived in style, they felt always an anxiety in the house. There was never enough money. The mother had a small income, and the father had a small income, but not nearly enough for the social position which they had to keep up. The father went in to town to some office. But though he had good prospects, these prospects never materialized. There was always the grinding sense of the shortage of money, though the style was always kept up.

At last the mother said: "I will see if *I* can't make something." But she did not know where to begin. She racked her brains, and tried this thing and the other, but could not find anything successful. The failure made deep lines come into her face. Her children were growing up, they would have to go to school. There must be more money, there must be more money. The father, who was always very handsome and expensive in his tastes, seemed as if he never *would* be able to do anything worth doing. And the mother, who had a great belief in herself, did not succeed any better, and her tastes were just as expensive.

And so the house came to be haunted by the unspoken phrase: *There must be more money! There must be more money!* The children could hear it all the time, though nobody said it aloud. They heard it at Christmas, when the expensive and splendid toys filled the nursery. Behind the shining modern rocking-horse, behind the smart doll's-house, a voice would start whispering: "There *must* be more money! There *must* be more money!" And the children would stop playing, to listen for a moment. They would look into each other's eyes, to see if they had all heard. And each one saw in the eyes of the other two that they too had heard. "There *must* be more money! There *must* be more money!"

It came whispering from the springs of the still-swaying rocking-horse, and even the horse, bending his wooden, champing head, heard it. The big doll, sitting so pink and smirking in her new pram, could hear it quite plainly, and seemed to be smirking all the more self-consciously because of it. The foolish puppy, too, that took the place of the teddy-bear, he was looking so extraordinarily foolish for no other reason but that he heard the secret whisper all over the house: "There *must* be more money!"

Yet nobody ever said it aloud. The whisper was everywhere, and therefore no one spoke it. Just as no one ever says: "We are breathing!" in spite of the fact that breath is coming and going all the time.

"Mother," said the boy Paul one day, "why don't we keep a car of our own? Why do we always use uncle's, or else a taxi?"

"Because we're the poor members of the family," said the mother.

"But why *are* we, mother?"

"Well—I suppose," she said slowly and bitterly, "it's because your father has no luck."

The boy was silent for some time.

"Is luck money, mother?" he asked rather timidly.

"No, Paul. Not quite. It's what causes you to have money."

"Oh!" said Paul vaguely. "I thought when Uncle Oscar said *filthy lucker,* it meant money."

"*Filthy lucre* does mean money," said the mother. "But it's lucre, not luck."

"Oh!" said the boy. "Then what *is* luck, mother?"

"It's what causes you to have money. If you're lucky you have money. That's why it's better to be born lucky than rich. If you're rich, you may lose your money. But if you're lucky, you will always get more money."

"Oh! Will you? And is father not lucky?"

"Very unlucky, I should say," she said bitterly.

The boy watched her with unsure eyes.

"Why?" he asked.

"I don't know. Nobody ever knows why one person is lucky and another unlucky."

"Don't they? Nobody at all? Does *nobody* know?"

"Perhaps God. But He never tells."

"He ought to, then. And aren't you lucky either, mother?"

"I can't be, if I married an unlucky husband."

"But by yourself, aren't you?"

"I used to think I was, before I married. Now I think I am very unlucky indeed."

"Why?"

"Well—never mind! Perhaps I'm not really," she said.

The child looked at her, to see if she meant it. But he saw, by the lines of her mouth, that she was only trying to hide something from him.

"Well, anyhow," he said stoutly, "I'm a lucky person."

"Why?" said his mother, with a sudden laugh.

He stared at her. He didn't even know why he had said it.

"God told me," he asserted, brazening it out.

"I hope He did, dear!" she said, again with a laugh, but rather bitter.

"He did, mother!"

"Excellent!" said the mother, using one of her husband's exclamations.

The boy saw she did not believe him; or, rather, that she paid no attention to his assertion. This angered him somewhat, and made him want to compel her attention.

He went off by himself, vaguely, in a childish way, seeking for the clue to "luck." Absorbed, taking no heed of other people, he went about with a sort of stealth, seeking inwardly for luck. He wanted luck, he wanted it, he wanted it. When the two girls were playing dolls in the nursery, he would sit on his big rocking-horse, charging madly into space, with a frenzy that made the little girls peer at him uneasily. Wildly the horse careered, the waving dark hair of the boy tossed, his eyes had a strange glare in them. The little girls dared not speak to him.

When he had ridden to the end of his mad little journey, he climbed down and stood in front of his rocking-horse, staring fixedly into its lowered face. Its red mouth was slightly open, its big eye was wide and glassy-bright.

"Now!" he would silently command the snorting steed. "Now, take me to where there is luck! Now take me!"

And he would slash the horse on the neck with the little whip he had asked Uncle Oscar for. He *knew* the horse could take him to where there was luck, if only he forced it. So he would mount again, and start on his furious ride, hoping at last to get there. He knew he could get there.

"You'll break your horse, Paul!" said the nurse.

"He's always riding like that! I wish he'd leave off!" said his elder sister Joan.

But he only glared down on them in silence. Nurse gave him up. She could make nothing of him. Anyhow he was growing beyond her.

One day his mother and his Uncle Oscar came in when he was on one of his furious rides. He did not speak to them.

"Hallo, you young jockey! Riding a winner?" said his uncle.

"Aren't you growing too big for a rocking-horse? You're not a very little boy any longer, you know," said his mother.

But Paul only gave a blue glare from his big, rather close-set eyes. He would speak to nobody when he was in full tilt. His mother watched him with an anxious expression on her face.

At last he suddenly stopped forcing his horse into the mechanical gallop, and slid down.

"Well, I got there!" he announced fiercely, his blue eyes still flaring, and his sturdy long legs straddling apart.

"Where did you get to?" asked his mother.

"Where I wanted to go," he flared back at her.

"That's right, son!" said Uncle Oscar. "Don't you stop till you get there. What's the horse's name?"

"He doesn't have a name," said the boy.

"Gets on without all right?" asked the uncle.

"Well, he has different names. He was called Sansovino last week."

"Sansovino, eh? Won the Ascot. How did you know his name?"

"He always talks about horse-races with Bassett," said Joan.

The uncle was delighted to find that his small nephew was posted with all the racing news. Bassett, the young gardener, who had been wounded in the left foot in the war and had got his present job through Oscar Cresswell, whose batman he had been, was a perfect blade of the "turf." He lived in the racing events, and the small boy lived with him.

Oscar Cresswell got it all from Bassett.

"Master Paul comes and asks me, so I can't do more than tell him, sir," said Bassett, his face terribly serious, as if he were speaking of religious matters.

"And does he ever put anything on a horse he fancies?"

"Well—I don't want to give him away—he's a young sport, a fine sport, sir. Would you mind asking him himself? He sort of takes a pleasure in it, and perhaps he'd feel I was giving him away, sir, if you don't mind."

Bassett was serious as a church.

The uncle went back to his nephew and took him off for a ride in the car.

"Say, Paul, old man, do you ever put anything on a horse?" the uncle asked.

The boy watched the handsome man closely.

"Why, do you think I oughtn't to?" he parried.

"Not a bit of it! I thought perhaps you might give me a tip for the Lincoln."

The car sped on into the country, going down to Uncle Oscar's place in Hampshire.

"Honour bright?" said the nephew.

"Honour bright, son!" said the uncle.

"Well, then, Daffodil."

"Daffodil! I doubt it, sonny. What about Mirza?"

"I only know the winner," said the boy. "That's Daffodil."

"Daffodil, eh?"

There was a pause. Daffodil was an obscure horse comparatively.

"Uncle!"

"Yes, son?"

"You won't let it go any further, will you? I promised Bassett."

"Bassett be damned, old man! What's he got to do with it?"

"We're partners. We've been partners from the first. Uncle, he lent me my first five shillings, which I lost. I promised him, honour bright, it was only between me and him; only you gave me that ten-shilling note I started winning with, so I thought you were lucky. You won't let it go any further, will you?"

The boy gazed at his uncle from those big, hot, blue eyes, set rather close together. The uncle stirred and laughed uneasily.

"Right you are, son! I'll keep your tip private. Daffodil, eh? How much are you putting on him?"

"All except twenty pounds," said the boy. "I keep that in reserve."

The uncle thought it a good joke.

"You keep twenty pounds in reserve, do you, you young romancer? What are you betting, then?"

"I'm betting three hundred," said the boy gravely. "But it's between you and me, Uncle Oscar! Honour bright?"

The uncle burst into a roar of laughter.

"It's between you and me all right, you young Nat Gould," he said, laughing. "But where's your three hundred?"

"Bassett keeps it for me. We're partners."

"You are, are you! And what is Bassett putting on Daffodil?"

"He won't go quite as high as I do, I expect. Perhaps he'll go a hundred and fifty."

"What, pennies?" laughed the uncle.

"Pounds," said the child, with a surprised look at his uncle. "Bassett keeps a bigger reserve than I do."

Between wonder and amusement Uncle Oscar was silent. He pursued the matter no further, but he determined to take his nephew with him to the Lincoln races.

"Now, son," he said, "I'm putting twenty on Mirza, and I'll put five for you on any horse you fancy. What's your pick?"

"Daffodil, uncle."

"No, not the fiver on Daffodil!"

"I should if it was my own fiver," said the child.

"Good! Good! Right you are! A fiver for me and a fiver for you on Daffodil."

The child had never been to a race-meeting before, and his eyes were blue fire. He pursed his mouth tight, and watched. A Frenchman just in front had put his money on Lancelot. Wild with excitement, he flayed his arms up and down, yelling *Lancelot! Lancelot!* in his French accent.

Daffodil came in first, Lancelot second, Mirza third. The child, flushed and with eyes blazing, was curiously serene. His uncle brought him four five-pound notes, four to one.

"What am I to do with these?" he cried, waving them before the boy's eyes.

"I suppose we'll talk to Bassett," said the boy. "I expect I have fifteen hundred now; and twenty in reserve; and this twenty."

His uncle studied him for some moments.

"Look here, son!" he said. "You're not serious about Bassett and that fifteen hundred, are you?"

"Yes, I am. But it's between you and me, uncle. Honour bright!"

"Honour bright all right, son! But I must talk to Bassett."

"If you'd like to be a partner, uncle, with Bassett and me, we could all be partners. Only, you'd have to promise, honour bright, uncle, not to let it go beyond us three. Bassett and I are lucky, and you must be lucky, because it was your ten shillings I started winning with...."

Uncle Oscar took both Bassett and Paul into Richmond Park for an afternoon, and there they talked.

"It's like this, you see, sir," Bassett said. "Master Paul would get me talking about racing events, spinning yarns, you know, sir. And he was always keen on knowing if I'd made or if I'd lost. It's about a year since, now, that I put five shilling on Blush of Dawn for him—and we lost. Then the luck turned, with that ten shillings he had from you, that we put on Singhalese. And since that time, it's been pretty steady, all things considering. What do you say, Master Paul?"

"We're all right when we're sure," said Paul. "It's when we're not quite sure that we go down."

"Oh, but we're careful then," said Bassett.

"But when are you *sure?*" smiled Uncle Oscar.

"It's Master Paul, sir," said Bassett, in a secret, religious voice. "It's as if he had it from heaven. Like Daffodil, now, for the Lincoln. That was as sure as eggs."

"Did you put anything on Daffodil?" asked Oscar Cresswell.

"Yes, sir. I made my bit."

"And my nephew?"

Bassett was obstinately silent, looking at Paul.

"I made twelve hundred, didn't I, Bassett? I told uncle I was putting three hundred on Daffodil."

"That's right," said Bassett, nodding.

"But where's the money?" asked the uncle.

"I keep it safe locked up, sir. Master Paul he can have it any minute he likes to ask for it."

"What, fifteen hundred pounds?"

"And twenty! And *forty,* that is, with the twenty he made on the course."

"It's amazing!" said the uncle.

"If Master Paul offers you to be partners, sir, I would, if I were you: if you'll excuse me," said Bassett.

Oscar Cresswell thought about it.

"I'll see the money," he said.

They drove home again, and sure enough, Bassett came round to the garden-house with fifteen hundred pounds in notes. The twenty pounds reserve was left with Joe Glee, in the Turf Commission deposit.

"You see, it's all right, uncle, when I'm *sure!* Then we go strong, for all we're worth. Don't we, Bassett?"

"We do that, Master Paul."

"And when are you sure?" said the uncle, laughing.

"Oh, well, sometimes I'm *absolutely* sure, like about Daffodil," said the boy; "and sometimes I have an idea; and sometimes I haven't even an idea, have I, Bassett? Then we're careful, because we mostly go down."

"You do, do you! And when you're sure, like about Daffodil, what makes you sure, sonny?"

"Oh, well, I don't know," said the boy uneasily. "I'm sure, you know, uncle; that's all."

"It's as if he had it from heaven, sir," Bassett reiterated.

"I should say so!" said the uncle.

But he became a partner. And when the Leger was coming on, Paul was "sure" about Lively Spark, which was a quite inconsiderable horse. The boy insisted on putting a thousand on the horse, Bassett went for five hundred, and Oscar Cresswell two hundred. Lively Spark came in first, and the betting had been ten to one against him. Paul had made ten thousand.

"You see," he said, "I was absolutely sure of him."

Even Oscar Cresswell had cleared two thousand.

"Look here, son," he said, "this sort of thing makes me nervous."

"It needn't, uncle! Perhaps I shan't be sure again for a long time."

"But what are you going to do with your money?" asked the uncle.

"Of course," said the boy, "I started it for mother. She said she had no luck, because father is unlucky, so I thought if *I* was lucky, it might stop whispering."

"What might stop whispering?"

"Our house. I *hate* our house for whispering."

"What does it whisper?"

"Why—why"—the boy fidgeted—"why, I don't know. But it's always short of money, you know, uncle."

"I know it, son, I know it."

"You know people send mother writs, don't you, uncle?"

"I'm afraid I do," said the uncle.

"And then the house whispers, like people laughing at you behind your back. It's awful, that is! I thought if I was lucky . . ."

"You might stop it," added the uncle.

The boy watched him with big blue eyes, that had an uncanny cold fire in them, and he said never a word.

"Well, then!" said the uncle. "What are we doing?"

"I shouldn't like mother to know I was lucky," said the boy.

"Why not, son?"

"She'd stop me."

"I don't think she would."

"Oh"—and the boy writhed in an odd way—"I *don't* want her to know, uncle."

"All right, son! We'll manage it without her knowing."

They managed it very easily. Paul, at the other's suggestion, handed over five thousand pounds to his uncle, who deposited it with the family lawyer, who was then to inform Paul's mother that a relative had put five thousand pounds into his hands, which sum was to be paid out a thousand pounds at a time, on the mother's birthday, for the next five years.

"So she'll have a birthday present of a thousand pounds for five successive years," said Uncle Oscar. "I hope it won't make it all the harder for her later."

Paul's mother had her birthday in November. The house had been "whispering" worse than ever lately, and, even in spite of his luck, Paul could not bear up against it. He was very anxious to see the effect of the birthday letter, telling his mother about the thousand pounds.

When there were no visitors, Paul now took his meals with his parents, as he was beyond the nursery control. His mother went into town nearly every day. She had discovered that she had an odd knack of sketching furs and dress materials, so she worked secretly in the studio of a friend who was the chief "artist" for the leading drapers. She drew the figures of ladies in furs and ladies in silk and sequins for the newspaper advertisements. This young woman artist earned several thousand pounds a year, but Paul's mother only made several hundreds, and she was again dissatisfied. She so wanted to be first in something, and she did not succeed, even in making sketches for drapery advertisements.

She was down to breakfast on the morning of her birthday. Paul watched her face as she read her letters. He knew the lawyer's letter. As his mother read it, her face hardened and became more expressionless. Then a cold, determined look came on her mouth. She hid the letter under the pile of others, and said not a word about it.

"Didn't you have anything nice in the post for your birthday, mother?" said Paul.

"Quite moderately nice," she said, her voice cold and absent.

She went away to town without saying more.

But in the afternoon Uncle Oscar appeared. He said Paul's mother had had a long interview with the lawyer, asking if the whole five thousand could not be advanced at once, as she was in debt.

"What do you think, uncle?" said the boy.

"I leave it to you, son."

"Oh, let her have it, then! We can get some more with the other," said the boy.

"A bird in the hand is worth two in the bush, laddie!" said Uncle Oscar.

"But I'm sure to *know* for the Grand National; or the Lincolnshire; or else the Derby. I'm sure to know for *one* of them," said Paul.

So Uncle Oscar signed the agreement, and Paul's mother touched the whole five thousand. Then something very curious happened. The voices in the house suddenly went mad, like a chorus of frogs on a spring evening. There were certain new furnishings, and Paul had a tutor. He was *really* going to Eton, his father's school, in the following autumn. There were flowers in the winter, and a blossoming of the luxury Paul's mother had been used to. And yet the voices in the house, behind the sprays of mimosa and almond blossom, and from under the piles of iridescent cushions, simply trilled and screamed in a sort of ecstasy: "There *must* be more money! Oh-h-h; there *must* be more money. Oh, now, now-w! Now-w-w—there *must* be more money!—more than ever! More than ever!"

It frightened Paul terribly. He studied away at his Latin and Greek with his tutors. But his intense hours were spent with Bassett. The Grand National had gone by: he had not "known," and had lost a hundred pounds. Summer was at hand. He was in agony for the Lincoln. But even for the Lincoln he didn't "know," and he lost fifty pounds. He became wild-eyed and strange, as if something were going to explode in him.

"Let it alone, son! Don't you bother about it!" urged Uncle Oscar. But it was as if the boy couldn't really hear what his uncle was saying.

"I've got to know for the Derby! I've got to know for the Derby!" the child reiterated, his big blue eyes blazing with a sort of madness.

His mother noticed how overwrought he was.

"You'd better go to the seaside. Wouldn't you like to go now to the seaside, instead of waiting? I think you'd better," she said, looking down at him anxiously, her heart curiously heavy because of him.

But the child lifted his uncanny blue eyes.

"I couldn't possibly go before the Derby, mother!" he said. "I couldn't possibly!"

"Why not?" she said, her voice becoming heavy when she was opposed. "Why not? You can still go from the seaside to see the Derby with your Uncle Oscar, if that's what you wish. No need for you to wait here. Besides, I think you care too much about these races. It's a bad sign. My family has been a gambling family, and you won't know till you grow up how much damage it has done. But it has done damage. I shall have to send Bassett away, and ask Uncle Oscar not to talk racing to you, unless you promise to be reasonable about it; go away to the seaside and forget it. You're all nerves!"

"I'll do what you like, mother, so long as you don't send me away till after the Derby," the boy said.

"Send you away from where? Just from this house?"

"Yes," he said, gazing at her.

"Why, you curious child, what makes you care about this house so much, suddenly? I never knew you loved it."

He gazed at her without speaking. He had a secret within a secret, something he had not divulged, even to Bassett or to his Uncle Oscar.

But his mother, after standing undecided and a little bit sullen for some moments, said:

"Very well, then! Don't go to the seaside till after the Derby, if you don't wish it. But promise me you won't let your nerves go to pieces. Promise you won't think so much about horse-racing and *events*, as you call them!"

"Oh, no," said the boy casually. "I won't think much about them, mother. You needn't worry. I wouldn't worry, mother, if I were you."

"If you were me, and I were you," said his mother, "I wonder what we *should* do!"

"But you know you needn't worry, mother, don't you?" the boy repeated.

"I should be awfully glad to know it," she said wearily.

"Oh, well, you *can*, you know. I mean, you *ought* to know you needn't worry," he insisted.

"Ought I? Then I'll see about it," she said.

Paul's secret of secrets was his wooden horse, that which had no name. Since he was emancipated from a nurse and a nursery-governess, he had had his rocking-horse removed to his own bedroom at the top of the house.

"Surely, you're too big for a rocking-horse!" his mother had remonstrated.

"Well, you see, mother, till I can have a *real* horse, I like to have *some* sort of animal about," had been his quaint answer.

"Do you feel he keeps you company?" she laughed.

"Oh, yes! He's very good, he always keeps me company, when I'm there," said Paul.

So the horse, rather shabby, stood in an arrested prance in the boy's bedroom.

The Derby was drawing near, and the boy grew more and more tense. He hardly heard what was spoken to him, he was very frail, and his eyes were really uncanny. His mother had sudden strange seizures of uneasiness about him. Sometimes, for half-an-hour, she would feel a sudden anxiety about him that was almost anguish. She wanted to rush to him at once, and know he was safe.

Two nights before the Derby, she was at a big party in town, when one of her rushes of anxiety about her boy, her first-born, gripped her heart till she could hardly speak. She fought with the feeling, might and main, for she believed in common-sense. But it was too strong. She had to leave the dance and go downstairs to telephone to the country. The children's nursery-governess was terribly surprised and startled at being rung up in the night.

"Are the children all right, Miss Wilmot?"

"Oh, yes, they are quite all right."

"Master Paul? Is he all right?"

"He went to bed as right as a trivet. Shall I run up and look at him?"

"No," said Paul's mother reluctantly. "No! Don't trouble. It's all right. Don't sit up. We shall be home fairly soon." She did not want her son's privacy intruded upon.

"Very good," said the governess.

It was about one o'clock when Paul's mother and father drove up to their house. All was still. Paul's mother went to her room and slipped off her white fur cloak. She had told her maid not to wait up for her. She heard her husband downstairs, mixing a whisky-and-soda.

And then, because of the strange anxiety at her heart, she stole upstairs to her son's room. Noiselessly she went along the upper corridor. Was there a faint noise? What was it?

She stood, with arrested muscles, outside his door, listening. There was a strange, heavy, and yet not loud noise. Her heart stood still. It was a soundless noise, yet rushing and powerful. Something huge, in violent, hushed motion. What was it? What in God's name was it? She ought to know. She felt that she knew the noise. She knew what it was.

Yet she could not place it. She couldn't say what it was. And on and on it went, like a madness.

Softly, frozen with anxiety and fear, she turned the door-handle.

The room was dark. Yet in the space near the window, she heard and saw something plunging to and fro. She gazed in fear and amazement.

Then suddenly she switched on the light, and saw her son, in his green pyjamas, madly surging on the rocking-horse. The blaze of light suddenly lit him up, as he urged the wooden horse, and lit her up, as she stood, blonde, in her dress of pale green and crystal, in the doorway.

"Paul!" she cried. "Whatever are you doing?"

"It's Malabar!" he screamed, in a powerful, strange voice. "It's Malabar!"

His eyes blazed at her for one strange and senseless second, as he ceased urging his wooden horse. Then he fell with a crash to the ground, and she, all her tormented motherhood flooding upon her, rushed to gather him up.

But he was unconscious, and unconscious he remained, with some brain-fever. He talked and tossed, and his mother sat stonily by his side.

"Malabar! It's Malabar! Bassett, Bassett, I *know!* It's Malabar!"

So the child cried, trying to get up and urge the rocking-horse that gave him his inspiration.

"What does he mean by Malabar?" asked the heart-frozen mother.

"I don't know," said the father stonily.

"What does he mean by Malabar?" she asked her brother Oscar.

"It's one of the horses running for the Derby," was the answer.

And, in spite of himself, Oscar Cresswell spoke to Bassett, and himself put a thousand on Malabar: at fourteen to one.

The third day of the illness was critical: they were waiting for a change. The boy, with his rather long, curly hair, was tossing ceaselessly on the pillow. He neither slept nor regained consciousness, and his eyes were like blue stones. His mother sat, feeling her heart had gone, turned actually into a stone.

In the evening, Oscar Cresswell did not come, but Bassett sent a message, saying could he come up for one moment, just one moment? Paul's mother was very angry at the intrusion, but on second thought she agreed. The boy was the same. Perhaps Bassett might bring him to consciousness.

The gardener, a shortish fellow with a little brown moustache, and sharp little brown eyes, tip-toed into the room, touched his imaginary cap to Paul's mother, and stole to the bedside, staring with glittering, smallish eyes, at the tossing, dying child.

"Master Paul!" he whispered. "Master Paul! Malabar came in first all right, a clean win. I did as you told me. You've made over seventy thousand pounds, you have; you've got over eighty thousand. Malabar came in all right, Master Paul."

"Malabar! Malabar! Did I say Malabar, mother? Did I say Malabar? Do you think I'm lucky, mother? I knew Malabar, didn't I? Over eighty thousand pounds! I call that lucky, don't you mother? Over eighty thousand pounds! I knew, didn't I know I knew? Malabar came in all right. If I ride my horse till I'm sure, then I tell you, Bassett, you can go as high as you like. Did you go for all you were worth, Bassett?"

"I went a thousand on it, Master Paul."

"I never told you, mother, that if I can ride my horse, and *get there,* then I'm absolutely sure—oh, absolutely! Mother, did I ever tell you? I *am* lucky!"

"No, you never did," said the mother.

But the boy died in the night.

And even as he lay dead, his mother heard her brother's voice saying to her: "My God, Hester, you're eighty-odd thousand to the good, and a poor devil of a son to the bad. But, poor devil, poor devil, he's best gone out of a life where he rides his rocking-horse to find a winner."

COMMENTARY
by D. H. Lawrence

The theme of "The Rocking-Horse Winner" has to do with the corrupting, the killing effects of money and other gross forms of materialism upon a so-called civilized modernity. In his letters Lawrence comments frequently upon money as a moral and emotional abstraction. For example, in a note to Charles Wilson, from the Hôtel Beau Rivage, Bandol, 28 December 1928, he writes:

The whole scheme of things is unjust and rotten, and money is just a disease upon humanity. It's time there was an *enormous* revolution— not to install Soviets, but to give life itself a chance. What's the good of an industrial system piling up rubbish, while nobody lives. We want a revolution not in the name of money or work or any of that, but of life—and let money and work be as casual in human life as they are in a bird's life, damn it all. Oh it's time the whole thing was changed, absolutely. And the men will have to do it—you've got to smash money and this beastly *possessive* spirit. I get more revolutionary every minute, but for *life's* sake. The dead materialism of Marx socialism and soviets seems to me no better than what we've got. What we want is life and *trust;* men trusting men, and making living a free thing, not a thing to be *earned.* But if men trusted men, we could soon have a new world, and send this one to the devil.*

Thirteen years earlier, he used the metaphor of disease to describe the pestilential influence of money upon both the individual and

The Collected Letters of D. H. Lawrence, ed. Harry T. Moore (London, 1962), II, 1110.

his society. In a letter addressed to Lady Cynthia Asquith (16 August 1915), Lawrence said: "We must rid ourselves of the idea of money. A rich man with a beautiful house is like a jewel on a leper's body.... What good is it to a sick, unclean man, if he wears jewels."*

The theme of Lawrence's short story takes on a uniquely tragic significance when it is related, as it must be, to the rocking-horse itself. Here we have a toy which appears quite naturally in a child's world. What is disturbing to the reader is the unnatural use to which the boy—who is neither a child nor a man—puts it. It soon becomes apparent to us that the toy—the horse—is a symbol with emotional value and meaning beyond the literal. What is not apparent to us is the fact that the horse had for a long time been endowed with a symbolic dimension in Lawrence's thinking. In a lengthy, bantering letter to Willard Johnson (9 January 1924) he seriously defined the character of the symbol. Addressed to "Dear Spoodle" from London on a bleak, wintry day, it begins:

Yesterday came the Horse [*The Laughing Horse***] capering a trifle woodenly, and today a fall of snow. Enough bright white snow on the ground to make a bit of daylight. I've been here exactly a month, in London, and day has never broke all the time. A dull, heavy, mortified half-light that seems to take the place of day in London in winter. I can't stand it.

However, with a bit of snow-brightness in the air, and a bit of a rather wooden neigh from the Horse in my ears, I pick up and write you a London letter.

Dear old Azure Horse, Turquoise Horse, Hobby Horse, Trojan Horse with a few scared heroes in your belly: Horse, laughing your Horse Laugh, you do actually ramp in with a bit of horse sense. I'm all for horse sense, oh Horse! Come down to it, and it's the Centaur. Good old Horse, be patted, and be persuaded to grin and to be a Centaur, getting your own back.

Even if you're only a Hobby Horse, with a wooden head and a Spoodle on your broom-stick flanks, you're welcome just now. Very welcome.

*Ibid., I, 362.
**The Laughing Horse* was an American magazine whose editor was Willard Johnson. Lawrence was one of its contributors.

Here's an apple. Be tempted, like Adam, and take it. And for the sake of all horses, be braver than Adam, who only bit a bite out and dropped the main. Eat up the whole gaudy apple, oh Horse. Let's have the Centaur back.

Dear old Horse, you'd never be azure or turquoise here in London. Oh, London is awful: so dark, so damp, so yellow-grey, so mouldering, damp, half-visible sort of way, as if they were all mouldering bits of rag that had fallen from an old garment. Horse, Horse, be as hobby as you like, but let me get on your back and ride away again to New Mexico. . . . Oh Horse, Horse, Horse, when you kick your heels you shatter an enclosure every time. And over here the Horse is dead: he'll kick his heels no more. I don't know whether it's the pale Galilean who has triumphed, or a paleness paler than the pallor even of Jesus. But a yellow and jaundiced paleness has triumphed over here, the turquoise Horse has been long dead, and churned into sausages. I find it unbearable.

Let the Horse laugh. I'm all for a horse that laughs.

. . . . .

Two-legged man is no good. If he's going to stand steady, he must stand on four feet. Like the Centaur. When Jesus was born, the spirits wailed round the Mediterranean: *Pan is dead. Great Pan is dead.* And at the Renaissance the Centaur gave a final groan, and expired. At least, I seem to remember him lamenting and about to expire, in the Uffizi.

It would be a terrible thing if the horse in us died for ever, as he seems to have died in Europe. How awful it would be, if at this present moment I sat in the yellow mummy-swathings of London atmosphere—the snow is melting—inside the dreadful mummy sarcophagus of Europe, and didn't know that the blue horse was still kicking his heels and making a few sparks fly, across the tops of the Rockies. It would be a truly sad case for me.

. . . . .

But talking seriously, Spoodle, man must be a Centaur. This two-legged forked radish is going flabby.

The Centaur's lament! Not at all. The Laugh of the Turquoise Man-Horse. Let the forked radish do the lamenting.

In modern symbolism, the Horse is supposed to stand for the passions. Passions be blowed. What does the Centaur stand for, Chiron or any other of that quondam four-footed gentry? Sense! Horse-sense! Sound, powerful, four-footed *sense,* that's what the Horse stands for. Horse-sense, I tell you. That's the Centaur. That's the blue Horse of the ancient Mediterranean, before the pale Galilean or the extra-pale German or

Nordic gentleman conquered. First of all, Sense, Good Sense, Sound Sense, Horse Sense. And then a laugh, a loud, sensible Horse Laugh. After that, these same passions, glossy and dangerous in the flanks. And after these again, hoofs, irresistible, splintering hoofs, that can kick the walls of the world down.

Horse-sense, Horse-laughter, Horse-passion, Horse-hoofs: ask the Indians if it is not so.

Tell me the Horse is dead? Tell me the Centaur has died out? It may easily be so, in Europe here, since the Renaissance. But in the wide blue skies of the Southwest, and far-away south over Mexico: over the grey deserts and the red deserts beneath the Rockies and the Sierra Madre; down the canyons and across the *mesas* and along the depths of the barancas goes the Turquoise Horse, uneasy, bethinking himself, and just on the point of bursting into a loud laugh, after all, laughing longest and laughing last.

Ask the Indians, if there isn't a little blue foal born every year, in the *pueblos,* out of the old dark earth-coloured mottled mare. Tell me the Centaur can't beget Centaurs?— Ask the Indian, ask the Navajo, ask the Mexican under his big hat.

It's no good. I've GOT to ride on a laughing horse. The forked radish has ceased to perambulate. I've *got* to ride a laughing horse. And I whistle for him, call him, spread corn for him, and hold out an apple to him, here in England. No go! No good! No answer! The poor devil's dead and churned into Cambridge sausages. Flabby flaccid forked radishes, sausages, pairs of sausages in forked skins: these seem to drift about in the soup of the London air. There's no answer.

There's no blue cave to stable the Turquoise Horse here. There's no dark earth-coloured mare to bear his foals. There's no far-away blue distance for him to roam across. He's dead.

And yet I've *got* to ride, centaur, on a blue stallion.

So, thanks be to the oldest of gods, comes a wooden little Laughing Horse sliding down from the blue air of the Rockies, riding on his hobby stick like a rocket, summonsing me to mount and away.

Hurray! Hup-a-la! Up we go! Like a witch on a broom-stick, riding west.*

*The Collected Letters of D. H. Lawrence, II, 767–770.

The Nuisance
Doris Lessing

Two narrow tracks, one of them deepened to a smooth dusty groove
by the incessant padding of bare feet, wound from the farm compound to the old well through half a mile of tall blond grass that
was soiled and matted because of the nearness of the clustering huts:
the compound had been on that ridge for twenty years.

The native women with their children used to loiter down
the track, and their shrill laughter and chattering sounded through
the trees as if one might suddenly have come on a flock of brilliant
noisy parrots. It seemed as if fetching water was more of a social
event to them than a chore. At the well itself they would linger half
the morning, standing in groups to gossip, their arms raised in that
graceful, eternally moving gesture to steady glittering or rusted
petrol tins balanced on head-rings woven of grass; kneeling to slap
bits of bright cloth on slabs of stone blasted long ago from the depths
of earth. Here they washed and scolded and dandled their children.
Here they scrubbed their pots. Here they sluiced themselves and
combed their hair.

Coming upon them suddenly there would be sharp exclamations;
a glimpse of soft brown shoulders and thighs withdrawing to the
bushes, or annoyed and resentful eyes. It was their well. And while
they were there, with their laughter, and gossip and singing, their
folded draperies, bright armbands, earthenware jars and metal combs,
grouped in attitudes of head-slowed indolence, it seemed as if the
bellowing of distant cattle, drone of tractor, all the noises of the
farm, were simply lending themselves to form a background to this
antique scene: Women, drawing water at the well.

When they left the ground would be scattered with the bright-
pink, fleshy skins of the native wild-plum which contracts the mouth
shudderingly with its astringency, or with the shiny green fragments
of the shells of kaffir oranges.

Without the women the place was ugly, paltry. The windlass,
coiled with greasy rope, propped for safety with a forked stick, was
sheltered by a tiny cock of thatch that threw across the track a long,

intensely black shadow. For the rest, veld; the sere, flattened, sun-dried veld.

They were beautiful, these women. But she whom I thought of vaguely as "The cross-eyed one," offended the sight. She used to lag behind the others on the road, either by herself, or in charge of the older children. Not only did she suffer from a painful squint, so that when she looked towards you it was with a confused glare of white eyeball; but her body was hideous. She wore the traditional dark-patterned blue stuff looped at the waist, and above it her breasts were loose, flat crinkling triangles.

She was a solitary figure at the well, doing her washing unaided and without laughter. She would strain at the windlass during the long slow ascent of the swinging bucket that clanged sometimes, far below, against the sides of naked rock until at that critical moment when it hung vibrating at the mouth of the well, she would set the weight of her shoulder in the crook of the handle and with a fearful snatching movement bring the water to safety. It would slop over, dissolving in a shower of great drops that fell tinkling to disturb the surface of that tiny, circular, dully-gleaming mirror which lay at the bottom of the plunging rock tunnel. She was clumsy. Because of her eyes her body lumbered.

She was the oldest wife of "The Long One," who was our most skilful driver.

"The Long One" was not so tall as he was abnormally thin. It was the leanness of those driven by inner restlessness. He could never keep still. His hands plucked at pieces of grass, his shoulder twitched to a secret rhythm of the nerves. Set a-top of that sinewy, narrow, taut body was a narrow head, with wide-pointed ears, which gave him an appearance of alert caution. The expression of the face was always violent, whether he was angry, laughing, or—most usually—sardonically critical. He had a tongue that was feared by every la-bourer of the farm. Even my father would smile ruefully after an altercation with his driver and say: "He's a man, that native. One must respect him, after all. He never lets you get away with anything."

In his own line he was an artist—his line being cattle. He handled oxen with a delicate brutality that was fascinating and horrifying to watch. Give him a bunch of screaming, rearing three-year-olds, due to take their first taste of the yoke, and he would fight them for hours under a blistering sun with the sweat running off him, his eyes glowing with a wicked and sombre satisfaction. Then he would use his whip, grunting savagely as the lash cut down into flesh, his tongue stuck calculatingly between his teeth as he measured the exact weight of the blow. But to watch him handle a team of sixteen fat tamed oxen was a different thing. It was like watching a circus act; there was the same suspense in it: it was a matter of pride to him that he did not need to use the whip. This did not by any means imply that he wished to spare the beasts pain, not at all; he liked to feed his pride on his own skill. Alongside the double line of ponderous cattle that strained across acres of heavy clods, danced, raved and screamed the Long One, with his twelve-foot-long lash circling in black patterns over their backs; and though his threatening yells were the yells of an inspired madman, and the heavy whip could be heard clean across the farm, so that on a moonlight night when they were ploughing late it sounded like the crack and whine of a rifle, never did the dangerous metal-tipped lash so much as touch a hair of their hides. If you examined the oxen as they were outspanned, they might be exhausted, driven to staggering-point, so that my father had to remonstrate, but there was never a mark on them.

"He knows how to handle oxen, but he can't handle his women."

We gave our natives labels such as that, since it was impossible ever to know them as their fellows knew them, in the round. That phrase summarised for us what the Long One offered in entertainment during the years he was with us. Coming back to the farm, after an absence, one would say in humorous anticipation: "And what has the Long One been up to now, with his harem?"

There was always trouble with his three wives. He used to come up to the house to discuss with my father, man to man, how the youngest wife was flirting with the boss-boy from the neighbouring compound, six miles off; or how she had thrown a big pot of smoking mealie-pap at the middle wife, who was jealous of her.

We grew accustomed to the sight of the Long One standing at the back door, at the sunset hour, when my father held audience after work. He always wore long khaki trousers that slipped down over thin bony hips and went bare-chested, and there would be a ruddy gleam on his polished black skin, and his spindly gesticulating form would be outlined against a sea of fiery colours. At the end of his tale of complaint he would relapse suddenly into a pose of resignation that was self-consciously weary. My father used to laugh until his face was wet and say: "That man is a natural-born comedian. He would have been on the stage if he had been born another colour."

But he was no buffoon. He would play up to my father's appreciation of the comic, but he would never play the ape, as some Africans did, for our amusement. And he was certainly no figure of fun to his fellows. That same thing in him that sat apart, watchfully critical, even of himself, gave his humour its mordancy, his tongue its sting. And he was terribly attractive to his women. I have seen him slouch down the road on his way from one team to another, his whip trailing behind in the dust, his trousers sagging in folds from hip-bone to ankle, his eyes broodingly directed in front of him, merely nodding as he passed a group of women among whom might be his wives. And it was as if he had lashed them with that whip. They would bridle and writhe; and then call provocatively after him, but with a note of real anger, to make him notice them. He would not so much as turn his head.

When the real trouble started, though, my father soon got tired of it. He liked to be amused, not seriously implicated in his labourers' problems. The Lone One took to coming up not occasionally, as he had been used to do, but every evening. He was deadly serious, and very bitter. He wanted my father to persuade the old wife, the cross-eyed one, to go back home to her own people. The woman was driving him crazy. A nagging woman in your house was like having a flea on your body; you could scratch but it always moved to another place, and there was no peace till you killed it.

"But you can't send her back, just because you are tired of her."

The Long One said his life had become insupportable. She grumbled, she sulked, she spoilt his food.

"Well, then your other wives can cook for you."

But it seemed there were complications. The two younger women hated each other, but they were united in one thing, that the old wife should stay, for she was so useful. She looked after the children; she did the hoeing in the garden; she picked relishes from the veld. Besides, she provided endless amusement with her ungainliness. She was the eternal butt, the fool, marked by fate for the entertainment of the whole-limbed and the comely.

My father referred at this point to a certain handbook on native lore, which stated definitively that an elder wife was entitled to be waited on by a young wife, perhaps as compensation for having to give up the pleasures of her lord's favour. The Long One and his ménage cut clean across this amiable theory. And my father, being unable to find a prescribed remedy (as one might look for a cure of a disease in a pharmacopoeia), grew angry. After some weeks of incessant complaint from the Long One he was told to hold his tongue and manage his women himself. That evening the man stalked furiously down the path, muttering to himself between teeth clenched on a grass-stem, on his way home to his two giggling younger wives and the ugly sour-faced old woman, the mother of his elder children, the drudge of his household and the scourge of his life.

It was some weeks later that my father asked casually one day: "And by the way, Long One, how are things with you? All right again?"

And the Long One answered simply: "Yes, baas. She's gone away."

"What do you mean, gone away?"

The Long One shrugged. She had just gone. She had left suddenly, without saying anything to anyone.

Now, the woman came from Nyasaland, which was days and days of weary walking away. Surely she hadn't gone by herself? Had a brother or an uncle come to fetch her? Had she gone with a band of passing Africans on their way home?

My father wondered a little, and then forgot about it. It wasn't his affair. He was pleased to have his most useful native back at work with an unharassed mind. And he was particularly pleased that the whole business was ended before the annual trouble over the water-carrying.

For there were two wells. The new one, used by ourselves, had fresh sparkling water that was sweet in the mouth; but in July of each year it ran dry. The water of the old well had a faintly unpleasant taste and was pale brown, but there was always plenty of it. For three or four months of the year, depending on the rains, we shared that well with the compound.

Now, the Long One hated fetching water three miles, four times a week, in the water-cart. The women of the compound disliked having to arrange their visits to the well so as not to get in the way of the water-carriers. There was always grumbling.

This year we had not even begun to use the old well when complaints started that the water tasted bad. The big baas must get the well cleaned.

My father said vaguely that he would clean the well when he had time.

Next day there came a deputation from the women of the compound. Half a dozen of them stood at the back door, arguing that if the well wasn't cleaned soon, all their children would be sick.

"I'll do it next week," he promised, with bad grace.

The following morning the Long One brought our first load of the season from the old well; and as we turned the taps on the barrels a foetid smell began to pervade the house. As for drinking it, that was out of the question.

"Why don't you keep the cover on the well?" my father said to the women, who were still loitering resentfully at the back door. He was really angry. "Last time the well was cleaned there were fourteen dead rats and a dead snake. We never get things in our well because we remember to keep the lid on."

But the women appeared to consider the lid being on, or off, was an act of God, and nothing to do with them.

We always went down to watch the well-emptying, which had the fascination of a ritual. Like the mealie-shelling, or the first rains, it marked a turning-point in the year. It seemed as if a besieged city were laying plans for the conservation of supplies. The sap was falling in tree and grass-root; the sun was withdrawing high, high, behind a veil of smoke and dust; the fierce dryness of the air was a new element, parching foliage as the heat cauterized it. The well-emptying was an act of faith, and of defiance. For a whole afternoon there would be no water on the farm at all. One well was completely dry. And this one would be drained, dependent on the mysterious ebbing and flowing of underground rivers. What if they should fail us?

There was an anxious evening, every year; and in the morning, when the Long One stood at the back door and said, beaming, that the bucket was bringing up fine new water, it was like a festival.

But this afternoon we could not stick it out. The smell was intolerable. We saw the usual complement of bloated rats, laid out on the stones around the well, and there was even the skeleton of a small buck that must have fallen in the dark. Then we left, along the road that was temporarily a river whose source was that apparently endless succession of buckets filled by greyish, evil water.

It was the Long One himself that came to tell us the news. Afterwards we tried to remember what look that always expressive face wore as he told it.

It seemed that in the last bucket but one had floated a human arm, or rather the fragments of one. Piece by piece they had fetched her up, the Cross-eyed Woman, his own first wife. They recognised her by her bangles. Last of all, the Long One went down to fetch up her head, which was missing.

"I thought you said your wife had gone home?" said my father.

"I thought she had. Where else could she have gone?"

"Well," said my father at last, disgusted by the whole thing, "if she had to kill herself, why couldn't she hang herself on a tree, instead of spoiling the well?"

"She might have slipped and fallen," said the Long One.

My father looked up at him suddenly. He stared for a few moments. Then: "Ye-yes," he said, "I suppose she might."

Later, we talked about the thing, saying how odd it was that natives should commit suicide; it seemed almost like an impertinence, as if they were claiming to have the same delicate feelings as ours.

But later still, apropos of nothing in particular, my father was heard to remark: "Well, I don't know, I'm damned if I know, but in any case he's a damned good driver."

COMMENTARY

by the Editors

Mrs. Lessing writes in a contemporary idiom and of modern concerns. But the creative process as she unfolds it in "The Nuisance" owes much of its organic strength to the oldfashioned virtues of simplicity and unity. This African world of hers is remote in time and place from Augustan Rome; yet she tells her story in a way that is as artistically sound in the twentieth century as it would have been two thousand years ago. "You who write," Horace advised, "take a subject equal to your powers, and consider at length how much your shoulders can bear. Neither proper words nor lucid order will be lacking to the writer who chooses a subject within his powers. The excellence and charm of the arrangement, I believe, consists in the ability to say only what needs to be said at the time, deferring or omitting many points for the moment. The author...must accept and reject as he proceeds."*

The easy authority of Mrs. Lessing's presentation reduces to irrelevance the distance between an African culture and ours. With eloquent, imaginative economy she makes everything familiar and inevitable. Her characters happen to be, for the most part, Africans, but they transcend geographical barriers in their human-ness. The undercurrent of a tense social theme cannot be ignored. As a good storyteller, however, the author has skillfully exercised an option in favor of individualized as opposed to social conduct. That is to say, she has chosen to emphasize people rather than issues. The latter are there, but we understand them better when we understand the former. A story, Mrs. Lessing seems to remind us, begins with people.

In the present instance, the characters who most invite our attention are "The Long One" and his nagging wife, respectively the protagonist and antagonist. The former dominates the overt action because he is a fully drawn personality, a "rounded" character whom we are able to identify physically as well as temperamentally. We see him as an intrinsically cruel man, arrogant, edgy, violent. But he is nonetheless capable of a taut self-control which always guarantees

*Trans. W. J. Bate, in *Criticism: The Major Texts* (New York, 1952), p. 51.

his advantage, whether he is quarreling with his peers or with his white employer. Even the latter, who prefers not taking "The Long One" seriously, concedes that "He never lets you get away with anything." The words, though spoken lightly, become a brutal prophecy. They apply to a dangerously determined man: one who can break a team of oxen to his will but, ironically, "can't handle his women," least of all "The cross-eyed one." It is out of this failure that the tension arises only to resolve itself in a macabre tragedy. As self-centered as he is vicious, he cannot adapt himself to human relationships which might exact from him any show of generosity or understanding. Consequently, he reacts to domestic irritations as he would to a flea on his person. There can be no peace for him until he removes the source of irritation or destroys it. Under such circumstances tragedy is inevitable, for the domineering husband and his shrewish woman are committed to a life of furious, irrational collisions. Both are, in fact, strangers to tolerance and esteem.

Realistically, the victor in this stubborn conflict is "The Long One." Realistically, we say, because the traditional role of the African female is one of subordination. "The cross-eyed one" must fulfill this social truth through a kind of personal expiation, whether through her destruction by suicide (which is not likely) or at the hands of her husband. The point is, she unconsciously doomed herself by refusing to make appropriate concessions to the male's domestic comfort. To be sure, Mrs. Lessing does not burden "The Nuisance" with such speculations. Nor does she have to, for the narrative itself tells us everything we need to know about this particular aspect of marital inequality and presumption. The portraiture of "The cross-eyed one," further, is a tacit declaration of the inferior status which she attempted to overreach. Whereas "The Long One" is placed dramatically in the foreground of the action, his eldest wife—except for a few paragraphs of description—is seen at a distance, where she belongs. His actions—barring the climactic one which ends in her death—are visible and predominantly aggressive. Hers are merely related, *talked about*.

Her refusal to observe the ritual of housewifely obedience evokes interesting echoes of the biblical Rebecca (Genesis, chapters 24–27). But it must be understood immediately that what we have here is an inversion of the scriptural legend. What wife was meeker and more dutiful than Rebecca? The parallels, even though the values of "The Nuisance" are reversed, enrich the texture of this story. Both women —legendary and fictional—have symbolic as well as real roles in a common "antique scene: Women, drawing water at the well." And both are affected by the pollution of their wells and the tedious efforts to restore them. Rebecca and "The cross-eyed one," moreover, come to their husbands from foreign lands. And both, at advanced ages, have the care of young children.

The differences, however, are manifest. For Rebecca, each experience is salutary. For "The cross-eyed one," on the other hand, each is a trial and destructive. When she takes care of the children, it is as a drudge not a loving mother. She is not honored by her family; she is ridiculed for her clumsiness and stupidity. Instead of the lovely, obedient Rebecca we have an ugly, quarrelsome shrew. By indirection we see her as another of those strangers whose intrusions are resented by the girls of "The Nuisance." "It was their well," even as the inhospitable herdsmen of Gerar insisted, "The water is ours" (Gen. 26:17). Before long we are to discover that when "The cross-eyed one" is no longer bearable to "The Long One," he too regards her as a stranger whom he wishes back in Nyasaland. The final, symbolic assertion of her alienation occurs in her death, because by it she has added to the pollution of the well.

The inverted parallels, we concede, may be the editors' wish rather than the author's intention. Even as accidents, however, they provide a basis for contrast which helps to illuminate a modern storyteller's art. Without pressing the analogy further, we may also look briefly at a setting whose initial details create a deceptively tranquil atmosphere. But Mrs. Lessing lures her readers into a mood of pastoral simplicity in order to heighten a tragic conflict that goes beyond the situation at hand. As is possible in any primitive element, outward serenity covers latent, unsuspected danger that is as real for men as for wild animals. In "The Nuisance" an aura of uncertainty or threat is compounded by the presence of the white settlers. They are detached, even amused, onlookers who are essentially as indifferent to the natives as the natives are to each other. Removed from their customary sophisticated environment, they seem to have lost the capacity for sympathy. There is in them, indeed, a callous absence of compassion—a muted warning by the author, we may take it, that, for all their sense of personal value and superiority, "civilized" men are themselves never very far from regression to their irrational instincts.

2. SYMBOLISM AND ALLEGORY

The writer of a short story can never be wholly indifferent to the external event. Yet if he is a successful artist he does not stop with the fact but attempts to probe its meaning, to move from the local and particular to the universal and abstract. In doing so, he gives to the fact a new—a symbolic—dimension. The term symbol means literally an act of throwing together or bringing into conjunction. Connotatively it suggests a process of comparison. As part of the terminology of literary criticism, a symbol is a sign—for example, a character, an event, an object—through which the author communicates abstract qualities not easily apparent in ordinary experience. It enables the artist to transcend the language of exposition and to expose the hidden meaning and emotional value of his subject.

Mark Schorer deftly shows how a specific fact to which many people have been exposed is transformed into a focal and massive symbol for William Carlos Williams in "The Use of Force." Let us assume, says Mr. Schorer,

that we have a writer who wishes to do nothing but report objectively the facts of a sick call made by a doctor to a patient, a frightened child. Since it is impossible to report all the facts of any situation, our author will have to report, as fully as possible or with as much economy, depending on the kind of author he is, the salient facts. It occurs to us at once that the facts that appear salient to him (say that he has been annoyed—for all the years of his practice by hovering, incompetent parents of sick children) are not necessarily the facts that would seem salient to—well, parents themselves or their sick child, if such persons, rather than the doctor, happened to be telling the story. So your author must—he cannot do anything else—select, and he selects inevitably those details that, in terms of his bias toward the situation, seem to him most relevant. He selects from among other possible details repeated examples of alarmed parental ineptitude. He writes of the child as "strong as a heifer," as clawing at him like a cat, and finally as trying to fly at him like some winged creature in outraged fury. The instruments of force, besides the muscles of two grown men, are a wooden tongue depressor (smashed) and a teaspoon that cannot be smashed. And with these details we have the symbolization of the author's own attitude and of the attitude within the attitude. Because what the story finally tells us is that the doctor's will to dominate the child is at least as furious as the child's determination not to be dominated.*

Williams' story at the literal level is a particularized account of a struggle between a doctor and a sick child. But the story suggests more to us than what we read on the surface. The struggle itself symbolizes a basic human drive for power and domination. And the implication is clear that what may be natural is not necessarily wholesome or commendable. In "The Use of Force" the symbol is at one with the structure of the story; without the conflict between doctor and child there would be neither plot nor characterization and hence no story. For purposes of convenient classification we call this a *structural symbol*.

There may also be within a story details of feeling and meaning which serve as *textural symbols*. They give to the narrative situation a certain buoyancy and energy; they quicken the reader's perception, engaging his mind and imagination at a level beyond the literal. Consider Lawrence's "Rocking-Horse Winner" for the use of a dominant textural symbol. The rocking horse in the story *is* a rocking horse in terms of narrative realism. Beyond that it is a highly contrived but effective symbol. In the mind of the boy the rocking horse stands for the racing horse which runs to win a steeple chase. The meaning of the symbol lies just below the expository surface of the story. More significantly, the rocking horse, with "its red mouth . . . slightly open, its big eye . . . wide and glassy bright" represents a child's world made hysterical and corrupt by the materialistic greed of adult demands. Only in the last paragraph does Paul's uncle offer an overt clue which helps to unravel the story's dominant symbol. "And even as [Paul] lay dead, his mother heard her brother's voice saying to her: 'My God, Hester, you're eighty-odd thousand to the good, and a poor devil of a son to the bad. But, poor devil, poor devil, he's best gone out of a life where he rides his rocking-horse to find a winner.'"

*Mark Schorer, ed., *The Story, a Critical Anthology* (New York, 1950, 1967), pp. 205–206.

We can also analyze a less obvious but equally effective symbol, this time the primroses in Elizabeth Bowen's "Coming Home." When Rosalind, elated by her triumph at school, returns to her house, she sees first a bowl of primroses on the hall table: "Darlingest must have put them there that morning. The hall was chilly; she could not think why the primroses gave her such a feeling of horror, then she remembered the wreath of primroses, and the scent of it, lying on the raw new earth of the grave."

The idea of death symbolized by the primroses permeates the entire story just as the specific flower dominates all the other blooms in the house. Rosalind has already been introduced to the concept of death for she has stood by an open grave. Yet she had not understood the meaning of ultimate separation; "nothing became real for her until she had had time to live it over again." What she had experienced at the grave—never realized because of the "shock"—she re-lives in the house made silent and empty by the absence of her mother. Wanting Darlingest and yet apart from her, Rosalind's adolescent mind conjures up the image of death once more. "The whole house was full of the scent and horror of the primroses. Rosalind dropped the exercise-book on the floor, looked at it, hesitated, and putting her hands over her mouth, went upstairs, choking back her sobs."

The child suffers acutely, intuits for the first time what she is suffering and why. She can never again be the same, spontaneous and generous in her love which—because of the human condition—cannot endure. Upon the return of her mother "she went down into the drawing-room past the primroses. The grey gloves were back on the table. This was the mauve and golden room that Darlingest had come back to, from under the Shadow of Death, expecting to find her little daughter." Rosalind was there but not "her little daughter."

A symbol provides one specialized strategy for extending meaning in depth; allegory is another such strategy and in part dependent upon the first. *Allegory* is a didactic narrative in which the characters, objects, and events are not to be limited to a realistic level but are to be interpreted as symbols and personifications. That is, each item in the narrative has its intellectual or abstract equivalent. The aim of allegory is to present at least two meanings: (1) a literal surface meaning, which is primary; (2) an abstract moralistic-didactic meaning, which is secondary. This dualism operates simultaneously, the connotations of the secondary level dependent for clarity and interpretation upon the primary. Thus we may read allegory for the narrative pleasure it affords. But to stop at the story line is to miss at least half of the intention.

In the passage which follows, Hawthorne (whose name is Aubepine in French) is defining and defending through the use of irony his own allegories.

We do not remember to have seen any translated specimens of the productions of M. de l'Aubepine—a fact the less to be wondered at, as his very name is unknown to many of his own countrymen as well as to the student of foreign literature. As a writer, he seems to occupy an unfortunate position between the Transcendentalists (who, under one name or another, have their share in all the current literature of the world) and the great body of pen-and-ink men who address the intellect and sympathies of the multitude. If not too refined, at all events too remote, too shadowy, and unsubstantial in his modes of development to suit the taste of the latter class, and yet too popular to satisfy the spiritual or metaphysical requisitions of the former, he must necessarily find himself without an audience, except here and there an individual or possibly an isolated clique. His writings to do them justice, are not altogether destitute of fancy and originality; they might have won him greater reputation but for an inveterate love of allegory, which is apt to invest his plots and characters with the aspect of scenery and people in the clouds, to steal away the human warmth out of his conceptions. His fictions are sometimes historical, sometimes of the present day, and sometimes, so far as can be discovered, have little or no reference either to time or space. In any case, he generally contents himself with a very slight embroidery of outward manners,—and endeavors to create an interest by some less obvious peculiarity of the subject. Occasionally a breath of Nature, a rain-drop of pathos and tenderness, or a gleam of humor, will find its way into the midst of his fantastic imagery, and make us feel as if, after all, we were yet within the limits of our native earth. We will only add to this very cursory notice that M. de l'Aubepine's productions, if the reader chance to take them in precisely the proper point of view,

may amuse a leisure hour as well as those of a brighter man; if otherwise, they can hardly fail to look excessively into nonsense.*

Hawthorne here is isolating the traditional charges against allegory: its failure to create rounded characters or a realistic plot and
setting. He is aware too that the genre makes only "the faintest possible counterfeit of real life," that because of its intellectuality it lacks
"warmth" and substance. Yet he offers no defense in its behalf for
he knows that successful allegory—like any successful short story—
stands on its own merits and is its own reason for being. Rather than
debate a truism, however, we present several stories which reveal the
creative versatility of fiction written in an allegorical manner. That
manner, it will be noted, was congenial to such nineteenth-century
American "classic" writers as Hawthorne himself, Herman Melville,
and Mark Twain. But it has also been turned to excellent account by
an author as modern as Bernard Malamud. And these examples, obviously, barely touch on possibilities which are limited neither by
history nor geography.

The Use of Force
William Carlos Williams

They were new patients to me, all I had was the name, Olson.
Please come down as soon as you can, my daughter is very sick.

When I arrived I was met by the mother, a big startled looking
woman, very clean and apologetic who merely said, Is this the doctor? and let me in. In the back, she added. You must excuse us,
doctor, we have her in the kitchen where it is warm. It is very damp
here sometimes.

The child was fully dressed and sitting on her fathers lap near

*From the headnote to "Rappaccini's Daughter," first published in *Dem-
ocratic Review* (December, 1844).

the kitchen table. He tried to get up, but I motioned for him not to bother, took off my overcoat and started to look things over. I could see that they were all very nervous, eyeing me up and down distrustfully. As often, in such cases, they weren't telling me more than they had to, it was up to me to tell them; that's why they were spending three dollars on me.

The child was fairly eating me up with her cold, steady eyes, and no expression to her face whatever. She did not move and seemed, inwardly, quiet; an unusually attractive little thing, and as strong as a heifer in appearance. But her face was flushed, she was breathing rapidly, and I realized that she had a high fever. She had magnificent blonde hair, in profusion. One of those picture children often reproduced in advertising leaflets and the photogravure sections of the Sunday papers.

She's had a fever for three days, began the father and we don't know what it comes from. My wife has given her things, you know, like people do, but it don't do no good. And there's been a lot of sickness around. So we tho't you'd better look her over and tell us what is the matter.

As doctors often do I took a trial shot at it as a point of departure. Has she had a sore throat?

Both parents answered me together, No . . . No, she says her throat don't hurt her.

Does your throat hurt you? added the mother to the child. But the little girl's expression didn't change nor did she move her eyes from my face.

Have you looked?

I tried to, said the mother, but I couldn't see.

As it happens we had been having a number of cases of diphtheria in the school to which this child went during that month and we were all, quite apparently, thinking of that, though no one had as yet spoken of the thing.

Well, I said, suppose we take a look at the throat first. I smiled in my best professional manner and asking for the child's first name I said, come on, Mathilda, open your mouth and let's take a look at your throat.

Nothing doing.

Aw, come on, I coaxed, just open your mouth wide and let me take a look. Look, I said opening both hands wide, I haven't anything in my hands. Just open up and let me see.

Such a nice man, put in the mother. Look how kind he is to you. Come on, do what he tells you to. He won't hurt you.

At that I ground my teeth in disgust. If only they wouldn't use the word "hurt" I might be able to get somewhere. But I did not allow myself to be hurried or disturbed but speaking quietly and slowly I approached the child again.

As I moved my chair a little nearer suddenly with one catlike movement both her hands clawed instinctively for my eyes and she almost reached them too. In fact she knocked my glasses flying and they fell, though unbroken, several feet away from me on the kitchen floor.

Both the mother and father almost turned themselves inside out in embarrassment and apology. You bad girl, said the mother, taking her and shaking her by one arm. Look what you've done. The nice man . . .

For heaven's sake, I broke in. Don't call me a nice man to her. I'm here to look at her throat on the chance that she might have diphtheria and possibly die of it. But that's nothing to her. Look here, I said to the child, we're going to look at your throat. You're old enough to understand what I'm saying. Will you open it now by yourself or shall we have to open it for you?

Not a move. Even her expression hadn't changed. Her breaths however were coming faster and faster. Then the battle began. I had to do it. I had to have a throat culture for her own protection. But first I told the parents that it was entirely up to them. I explained the danger but said that I would not insist on a throat examination so long as they would take the responsibility.

If you don't do what the doctor says you'll have to go to the hospital, the mother admonished her severely.

Oh yeah? I had to smile to myself. After all, I had already fallen in love with the savage brat, the parents were contemptible to me. In the ensuing struggle they grew more and more abject, crushed, exhausted while she surely rose to magnificent heights of insane fury of effort bred of her terror of me.

The father tried his best, and he was a big man but the fact that she was his daughter, his shame at her behavior and his dread of hurting her made him release her just at the critical times when I had almost achieved success, till I wanted to kill him. But his dread also that she might have diphtheria made him tell me to go on, go on though he himself was almost fainting, while the mother moved back and forth behind me raising and lowering her hands in an agony of apprehension.

Put her in front of you on your lap, I ordered, and hold both her wrists.

But as soon as he did the child let out a scream. Don't, you're hurting me. Let go of my hands. Let them go I tell you. Then she shrieked terrifyingly, hysterically. Stop it! Stop it! You're killing me!

Do you think she can stand it, doctor! said the mother.

You get out, said the husband to his wife. Do you want her to die of diphtheria?

Come on now, hold her, I said.

Then I grasped the child's head with my left hand and tried to get the wooden tongue depressor between her teeth. She fought, with clenched teeth, desperately! But now I also had grown furious —at a child. I tried to hold myself down but I couldn't. I know how to expose a throat for inspection. And I did my best. When finally I got the wooden spatula behind the last teeth and just the point of it into the mouth cavity, she opened up for an instant but before I could see anything she came down again and gripping the wooden blade between her molars she reduced it to splinters before I could get it out again.

Aren't you ashamed, the mother yelled at her. Aren't you ashamed to act like that in front of the doctor?

Get me a smooth-handled spoon of some sort, I told the mother. We're going through with this. The child's mouth was already bleeding. Her tongue was cut and she was screaming in wild hysterical shrieks. Perhaps I should have desisted and come back in an hour or more. No doubt it would have been better. But I have seen at least two children lying dead in bed of neglect in such cases, and feeling that I must get a diagnosis now or never I went at it again. But the worst of it was that I too had got beyond reason. I could have torn the child apart in my own fury and enjoyed it. It was a pleasure to attack her. My face was burning with it.

The damned little brat must be protected against her own idiocy, one says to one's self at such times. Others must be protected against her. It is a social necessity. And all these things are true. But a blind fury, a feeling of adult shame, bred of a longing for muscular release are the operatives. One goes on to the end.

In a final unreasoning assault I overpowered the child's neck and jaws. I forced the heavy silver spoon back of her teeth and down her throat till she gagged. And there it was—both tonsils covered with membrane. She had fought valiantly to keep me from knowing her secret. She had been hiding that sore throat for three days at least and lying to her parents in order to escape just such an outcome as this.

Now truly she was furious. She had been on the defensive before but now she attacked. Tried to get off her father's lap and fly at me while tears of defeat blinded her eyes.

Ethan Brand

A CHAPTER FROM AN ABORTIVE ROMANCE

Nathaniel Hawthorne

Bartram the lime-burner, a rough, heavy-looking man, begrimed with charcoal, sat watching his kiln at nightfall, while his little son played at building houses with the scattered fragments of marble, when, on the hillside below them, they heard a roar of laughter, not mirthful, but slow, and even solemn, like a wind shaking the boughs of the forest.

"Father, what is that?" asked the little boy, leaving his play, and pressing betwixt his father's knees.

"O, some drunken man, I suppose," answered the lime-burner; "some merry fellow from the bar-room in the village, who dared not laugh loud enough within doors lest he should blow the roof of the house off. So here he is, shaking his jolly sides at the foot of Graylock."

"But, father," said the child, more sensitive than the obtuse, middle-aged clown, "he does not laugh like a man that is glad. So the noise frightens me!"

"Don't be a fool, child!" cried his father gruffly. "You will never make a man, I do believe; there is too much of your mother in you. I have known the rustling of a leaf startle you. Hark! Here comes the merry fellow now. You shall see that there is no harm in him."

Bartram and his little son, while they were talking thus, sat watching the same lime-kiln that had been the scene of Ethan Brand's solitary and meditative life, before he began his search for the Unpardonable Sin. Many years, as we have seen, had now elapsed, since that portentous night when the IDEA was first developed. The kiln, however, on the mountain-side, stood unimpaired, and was in nothing changed since he had thrown his dark thoughts into the intense glow of its furnace, and melted them, as it were, into the one thought that took possession of his life. It was a rude, round, tower-like structure about twenty feet high, heavily built of rough stones, and with a hillock of earth heaped about the larger part of its circumference; so that the blocks and fragments of marble might be drawn by cartloads, and thrown in at the top. There was an opening at the bottom of the tower, like an oven mouth, but large enough to admit a man in a stooping posture, and provided with a massive iron door. With the smoke and jets of flame issuing from the chinks and crevices of this door, which seemed to give admittance into the hillside, it resembled nothing so much as the private entrance to the infernal regions, which the shepherds of the Delectable Mountains were accustomed to show to pilgrims.

There are many such lime-kilns in that tract of country, for the purpose of burning the white marble which composes a large part of the substance of the hills. Some of them, built years ago, and long deserted, with weeds growing in the vacant round of the interior, which is open to the sky, and grass and wild flowers rooting themselves into the chinks of the stones, look already like relics of antiquity, and may yet be overspread with the lichens of centuries to come. Others, where the lime-burner still feeds his daily and nightlong fire, afford points of interest to the wanderer among the hills, who seats himself on a log of wood or a fragment of marble, to hold a chat with the solitary man. It is a lonesome, and, when the character is inclined to thought, may be an intensely thoughtful occupation; as it proved in the case of Ethan Brand, who had mused to such strange purpose, in days gone by, while the fire in this very kiln was burning.

The man who now watched the fire was of a different order, and troubled himself with no thoughts save the very few that were requisite to his business. At frequent intervals, he flung back the clashing weight of the iron door, and, turning his face from the insufferable glare, thrust in huge logs of oak, or stirred the immense brands with a long pole. Within the furnace were seen the curling and riotous flames, and the burning marble, almost molten with the intensity of heat; while without, the reflection of the fire quivered on the dark intricacy of the surrounding forest, and showed in the foreground a bright and ruddy little picture of the hut, the spring beside its door, the athletic and coal-begrimed figure of the lime-burner, and the half-frightened child, shrinking into the protection of his father's shadow. And when, again, the iron door was closed, then reappeared the tender light of the half-full moon, which vainly strove to trace out the indistinct shapes of the neighboring mountains; and, in the upper sky, there was a flitting congregation of clouds, still faintly tinged with the rosy sunset, though thus far down into the valley the sunshine had vanished long and long ago.

The little boy now crept still closer to his father, as footsteps were heard ascending the hillside, and a human form thrust aside the bushes that clustered beneath the trees.

"Halloo! who is it?" cried the lime-burner, vexed at his son's timidity, yet half infected by it. "Come forward and show yourself, like a man, or I'll fling this chunk of marble at your head!"

"You offer me a rough welcome," said a gloomy voice, as the unknown man drew nigh. "Yet I neither claim nor desire a kinder one, even at my own fireside."

To obtain a distincter view, Bartram threw open the iron door of the kiln, whence immediately issued a gush of fierce light, that smote full upon the stranger's face and figure. To a careless eye there appeared nothing very remarkable in his aspect, which was that of a man in a coarse, brown, country-made suit of clothes, tall and thin, with the staff and heavy shoes of a wayfarer. As he advanced, he fixed his eyes—which were very bright—intently upon the brightness of the furnace, as if he beheld, or expected to behold, some object worthy of note within it.

"Good-evening, stranger," said the lime-burner; "whence come you, so late in the day?"

"I come from my search," answered the wayfarer; "for, at last, it is finished."

"Drunk!—or crazy!" muttered Bartram to himself. "I shall have trouble with the fellow. The sooner I drive him away, the better."

The little boy, all in a tremble, whispered to his father, and begged him to shut the door of the kiln, so that there might not be so much light; for that there was something in the man's face which he was afraid to look at, yet could not look away from. And, indeed, even the lime-burner's dull and torpid sense began to be impressed by an indescribable something in that thin, rugged, thoughtful visage, with the grizzled hair hanging wildly about it, and those deeply sunken eyes, which gleamed like fires within the entrance of a mysterious cavern. But, as he closed the door, the stranger turned towards him, and spoke in a quiet, familiar way, that made Bartram feel as if he were a sane and sensible man, after all.

"Your task draws to an end, I see," said he. "This marble has already been burning three days. A few hours more will convert the stone to lime."

"Why, who are you?" exclaimed the lime-burner. "You seem as well acquainted with my business as I am myself."

"And well I may be," said the stranger; "for I followed the same craft many a long year, and here, too, on this very spot. But you are a new-comer in these parts? Did you ever hear of Ethan Brand?"

"The man that went in search of the Unpardonable Sin?" asked Bartram with a laugh.

"The same," answered the stranger. "He has found what he sought, and therefore he comes back again."

"What! then you are Ethan Brand himself?" cried the lime-burner in amazement. "I am a new-comer here, as you say, and they call it eighteen years since you left the foot of Graylock. But, I can tell you, the good folks still talk about Ethan Brand, in the village yonder, and what a strange errand took him away from his lime-kiln. Well, and so you have found the Unpardonable Sin?"

"Even so!" said the stranger calmly.

"If the question is a fair one," proceeded Bartram, "where might it be?"

Ethan Brand laid his finger on his own heart.

"Here!" replied he.

And then, without mirth in his countenance, but as if moved by an involuntary recognition of the infinite absurdity of seeking throughout the world for what was the closest of all things to himself, and looking into every heart, save his own, for what was hidden in no other breast, he broke into a laugh of scorn. It was the same slow, heavy laugh, that had almost appalled the lime-burner when it heralded the wayfarer's approach.

The solitary mountain-side was made dismal by it. Laughter, when out of place, mistimed, or bursting forth from a disordered state of feeling, may be the most terrible modulation of the human voice. The laughter of one asleep, even if it be a little child,—the mad-man's laugh,—the wild, screaming laugh of a born idiot,—are sounds that we sometimes tremble to hear, and would always willingly forget. Poets have imagined no utterance of fiends or hobgoblins so fearfully appropriate as a laugh. And even the obtuse lime-burner felt his nerves shaken, as this strange man looked inward at his own heart, and burst into laughter that rolled away into the night, and was indistinctly reverberated among the hills.

"Joe," said he to his little son, "scamper down to the tavern in the village, and tell the jolly fellows there that Ethan Brand has come back, and that he has found the Unpardonable Sin!"

The boy darted away on his errand, to which Ethan Brand made no objection, nor seemed hardly to notice it. He sat on a log of wood, looking steadfastly at the iron door of the kiln. When the child was out of sight, and his swift and light footsteps ceased to be heard treading first on the fallen leaves and then on the rocky mountain-path, the lime-burner began to regret his departure. He felt that the little fellow's presence had been a barrier between his guest and himself, and that he must now deal, heart to heart, with a man who, on his own confession, had committed the one only crime for which Heaven could afford no mercy. That crime, in its indistinct blackness, seemed to overshadow him. The lime-burner's own sins rose up within him, and made his memory riotous with a throng of evil shapes that asserted their kindred with the Master Sin, whatever it might be, which it was within the scope of man's corrupted nature to conceive and cherish. They were all of one family; they went to and fro between his breast and Ethan Brand's, and carried dark greetings from one to the other.

Then Bartram remembered the stories which had grown traditionary in reference to this strange man, who had come upon him like a shadow of the night, and was making himself at home in his old place, after so long absence, that the dead people, dead and buried for years, would have had more right to be at home, in any familiar spot, than he. Ethan Brand, it was said, had conversed with Satan himself in the lurid blaze of this very kiln. The legend had been matter of mirth heretofore, but looked grisly now. According to this tale, before Ethan Brand departed on his search, he had been accustomed to evoke a fiend from the hot furnace of the lime-kiln, night after night, in order to confer with him about the Unpardonable Sin; the man and the fiend each laboring to frame the image of some mode of guilt which could neither be atoned for nor forgiven. And, with the first gleam of light upon the mountain-top, the fiend crept in at the iron door, there to abide the intensest element of fire until again summoned forth to share in the dreadful task of extending man's possible guilt beyond the scope of Heaven's else infinite mercy.

While the lime-burner was struggling with the horror of these thoughts, Ethan Brand rose from the log, and flung open the door of the kiln. The action was in such accordance with the idea in Bartram's mind, that he almost expected to see the Evil One issue forth, red-hot, from the raging furnace.

"Hold! hold!" cried he, with a tremulous attempt to laugh; for he was ashamed of his fears, although they overmastered him. "Don't, for mercy's sake, bring out your Devil now!"

"Man!" sternly replied Ethan Brand, "what need have I of the Devil? I have left him behind me, on my track. It is with such half-way sinners as you that he busies himself. Fear not, because I open the door. I do but act by old custom, and am going to trim your fire like a lime-burner, as I was once."

He stirred the vast coals, thrust in more wood, and bent forward to gaze into the hollow prison house of the fire, regardless of the fierce glow that reddened upon his face. The lime-burner sat watching him, and half suspected this strange guest of a purpose, if not to evoke a fiend, at least to plunge bodily into the flames, and thus vanish from the sight of man. Ethan Brand, however, drew quietly back, and closed the door of the kiln.

"I have looked," said he, "into many a human heart that was seven times hotter with sinful passions than yonder furnace is with fire. But I found not there what I sought. No, not the Unpardonable Sin!"

"What is the Unpardonable Sin?" asked the lime-burner; and then he shrank farther from his companion, trembling lest his question should be answered.

"It is a sin that grew within my own breast," replied Ethan Brand, standing erect, with a pride that distinguishes all enthusiasts of his stamp. "A sin that grew nowhere else! The sin of an intellect that triumphed over the sense of brotherhood with man and reverence for God, and sacrificed everything to its own mighty claims! The only sin that deserves a recompense of immortal agony! Freely, were it to do again, would I incur the guilt. Unshrinkingly I accept the retribution!"

"The man's head is turned," muttered the lime-burner to himself. "He may be a sinner like the rest of us,—nothing more likely,—but, I'll be sworn, he is a madman too."

Nevertheless, he felt uncomfortable at his situation, alone with Ethan Brand on the wild mountain-side, and was right glad to hear the rough murmur of tongues, and the footsteps of what seemed a pretty numerous party, stumbling over the stones and rustling through the underbrush. Soon appeared the whole lazy regiment that was wont to infest the village tavern, comprehending three or four individuals who had drunk flip beside the bar-room fire through all the winters, and smoked their pipes beneath the stoop through all the summers, since Ethan Brand's departure. Laughing boisterously, and mingling all their voices together in unceremonious talk, they now burst into the moonshine and narrow streaks of firelight that illuminated the open space before the lime-kiln. Bartram set the door ajar again, flooding the spot with light, that the whole company might get a fair view of Ethan Brand, and he of them.

There, among other old acquaintances, was a once ubiquitous man, now almost extinct, but whom we were formerly sure to encounter at the hotel of every thriving village throughout the country. It was the stage agent. The present specimen of the genus was a wilted and smoke-dried man, wrinkled and red-nosed, in a smartly cut, brown, bobtailed coat, with brass buttons, who, for a length of time unknown, had kept his desk and corner in the bar-room, and was still puffing what seemed to be the same cigar that he had lighted twenty years before. He had great fame as a dry joker, though, perhaps, less on account of any intrinsic humor than from a certain flavor of brandy toddy and tobacco smoke, which impregnated all his ideas and expressions, as well as his person. Another well-remembered, though strangely altered, face was that of Lawyer Giles, as people still called him in courtesy; an elderly ragamuffin, in his soiled shirtsleeves and tow-cloth trousers. This poor fellow had been an attorney, in what he called his better days, a sharp practitioner, and in great vogue among the village litigants; but flip, and sling, and toddy, and cocktails, imbibed at all hours, morning, noon, and night, had caused him to slide from intellectual to various kinds and degrees of bodily labor, till at last, to adopt his own phrase, he slid into a soap-vat. In other words, Giles was now a soap-boiler, in a small way. He had come to be but the fragment of a human being, a part of one foot having been chopped off by an axe, and an entire hand torn away by the devilish grip of a steam-engine. Yet, though the corporeal hand was gone, a spiritual member remained; for, stretching forth the stump, Giles steadfastly averred that he felt an invisible thumb and fingers with as vivid a sensation as before the real ones were amputated. A maimed and miserable wretch he was; but one, nevertheless, whom the world could not trample on, and had no right to scorn, either in this or any previous stage of his misfortunes, since he had still kept up the courage and spirit of a man, asked nothing in charity, and with his one hand—and that the left one— fought a stern battle against want and hostile circumstances.

Among the throng, too, came another personage, who, with certain points of similarity to Lawyer Giles, had many more of difference. It was the village doctor; a man of some fifty years, whom, at an earlier period of his life, we introduced as paying a professional visit to Ethan Brand during the latter's supposed insanity. He was now a purple-visaged, rude, and brutal, yet half-gentlemanly figure, with something wild, ruined, and desperate in his talk, and in all the details of his gesture and manners. Brandy possessed this man like an evil spirit, and made him as surly and savage as a wild beast, and as miserable as a lost soul; but there was supposed to be in him such wonderful skill, such native gifts of healing, beyond any which medical science could impart, that society caught hold of him, and would not let him sink out of its reach. So, swaying to and fro upon his horse, and grumbling thick accents at the bedside, he visited all the sick-chambers for miles about among the mountain towns, and sometimes raised a dying man, as it were, by miracle, or quite as often, no doubt, sent his patient to a grave that was dug many a year too soon. The doctor had an everlasting pipe in his mouth, and, as somebody said, in allusion to his habit of swearing, it was always alight with hell-fire.

These three worthies pressed forward, and greeted Ethan Brand each after his own fashion, earnestly inviting him to partake of the contents of a certain black bottle, in which, as they averred, he would find something far better worth seeking for than the Unpardonable Sin. No mind, which has wrought itself by intense and solitary meditation into a high state of enthusiasm, can endure the kind of contact with low and vulgar modes of thought and feeling to which Ethan Brand was now subjected. It made him doubt—and, strange to say, it was a painful doubt—whether he had indeed found the Unpardonable Sin, and found it within himself. The whole question on which he had exhausted life, and more than life, looked like a delusion.

"Leave me," he said bitterly, "ye brute beasts, that have made yourselves so, shrivelling up your souls with fiery liquors! I have done with you. Years and years ago, I groped into your hearts and found nothing there for my purpose. Get ye gone!"

"Why, you uncivil scoundrel," cried the fierce doctor, "is that the way you respond to the kindness of your best friends? Then let me tell you the truth. You have no more found the Unpardonable Sin than yonder boy Joe has. You are but a crazy fellow,—I told you so twenty years ago,—neither better nor worse than a crazy fellow, and the fit companion of old Humphrey, here!"

He pointed to an old man, shabbily dressed, with long white hair, thin visage, and unsteady eyes. For some years past this aged person had been wandering about among the hills, inquiring of all travellers whom he met for his daughter. The girl, it seemed, had gone off with a company of circus performers, and occasionally tidings of her came to the village, and fine stories were told of her glittering appearance as she rode on horseback in the ring, or performed marvellous feats on the tight-rope.

The white-haired father now approached Ethan Brand, and gazed unsteadily into his face.

"They tell me you have been all over the earth," said he, wringing his hands with earnestness. "You must have seen my daughter, for she makes a grand figure in the world, and everybody goes to see her. Did she send any word to her old father, or say when she was coming back?"

Ethan Brand's eye quailed beneath the old man's. That daughter, from whom he so earnestly desired a word of greeting, was the Esther of our tale, the very girl whom, with such cold and remorseless purpose, Ethan Brand had made the subject of a psychological experiment, and wasted, absorbed, and perhaps annihilated her soul, in the process.

"Yes," murmured he, turning away from the hoary wanderer, "it is no delusion. There is an Unpardonable Sin!"

While these things were passing, a merry scene was going forward in the area of cheerful light, beside the spring and before the door of the hut. A number of the youth of the village, young men and girls, had hurried up the hillside, impelled by curiosity to see Ethan Brand, the hero of so many a legend familiar to their childhood. Finding nothing, however, very remarkable in his aspect,—nothing but a sunburnt wayfarer, in plain garb and dusty shoes, who sat looking into the fire as if he fancied pictures among the coals,—these young people speedily grew tired of observing him. As it happened, there was other amusement at hand. An old German Jew travelling with a diorama on his back, was passing down the mountain road towards the village just as the party turned aside from it, and, in hopes of eking out the profits of the day, the showman had kept them company to the lime-kiln.

"Come, old Dutchman," cried one of the young men, "let us see your pictures, if you can swear they are worth looking at!"

"O yes, Captain," answered the Jew,—whether as a matter of courtesy or craft, he styled everybody Captain,—"I shall show you, indeed, some very superb pictures!"

So, placing his box in a proper position, he invited the young men and girls to look through the glass orifices of the machine, and proceeded to exhibit a series of the most outrageous scratchings and daubings, as specimens of the fine arts, that ever an itinerant showman had the face to impose upon his circle of spectators. The pictures were worn out, moreover, tattered, full of cracks and wrinkles, dingy with tobacco smoke, and otherwise in a most pitiable condition. Some purported to be cities, public edifices, and ruined castles in Europe; others represented Napoleon's battles and Nelson's sea fights; and in the midst of these would be seen a gigantic, brown, hairy hand,—which might have been mistaken for the Hand of Destiny, though, in truth, it was only the showman's,—pointing its forefinger to various scenes of the conflict, while its owner gave historical illustrations. When, with much merriment at its abominable deficiency of merit, the exhibition was concluded, the German bade little Joe put his head into the box. Viewed through the magnifying-glasses, the boy's round, rosy visage assumed the strangest imaginable aspect of an immense Titanic child, the mouth grinning broadly, and the eyes and every other feature overflowing with fun at the joke.

Suddenly, however, that merry face turned pale, and its expression changed to horror, for this easily impressed and excitable child had become sensible that the eye of Ethan Brand was fixed upon him through the glass.

"You make the little man to be afraid, Captain," said the German Jew, turning up the dark and strong outline of his visage from his stooping posture. "But look again, and, by chance, I shall cause you to see somewhat that is very fine, upon my word!"

Ethan Brand gazed into the box for an instant, and then starting back, looked fixedly at the German. What had he seen? Nothing, apparently; for a curious youth, who had peeped in almost at the same moment, beheld only a vacant space of canvas.

"I remember you now," muttered Ethan Brand to the showman.

"Ah, Captain," whispered the Jew of Nuremberg, with a dark smile, "I find it to be a heavy matter in my showbox,—this Unpardonable Sin! By my faith, Captain, it has wearied my shoulders, this long day, to carry it over the mountain."

"Peace," answered Ethan Brand sternly, "or get thee into the furnace yonder!"

The Jew's exhibition had scarcely concluded, when a great, elderly dog—who seemed to be his own master, as no person in the company laid claim to him—saw fit to render himself the object of public notice. Hitherto, he had shown himself a very quiet, well-disposed old dog, going round from one to another, and, by way of being sociable, offering his rough head to be patted by any kindly hand that would take so much trouble. But now, all of a sudden, this grave and venerable quadruped, of his own mere motion, and without the slightest suggestion from anybody else, began to run round after his tail, which, to heighten the absurdity of the proceeding, was a great deal shorter than it should have been. Never was seen such headlong eagerness in pursuit of an object that could not possibly be attained; never was heard such a tremendous outbreak of growling, snarling, barking, and snapping,—as if one end of the ridiculous brute's body were at deadly and most unforgivable enmity with the other. Faster and faster, round about went the cur; and faster and still faster fled the unapproachable brevity of his tail; and louder and fiercer grew his yells of rage and animosity; until, utterly exhausted, and as far from the goal as ever, the foolish old dog ceased his performance as suddenly as he had begun it. The next moment he was as mild, quiet, sensible, and respectable in his deportment, as when he first scraped acquaintance with the company.

As may be supposed, the exhibition was greeted with universal laughter, clapping of hands, and shouts of encore, to which the canine performer responded by wagging all that there was to wag of his tail, but appeared totally unable to repeat his very successful effort to amuse the spectators.

Meanwhile, Ethan Brand had resumed his seat upon the log, and moved, it might be, by a perception of some remote analogy between his own case and that of this self-pursuing cur, he broke into the awful laugh which, more than any other token, expressed the condition of his inward being. From that moment, the merriment of the party was at an end; they stood aghast, dreading lest the inauspicious sound should be reverberated around the horizon, and that mountain would thunder it to mountain, and so the horror be prolonged upon their ears. Then, whispering one to another that it was late,—that the moon was almost down,—that the August night was growing chill,—they hurried homewards, leaving the lime-burner and little Joe to deal as they might with their unwelcome guest. Save for these three human beings, the open space on the hillside was a solitude, set in a vast gloom of forest. Beyond that darksome verge, the firelight glimmered on the stately trunks and almost black foliage of pines, intermixed with the lighter verdure of sapling oaks, maples, and poplars, while here and there lay the gigantic corpses of dead trees, decaying on the leaf-strewn soil. And it seemed to little Joe—a timorous and imaginative child—that the silent forest was holding its breath until some fearful thing should happen.

Ethan Brand thrust more wood into the fire, and closed the door of the kiln; then looking over his shoulder at the lime-burner and his son, he bade, rather than advised, them to retire to rest.

"For myself, I cannot sleep," said he. "I have matters that it concerns me to meditate upon. I will watch the fire, as I used to do in the old time."

"And call the Devil out of the furnace to keep you company, I suppose," muttered Bartram, who had been making intimate acquaintance with the black bottle above mentioned. "But watch, if you like, and call as many devils as you like! For my part, I shall be all the better for a snooze. Come, Joe!"

As the boy followed his father into the hut, he looked back at the wayfarer, and the tears came into his eyes, for his tender spirit had an intuition of the bleak and terrible loneliness in which this man had enveloped himself.

When they had gone, Ethan Brand sat listening to the crackling of the kindled wood, and looking at the little spirts of fire that issued through the chinks of the door. These trifles, however, once so familiar, had but the slightest hold of his attention, while deep within his mind he was reviewing the gradual but marvellous change that had been wrought upon him by the search to which he had devoted himself. He remembered how the night dew had fallen upon him,—how the dark forest had whispered to him,—how the stars had gleamed upon him,—a simple and loving man, watching his fire in the years gone by, and ever musing as it burned. He remembered with what tenderness, with what love and sympathy for mankind, and what pity for human guilt and woe, he had first begun to contemplate those ideas which afterwards became the inspiration of his life; with what reverence he had then looked into the heart of man, viewing it as a temple originally divine, and, however desecrated, still to be held sacred by a brother; with what awful fear he had deprecated the success of his pursuit, and prayed that the Unpardonable Sin might never be revealed to him. Then ensued that vast intellectual development, which, in its progress, disturbed the counterpoise between his mind and heart. The Idea that possessed his life had operated as a means of education; it had gone on cultivating his powers to the highest point of which they were susceptible; it had raised him from the level of an unlettered laborer to stand on a star-lit eminence, whither the philosophers of the earth, laden with the lore of universities, might vainly strive to clamber after him. So much for the intellect! But where was the heart? That, indeed, had withered,—had contracted,—had hardened,—had perished! It had ceased to partake of the universal throb. He had lost his hold of the magnetic chain of humanity. He was no longer a brother-man, opening the chambers or the dungeons of our common nature by the key of holy sympathy, which gave him a right to share in all its secrets; he was now a cold observer, looking on mankind as the subject of his experiment, and, at length, converting man and woman to be his puppets, and pulling the wires that moved them to such degrees of crime as were demanded for his study.

Thus Ethan Brand became a fiend. He began to be so from the moment that his moral nature had ceased to keep the pace of improvement with his intellect. And now, as his highest effort and inevitable development,—as the bright and gorgeous flower, and rich, delicious fruit of his life's labor,—he had produced the Unpardonable Sin!

"What more have I to seek? what more to achieve?" said Ethan Brand to himself. "My task is done, and well done!"

Starting from the log with a certain alacrity in his gait and ascending the hillock of earth that was raised against the stone circumference of the lime-kiln, he thus reached the top of the structure. It was a space of perhaps ten feet across, from edge to edge, presenting a view of the upper surface of the immense mass of broken marble with which the kiln was heaped. All these innumerable blocks and fragments of marble were red-hot and vividly on fire, sending up great spouts of blue flame, which quivered aloft and danced madly, as within a magic circle, and sank and rose again, with continual and multitudinous activity. As the lonely man bent forward over this terrible body of fire, the blasting heat smote up against his person with a breath that, it might be supposed, would have scorched and shrivelled him up in a moment.

Ethan Brand stood erect, and raised his arms on high. The blue flames played upon his face, and imparted the wild and ghastly light which alone could have suited its expression; it was that of a fiend on the verge of plunging into his gulf of intensest torment.

"O Mother Earth," cried he, "who art no more my Mother, and into whose bosom this frame shall never be resolved! O mankind, whose brotherhood I have cast off, and trampled thy great heart beneath my feet! O stars of heaven, that shone on me of old, as if to light me onward and upward!—farewell all, and forever. Come, deadly element of Fire,—henceforth my familiar friend! Embrace me, as I do thee!"

That night the sound of a fearful peal of laughter rolled heavily through the sleep of the lime-burner and his little son; dim shapes of horror and anguish haunted their dreams, and seemed still present in the rude hovel, when they opened their eyes to the daylight.

"Up, boy, up!" cried the lime-burner, staring about him. "Thank Heaven, the night is gone, at last; and rather than pass such another, I would watch my lime-kiln, wide awake, for a twelvemonth. This Ethan Brand, with his humbug of an Unpardonable Sin, has done me no such mighty favor, in taking my place!"

He issued from the hut, followed by little Joe, who kept fast hold of his father's hand. The early sunshine was already pouring its gold upon the mountain-tops, and though the valleys were still in shadow, they smiled cheerfully in the promise of the bright day that was hastening onward. The village, completely shut in by hills, which swelled away gently about it, looked as if it had rested peacefully in the hollow of the great hand of Providence. Every dwelling was distinctly visible; the little spires of the two churches pointed upwards, and caught a fore-glimmering of brightness from the sun-gilt skies upon their gilded weather-cocks. The tavern was astir, and the figure of the old, smoke-dried stage agent, cigar in mouth, was seen beneath the stoop. Old Graylock was glorified with a golden cloud upon his head. Scattered likewise over the breasts of the surrounding mountains, there were heaps of hoary mist, in fantastic shapes, some of them far down into the valley, others high up towards the summits, and still others, of the same family of mist or cloud, hovering in the gold radiance of the upper atmosphere. Stepping from one to another of the clouds that rested on the hills, and thence to the loftier brotherhood that sailed in air, it seemed almost as if a mortal man might thus ascend into the heavenly regions. Earth was so mingled with sky that it was a day-dream to look at it.

To supply that charm of the familiar and homely, which Nature so readily adopts into a scene like this, the stage-coach was rattling down the mountain road, and the driver sounded his horn, while Echo caught up the notes, and intertwined them into a rich and varied and elaborate harmony, of which the original performer could lay claim to little share. The great hills played a concert among themselves, each contributing a strain of airy sweetness.

Little Joe's face brightened at once.

"Dear father," cried he, skipping cheerily to and fro, "that strange man is gone, and the sky and the mountains all seem glad of it!"

"Yes," growled the lime-burner with an oath, "but he has let the fire go down, and no thanks to him if five hundred bushels of lime are not spoiled. If I catch the fellow hereabouts again, I shall feel like tossing him into the furnace!"

With his long pole in his hand, he ascended to the top of the kiln. After a moment's pause, he called to his son.

"Come up here, Joe!" said he.

So little Joe ran up the hillock, and stood by his father's side. The marble was all burnt into perfect, snow-white lime. But on its surface, in the midst of the circle,—snow-white too, and thoroughly converted into lime,—lay a human skeleton, in the attitude of a person who, after long toil, lies down to long repose. Within the ribs—strange to say—was the shape of a human heart.

"Was the fellow's heart made of marble?" cried Bartram, in some perplexity at this phenomenon. "At any rate, it is burnt into what looks like special good lime; and, taking all the bones together, my kiln is half a bushel the richer for him."

So saying, the rude lime-burner lifted his pole, and, letting it fall upon the skeleton, the relics of Ethan Brand were crumbled into fragments.

COMMENTARY
by Nathaniel Hawthorne

In his notebooks Hawthorne described a visit, accompanied by a friend, to a lime-kiln and their conversation. Both the visit and the talk helped to suggest structural details and symbols for "Ethan Brand."

September 7, 1838

Mr. Leach and I took a walk by moonlight, last evening, on the road that leads over the mountain. Remote from houses, far up on the hill side, we found a lime-kiln burning near the road side; and approaching it, a watcher started from the ground, where he had been lying at his length. There are several of these lime-kilns in this vicinity; they are built circular with stones, like a round tower, eighteen or twenty feet high; having a hillock heaped around a considerable of their circumference, so that the marble may be brought and thrown in by cart loads at the top. At the bottom there is a door-way large enough to admit a man in a stooping posture. Thus an edifice of great solidity is composed, which will endure for centuries, unless needless pains are taken to tear it down. There is one on the hill side close to the village, where in weeds grow at the bottom, and grass, and shrubs too are rooted in the interstices of the stones; and its low doorway has a dungeonlike aspect; and we look down from the top as into a roofless tower. It apparently has not been used for many years; and the lime, and weather-stained fragments of marble are scattered about.

But in the one we saw last night, a hard wood fire was burning merrily beneath the superincumbent marble—the kiln being heaped full; and shortly after we came, the man (a dark, black-bearded figure in shirt-sleeves) opened the iron door, through the chinks of which the fire was gleaming, and thrust in huge logs of wood, and stirred the immense coals with a long pole; and showed us the glowing lime-stone, —the lower layer of it. The glow of the fire was powerful, at the distance of several yards from the open door. He talked very sociably with us,—being doubtless glad to have two visitors to vary his solitary night-watch; for it would not do for him to get asleep; since the fire should be refreshed as often as every twenty minutes. We ascended the hillock to the top of the kiln; and the marble was red-hot and burning with a bluish lambent flame, quivering up, sometimes, nearly a yard high, and resembling the flame of anthracite coal—only, the marble being in larger fragments, the flame was higher. The kiln was perhaps six or eight feet across. Four hundred bushels of marble were then in a state of combustion. The expense of converting this quantity into lime is about fifty dollars; and it sells for 25cts per bushel at the kiln. We talked with the man about whether he would run across the top of the intensely burning kiln for a thousand dollars, barefooted; and he said he would for ten;—he said that the lime had been burning 48 hours, and would be finished in 36 more, and cooled sufficiently to handle in 12 more. He liked the business of watching it better by night than day; because the days were often hot; but such a mild and beautiful night as the last was just right. Here a poet might make verses, with moonlight in them—and a gleam of fierce firelight flickering through them. It is a shame to use this brilliant, white, almost transparent marble, in this way. A man said of it, the other day, that into some pieces of it, when polished, one could see a considerable distance; and instanced a certain gravestone.

Mr. Leach told me how a girl, to whom he was once paying attention with some idea of marrying her, made a confession of having forfeited her chastity. He had heard rumors of her having been indiscreet, with reference to a man who was formerly attentive to her—but had no idea of anything more than a merely pardonable indiscretion, in having trusted herself in long and solitary walk with this man. He began to talk with her on this subject, intending gently to reprehend her; but she became greatly agitated, and fell a weeping bitterly—her thoughts flying immediately to her guilt, and probably thinking that he was aware or suspicious of the full extent of it. She told so much, or betrayed so much, that he besought her to say no more. "That was the only time, Mr. Leach," sobbed she, "that I ever strayed from the path of virtue." Much might be made of such a scene—the lover's astoundment, at discovering so much more than he expected. Mr. Leach spoke to me as if one deviation from chastity might not be an altogether insuperable objection to making a girl his wife! . . .*

*The American Notebooks, ed. Randall Stewart (New Haven, 1932), pp. 66–8.

The Bell-Tower
Herman Melville

In the south of Europe, nigh a once frescoed capital, now with dank mould cankering its bloom, central in a plain, stands what, at distance, seems the black mossed stump of some immeasurable pine, fallen, in forgotten days, with Anak and the Titan.

As all along where the pine tree falls, its dissolution leaves a mossy mound—last-flung shadow of the perished trunk; never lengthening, never lessening; unsubject to the fleet falsities of the sun; shade immutable, and true gauge which cometh by prostration—so westward from what seems the stump, one steadfast spear of lichened ruin veins the plain.

From that tree-top, what birded chimes of silver throats had rung. A stone pine; a metallic aviary in its crown: the Bell-Tower, built by the great mechanician, the unblest foundling, Bannadonna.

Like Babel's, its base was laid in a high hour of renovated earth, following the second deluge, when the waters of the Dark Ages had dried up, and once more the green appeared. No wonder that, after so long and deep submersion, the jubilant expectation of the race should, as with Noah's sons, soar into Shinar aspiration.

In firm resolve, no man in Europe at that period went beyond Bannadonna. Enriched through commerce with the Levant, the state in which he lived voted to have the noblest Bell-Tower in Italy. His repute assigned him to be architect.

Stone by stone, month by month, the tower rose. Higher, higher; snail-like in pace, but torch or rocket in its pride.

After the masons would depart, the builder, standing alone upon its ever-ascending summit, at close of every day, saw that he overtopped still higher walls and trees. He would tarry till a late hour there, wrapped in schemes of other and still loftier piles. Those who of saints' days thronged the spot—hanging to the rude poles of scaffolding, like sailors on yards, or bees on boughs, unmindful of lime and dust, and falling chips of stone—their homage not the less inspired him to self-esteem.

At length the holiday of the Tower came. To the sound of viols, the climax-stone slowly rose in air, and, amid the firing of ordnance, was laid by Bannadonna's hands upon the final course. Then mounting it, he stood erect, alone, with folded arms, gazing upon the white summits of blue inland Alps, and whiter crests of bluer Alps off-shore—sights invisible from the plain. Invisible, too, from thence was that eye he turned below, when, like the cannon booms, came up to him the people's combustions of applause.

That which stirred them so was, seeing with what serenity the builder stood three hundred feet in air, upon an unrailed perch. This none but he durst do. But his periodic standing upon the pile, in each stage of its growth—such discipline had its last result.

Little remained now but the bells. These, in all respects, must correspond with their receptacle.

The minor ones were prosperously cast. A highly enriched one followed, of a singular make, intended for suspension in a manner before unknown. The purpose of this bell, its rotary motion, and connection with the clock-work, also executed at the time, will, in the sequel, receive mention.

In the one erection, bell-tower and clock-tower were united, though, before that period, such structures had commonly been built distinct; as the Campanile and Torre del 'Orologio of St. Mark to this day attest.

But it was upon the great state-bell that the founder lavished his more daring skill. In vain did some of the less elated magistrates here caution him; saying that though truly the tower was Titanic, yet limit should be set to the dependent weight of its swaying masses. But undeterred, he prepared his mammoth mould, dented with mythological devices; kindled his fires of balsamic firs; melted his tin and copper, and, throwing in much plate, contributed by the public spirit of the nobles, let loose the tide.

The unleashed metals bayed like hounds. The workmen shrunk. Through their fright, fatal harm to the bell was dreaded. Fearless as Shadrach, Bannadonna, rushing through the glow, smote the chief culprit with his ponderous ladle. From the smitten part, a splinter was dashed into the seething mass, and at once was melted in.

Next day a portion of the work was heedfully uncovered. All seemed right. Upon the third morning, with equal satisfaction, it was bared still lower. At length, like some old Theban king, the whole cooled casting was disinterred. All was fair except in one strange spot. But as he suffered no one to attend him in these inspections, he concealed the blemish by some preparation which none knew better to devise.

The casting of such a mass was deemed no small triumph for the caster; one, too, in which the state might not scorn to share. The homicide was overlooked. By the charitable that deed was but imputed to sudden transports of esthetic passion, not to any flagitious quality. A kick from an Arabian charger; not sign of vice, but blood.

His felony remitted by the judge, absolution given him by the priest, what more could even a sickly conscience have desired.

Honoring the tower and its builder with another holiday, the republic witnessed the hoisting of the bells and clockwork amid shows and pomps superior to the former.

Some months of more than usual solitude on Bannadonna's part ensued. It was not unknown that he was engaged upon something for the belfry, intended to complete it, and surpass all that had gone before. Most people imagined that the design would involve a casting like the bells. But those who thought they had some further insight, would shake their heads, with hints, that not for nothing did the mechanician keep so secret. Meantime, his seclusion failed not to invest his work with more or less of that sort of mystery pertaining to the forbidden.

Ere long he had a heavy object hoisted to the belfry, wrapped in a dark sack or cloak—a procedure sometimes had in the case of an elaborate piece of sculpture, or statue, which, being intended to grace the front of the new edifice, the architect does not desire exposed to critical eyes, till set up, finished, in its appointed place. Such was the impression now. But, as the object rose, a statuary present observed, or thought he did, that it was not entirely rigid, but was, in a manner, pliant. At last, when the hidden thing had attained its final height, and, obscurely seen from below, seemed almost of itself to step into the belfry, as if with little assistance from the crane, a shrewd old blacksmith present ventured the suspicion that it was but a living man. This surmise was thought a foolish one, while the general interest failed not to augment.

Not without demur from Bannadonna, the chief-magistrate of the town, with an associate—both elderly men—followed what seemed the image up the tower. But, arrived at the belfry, they had little recompense. Plausibly entrenching himself behind the conceded mysteries of his art, the mechanician withheld present explanation. The magistrates glanced toward the cloaked object, which, to their surprise, seemed now to have changed its attitude, or else had before been more perplexingly concealed by the violent muffling action of the wind without. It seemed now seated upon some sort of frame, or chair, contained within the domino. They observed that nigh the top, in a sort of square, the web of the cloth, either from accident or design, had its warp partly withdrawn, and the cross threads plucked out here and there, so as to form a sort of woven grating. Whether it were the low wind or no, stealing through the stone lattice-work, or only their own perturbed imaginations, is uncertain, but they thought they discerned a slight sort of fitful, spring-like motion, in the domino. Nothing, however incidental or insignificant, escaped their uneasy eyes. Among other things, they pried out, in a corner, an earthen cup, partly corroded and partly encrusted, and one whispered to the other, that this cup was just such a one as might, in mockery, be offered to the lips of some brazen statue, or, perhaps, still worse.

But, being questioned, the mechanician said, that the cup was simply used in his founder's business, and described the purpose; in short, a cup to test the condition of metals in fusion. He added, that it had got into the belfry by the merest chance.

Again, and again, they gazed at the domino, as at some suspicious incognito at a Venetian mask. All sorts of vague apprehensions stirred them. They even dreaded lest, when they should descend, the mechanician, though without a flesh and blood companion, for all that, would not be left alone.

Affecting some merriment at their disquietude, he begged to relieve them, by extending a coarse sheet of workman's canvas between them and the object.

Meantime he sought to interest them in his other work; nor, now that the domino was out of sight, did they long remain insensible to the artistic wonders lying round them; wonders hitherto beheld but in their unfinished state; because, since hoisting the bells, none but the caster had entered within the belfry. It was one trait of his, that, even in details, he would not let another do what he could, without too great loss of time, accomplish for himself. So, for several preceding weeks, whatever hours were unemployed in his secret design, had been devoted to elaborating the figures on the bells.

The clock-bell, in particular, now drew attention. Under a patient chisel, the latent beauty of its enrichments, before obscured by the cloudings incident to casting, that beauty in its shyest grace, was now revealed. Round and round the bell, twelve figures of gay girls, garlanded, hand-in-hand, danced in a choral ring—the embodied hours.

"Bannadonna," said the chief, "this bell excels all else. No added touch could here improve. Hark!" hearing a sound, "was that the wind?"

"The wind, Excellenza," was the light response. "But the figures, they are not yet without their faults. They need some touches yet. When those are given, and the ——block yonder," pointing towards the canvas screen, "when Haman there, as I merrily call him,—him? it, I mean——when Haman is fixed on this, his lofty tree, then, gentlemen, will I be most happy to receive you here again."

The equivocal reference to the object caused some return of restlessness. However, on their part, the visitors forbore further allusion to it, unwilling, perhaps, to let the foundling see how easily it lay within his plebeian art to stir the placid dignity of nobles.

"Well, Bannadonna," said the chief, "how long ere you are ready to set the clock going, so that the hour shall be sounded? Our interest in you, not less than in the work itself, makes us anxious to be assured of your success. The people, too,—why, they are shouting now. Say the exact hour when you will be ready."

"To-morrow, Excellenza, if you listen for it,—or should you not, all the same—strange music will be heard. The stroke of one shall be the first from yonder bell," pointing to the bell adorned with girls and garlands, "that stroke shall fall there, where the hand of Una clasps Dua's. The stroke of one shall sever that loved clasp. To-morrow, then, at one o'clock, as struck here, precisely here," advancing and placing his finger upon the clasp, "the poor mechanic will be most happy once more to give you liege audience, in this his littered shop. Farewell till then, illustrious magnificoes, and hark ye for your vassal's stroke."

His still, Vulcanic face hiding its burning brightness like a forge, he moved with ostentatious deference towards the scuttle, as if so far to escort their exit. But the junior magistrate, a kind-hearted man, troubled at what seemed to him a certain sardonical disdain, lurking beneath the foundling's humble mien, and in Christian sympathy more distressed at it on his account than on his own, dimly surmising what might be the final fate of such a cynic solitaire, not perhaps uninfluenced by the general strangeness of surrounding things, this good magistrate had glanced sadly, sideways from the speaker, and thereupon his foreboding eye had started at the expression of the unchanging face of the Hour Una.

"How is this, Bannadonna?" he lowly asked, "Una looks unlike her sisters."

"In Christ's name, Bannadonna," impulsively broke in the chief, his attention, for the first attracted to the figure, by his associate's remark, "Una's face looks just like that of Deborah, the prophetess, as painted by the Florentine, Del Fonca."

"Surely, Bannadonna," lowly resumed the milder magistrate, "you meant the twelve should wear the same jocundly abandoned air. But see, the smile of Una seems but a fatal one. 'Tis different."

While his mild associate was speaking, the chief glanced, inquiringly, from him to the caster, as if anxious to mark how the discrepancy would be accounted for. As the chief stood, his advanced foot was on the scuttle's curb.

Bannadonna spoke:

"Excellenza, now that, following your keener eye, I glance upon the face of Una, I do, indeed perceive some little variance. But look all round the bell, and you will find no two faces entirely correspond. Because there is a law in art—— but the cold wind is rising more; these lattices are but a poor defense. Suffer me, magnificoes, to conduct you, at least, partly on your way. Those in whose well-being there is a public stake, should be heedfully attended."

"Touching the look of Una, you were saying, Bannadonna, that there was a certain law in art," observed the chief, as the three now descended the stone shaft, "pray, tell me, then——."

"Pardon; another time, Excellenza;—the tower is damp."

"Nay, I must rest, and hear it now. Here,—here is a wide landing, and through this leeward slit, no wind, but ample light. Tell us of your law; and at large."

"Since, Excellenza, you insist, know that there is a law in art, which bars the possibility of duplicates. Some years ago, you may remember, I graved a small seal for your republic, bearing, for its chief device, the head of your own ancestor, its illustrious founder. It becoming necessary, for the customs' use, to have innumerable impressions for bales and boxes, I graved an entire plate, containing one hundred of the seals. Now, though, indeed, my object was to have those hundred heads identical, and though, I dare say, people think them so, yet, upon closely scanning an uncut impression from the plate, no two of those five-score faces, side by side, will be found alike. Gravity is the air of all; but, diversified in all. In some, benevolent; in some, ambiguous; in two or three, to a close scrutiny, all but incipiently malign, the variation of less than a hair's breadth in the linear shadings round the mouth sufficing to all this. Now, Excellenza, transmute that general gravity into joyousness, and subject it to twelve of those variations I have described, and tell me, will you not have my hours here, and Una one of them? But I like——."

"Hark! is that——a footfall above?"

"Mortar, Excellenza; sometimes it drops to the belfry-floor from the arch where the stone-work was left undressed. I must have it seen to. As I was about to say: for one, I like this law forbidding duplicates. It evokes fine personalities. Yes, Excellenza, that strange, and—to you—uncertain smile, and those fore-looking eyes of Una, suit Bannadonna very well."

"Hark!—sure we left no soul above?"

"No soul, Excellenza; rest assured, no *soul.*—Again the mortar."

"It fell not while we were there."

"Ah, in your presence, it better knew its place, Excellenza," blandly bowed Bannadonna.

"But, Una," said the milder magistrate, "she seemed intently gazing on you; one would have almost sworn that she picked you out from among us three."

"If she did, possibly, it might have been her finer apprehension, Excellenza."

"How, Bannadonna? I do not understand you."

"No consequence, no consequence, Excellenza—but the shifted wind is blowing through the slit. Suffer me to escort you on; and then, pardon, but the toiler must to his tools."

"It may be foolish, Signor," said the milder magistrate, as, from the third landing, the two now went down unescorted, "but, somehow, our great mechanician moves me strangely. Why, just now, when he so superciliously replied, his walk seemed Sisera's, God's vain foe, in Del Fonca's painting. And that young, sculptured Deborah, too. Ay, and that——."

"Tush, tush, Signor!" returned the chief. "A passing whim. Deborah?—Where's Jael, pray?"

"Ah," said the other, as they now stepped upon the sod, "Ah, Signor, I see you leave your fears behind you with the chill and gloom; but mine, even in this sunny air, remain. Hark!"

It was a sound from just within the tower door, whence they had emerged. Turning, they saw it closed.

"He has slipped down and barred us out," smiled the chief; "but it is his custom."

Proclamation was now made, that the next day, at one hour after meridian, the clock would strike, and—thanks to the mechanician's powerful art—with unusual accompaniments. But what those should be, none as yet could say. The announcement was received with cheers.

By the looser sort, who encamped about the tower all night, lights were seen gleaming through the topmost blind-work, only disappearing with the morning sun. Strange sounds, too, were heard, or were thought to be, by those whom anxious watching might not have left mentally undisturbed—sounds, not only of some ringing implement, but also—so they said—half-suppressed screams and plainings, such as might have issued from some ghostly engine, overplied.

Slowly the day drew on; part of the concourse chasing the weary time with songs and games, till, at last, the great blurred sun rolled, like a football, against the plain.

At noon, the nobility and principal citizens came from the town in cavalcade, a guard of soldiers, also, with music, the more to honor the occasion.

Only one hour more. Impatience grew. Watches were held in hands of feverish men, who stood, now scrutinizing their small dial-plates, and then, with neck thrown back, gazing toward the belfry, as if the eye might foretell that which could only be made sensible to the ear; for, as yet, there was no dial to the tower-clock.

The hour hands of a thousand watches now verged within a hair's breadth of the figure 1. A silence, as of the expectation of some Shiloh, pervaded the swarming plain. Suddenly a dull, mangled sound—naught ringing in it; scarcely audible, indeed, to the outer circles of the people—that dull sound dropped heavily from the belfry. At the same moment, each man stared at his neighbor blankly. All watches were upheld. All hour-hands were at—had passed—the figure 1. No bell-stroke from the tower. The multitude became tumultuous.

Waiting a few moments, the chief magistrate, commanding silence, hailed the belfry, to know what thing unforeseen had happened there.

No response.

He hailed again and yet again.

All continued hushed.

By his order, the soldiers burst in the tower-door; when, stationing guards to defend it from the now surging mob, the chief, accompanied by his former associate, climbed the winding stairs. Half-way up, they stopped to listen. No sound. Mounting faster, they reached the belfry; but, at the threshold, started at the spectacle disclosed. A spaniel, which, unbeknown to them, had followed them thus far, stood shivering as before some unknown monster in a brake: or, rather, as if it snuffed footsteps leading to some other world. Bannadonna lay, prostrate and bleeding, at the base of the bell which was adorned with girls and garlands. He lay at the feet of the hour Una; his head coinciding, in a vertical line, with her left hand, clasped by the hour Dua. With downcast face impending over him, like Jael over nailed Sisera in the tent, was the domino; now no more becloaked.

It had limbs, and seemed clad in a scaly mail, lustrous as a dragon-beetle's. It was manacled, and its clubbed arms were uplifted, as if, with its manacles, once more to smite its already smitten victim. One advanced foot of it was inserted beneath the dead body, as if in the act of spurning it.

Uncertainty falls on what now followed.

It were but natural to suppose that the magistrates would, at first, shrink from immediate personal contact with what they saw. At the least, for a time, they would stand in involuntary doubt; it may be, in more or less of horrified alarm. Certain it is, that an arquebuss was called for from below. And some add, that its report, followed by a fierce whiz, as of the sudden snapping of a main-spring, with a steely din, as if a stack of sword-blades should be dashed upon a pavement, these blended sounds came ringing to the plain attracting every eye far upward to the belfry, whence, through the lattice-work, thins wreaths of smoke were curling.

Some averred that it was the spaniel, gone mad by fear, which was shot. This, others denied. True it was, the spaniel never more was seen; and, probably, for some unknown reason, it shared the burial now to be related of the domino. For, whatever the preceding circumstances may have been, the first instinctive panic over, or else all ground of reasonable fear removed, the two magistrates, by themselves, quickly rehooded the figure in the dropped cloak wherein it had been hoisted. The same night, it was secretly lowered to the ground, smuggled to the beach, pulled far out to sea, and sunk. Nor to any after urgency, even in free convivial hours, would the twain ever disclose the full secrets of the belfry.

From the mystery unavoidably investing it, the popular solution of the foundling's fate involved more or less of supernatural agency. But some few less unscientific minds pretended to find little difficulty in otherwise accounting for it. In the chain of circumstantial inferences drawn, there may, or may not, have been some absent or defective links. But, as the explanation in question is the only one which tradition has explicitly preserved, in dearth of better, it will here be given. But, in the first place, it is requisite to present the supposition entertained as to the entire motive and mode, with their origin, of the secret design of Bannadonna; the minds abovementioned assuming to penetrate as well into his soul as into the event. The disclosure will indirectly involve reference to peculiar matters, none of the clearest, beyond the immediate subject.

At that period, no large bell was made to sound otherwise than as at present, by agitation of a tongue within, by means of ropes, or percussion from without, either from cumbrous machinery, or stalwart watchmen, armed with heavy hammers, stationed in the belfry, or in sentry-boxes on the open roof, according as the bell was sheltered or exposed.

It was from observing these exposed bells, with their watchmen, that the foundling, as was opined, derived the first suggestion of his scheme. Perched on a great mast or spire, the human figure, viewed from below, undergoes such a reduction in its apparent size, as to obliterate its intelligent features. It evinces no personality. Instead of bespeaking volition, its gestures rather resemble the automatic ones of the arms of a telegraph.

Musing, therefore, upon the purely Punchinello aspect of the human figure thus beheld, it had indirectly occurred to Bannadonna to devise some metallic agent, which should strike the hour with its mechanic hand, with even greater precision than the vital one. And, moreover, as the vital watchman on the roof, sallying from his retreat at the given periods, walked to the bell with uplifted mace, to smite it, Bannadonna had resolved that his invention should likewise possess the power of locomotion, and, along with that, the appearance, at least, of intelligence and will.

If the conjectures of those who claimed acquaintance with the intent of Bannadonna be thus far correct, no unenterprising spirit could have been his. But they stopped not here; intimating that though, indeed, his design had, in the first place, been prompted by the sight of the watchman, and confined to the devising of a subtle substitute for him: yet, as is not seldom the case with projectors, by insensible gradations, proceeding from comparatively pigmy aims to Titanic ones, the original scheme had, in its anticipated eventualities, at last, attained to an unheard of degree of daring. He still bent his efforts upon the locomotive figure for the belfry, but only as a partial type of an ulterior creature, a sort of elephantine Helot, adapted to further, in a degree scarcely to be imagined, the universal conveniences and glories of humanity; supplying nothing less than a supplement to the Six Days' Work; stocking the earth with a new serf, more useful than the ox, swifter than the dolphin, stronger than the lion, more cunning than the ape, for industry an ant, more fiery than serpents, and yet, in patience, another ass. All excellences of all God-made creatures, which served man, were here to receive advancement, and then to be combined in one. Talus was to have been the all-accomplished Helot's name. Talus, iron slave to Bannadonna, and, through him, to man.

Here, it might well be thought that, were these last conjectures as to the foundling's secrets not erroneous, then must he have been hopelessly infected with the craziest chimeras of his age; far outgoing Albert Magus and Cornelius Agrippa. But the contrary was averred. However marvelous his design, however apparently transcending not alone the bounds of human invention, but those of divine creation, yet the proposed means to be employed were alleged to have been confined within the sober forms of sober reason. It was affirmed that, to a degree of more than skeptic scorn, Bannadonna had been without sympathy for any of the vain-glorious irrationalities of his time. For example, he had not concluded, with the visionaries among the metaphysicians, that between the finer mechanic forces and the ruder animal vitality some germ of correspondence might prove discoverable. As little did his scheme partake of the enthusiasm of some natural philosophers, who hoped, by physiological and chemical inductions, to arrive at a knowledge of the source of life, and so qualify themselves to manufacture and improve upon it. Much less had he aught in common with the tribe of alchemists, who sought, by a species of incantations, to evoke some surprising vitality from the laboratory. Neither had he imagined, with certain sanguine theosophists, that, by faithful adoration of the Highest, unheard-of powers would be vouchsafed to man. A practical materialist, what Bannadonna had aimed at was to have been reached, not by logic, not by crucible, not by conjuration, not by altars; but by plain vice-bench and hammer. In short, to solve nature, to steal into her, to intrigue beyond her, to procure some one else to bind her to his hand;—

these, one and all, had not been his objects; but, asking no favors from any element or any being, of himself, to rival her, outstrip her, and rule her. He stooped to conquer. With him, common sense was theurgy; machinery, miracle; Prometheus, the heroic name for machinist; man, the true God.

Nevertheless, in initial step, so far as the experimental automaton for the belfry was concerned, he allowed fancy some little play; or, perhaps, what seemed his fancifulness was but his utilitarian ambition collaterally extended. In figure, the creature for the belfry should not be likened after the human pattern, nor any animal one, nor after the ideals, however wild, of ancient fable, but equally in aspect as in organism be an original production; the more terrible to behold, the better.

Such, then, were the suppositions as to the present scheme, and the reserved intent. How, at the very threshold, so unlooked for a catastrophe overturned all, or rather, what was the conjecture here, is now to be set forth.

It was thought that on the day preceding the fatality, his visitors having left him, Bannadonna had unpacked the belfry image, adjusted it, and placed it in the retreat provided—a sort of sentry-box in one corner of the belfry; in short, throughout the night, and for some part of the ensuing morning, he had been engaged in arranging everything connected with the domino; the issuing from the sentry-box each sixty minutes; sliding along a grooved way, like a railway; advancing to the clock-bell, with uplifted manacles; striking it at one of the twelve junctions of the four-and-twenty hands; then wheeling, circling the bell, and retiring to its post, there to bide for another sixty minutes, when the same process was to be repeated; the bell, by a cunning mechanism, meantime turning on its vertical axis, so as to present, to the descending mace, the clasped hands of the next two figures, when it would strike two, three, and so on, to to end. The musical metal in this time-bell being so managed in the fusion, by some art, perishing with its originator, that each of the clasps of the four-and-twenty hands should give forth its own peculiar resonance when parted.

But on the magic metal, the magic and metallic stranger never struck but that one stroke, drove but that one nail, severed but that one clasp, by which Bannadonna clung to his ambitious life. For, after winding up the creature in the sentry-box, so that, for the present, skipping the intervening hours, it should not emerge till the hour of one, but should then infallibly emerge, and, after deftly oiling the grooves whereon it was to slide, it was surmised that the mechanician must then have hurried to the bell, to give his final touches to its sculpture. True artist, he here became absorbed; and absorption still further intensified, it may be, by his striving to abate that strange look of Una; which, though, before others, he had treated with such unconcern, might not, in secret, have been without its thorn.

And so, for the interval, he was oblivious of his creature; which, not oblivious of him, and true to its creation, and true to its heedful winding up, left its post precisely at the given moment; along its well-oiled route, slid noiselessly towards its mark; and, aiming at the hand of Una, to ring one clangorous note, dully smote the intervening brain of Bannadonna, turned backwards to it; the manacled arms then instantly up-springing to their hovering poise. The falling body clogged the thing's return; so there it stood, still impending over Bannadonna, as if whispering some post-mortem terror. The chisel lay dropped from the hand, but beside the hand; the oil-flask spilled across the iron track.

In his unhappy end, not unmindful of the rare genius of the mechanician, the republic decreed him a stately funeral. It was resolved that the great bell—the one whose casting had been jeopardized through the timidity of the ill-starred workman—should be rung upon the entrance of the bier into the cathedral. The most robust man of the country round was assigned the office of bell-ringer.

But as the pall-bearers entered the cathedral porch, naught but a broken and disastrous sound, like that of some lone Alpine landslide, fell from the tower upon their ears. And then, all was hushed.

Glancing backwards, they saw the groined belfry crashed sideways in. It afterwards appeared that the powerful peasant, who had the bell-rope in charge, wishing to test at once the full glory of the bell, had swayed down upon the rope with one concentrate jerk. The mass of quaking metal, too ponderous for its frame, and strangely feeble somewhere at its top, loosed from its fastening, tore sideways down, and tumbling in one sheer fall, three hundred feet to the soft sward below, buried itself inverted and half out of sight.

Upon its disinterment, the main fracture was found to have started from a small spot in the ear; which, being scraped, revealed a defect, deceptively minute, in the casting; which defect must subsequently have been pasted over with some unknown compound.

The remolten metal soon reassumed its place in the tower's repaired superstructure. For one year the metallic choir of birds sang musically in its belfry-bough-work of sculptured blinds and traceries. But on the first anniversary of the tower's completion—at early dawn, before the concourse had surrounded it—an earthquake came; one loud crash was heard. The stone-pine, with all its bower of songsters, lay overthrown upon the plain.

So the blind slave obeyed its blinder lord; but, in obedience, slew him. So the creator was killed by the creature. So the bell was too heavy for the tower. So the bell's main weakness was where man's blood had flawed it. And so pride went before the fall.

COMMENTARY
by the Editors

There are obvious similarities between this story by Melville and Hawthorne's "Ethan Brand." Both prove the theme of satanic pride in an individual who, lacking humanity of his own, regards other men as "automatons." Both stories rely on textural symbols of heartlessness to describe the deaths of their protagonists on a tower or tower-like structure. And in the two stories the roles played by minor characters are similar. Bartram and his son Joe find their counterparts in the magistrate and the junior magistrate. Melville knew Hawthorne's story several years before he wrote his own in 1855. In the letter which follows he makes clear his attitude toward "Ethan Brand," an attitude which helped him later to shape his own "Bell-Tower." On 1 June 1851, from Pittsfield, he wrote to Hawthorne:

By the way, in the last "Dollar Magazine" I read "The Unpardonable Sin." He was a sad fellow, that Ethan Brand. I have no doubt you are by this time responsible for many a shake and tremor of the tribe of "general readers." It is a frightful poetical creed that the cultivation of the brain eats out the heart. But it's my *prose* opinion that in most cases, in those men who have fine brains and work them well, the heart extends to the hams. And though you smoke them with the fire of tribulation, yet, like veritable hams, the head only gives the richer and better flavor. I stand for the heart. To the dogs with the head! I had rather be a fool with a heart than Jupiter Olympus with his head. The reason the mass of men fear God, and *at bottom dislike* Him, is because they rather distrust His heart, and fancy Him all brain like a watch.*

The Facts Concerning the Recent Carnival of Crime in Connecticut
Mark Twain

I was feeling blithe, almost jocund. I put a match to my cigar, and just then the morning's mail was handed in. The first superscription I glanced at was in a handwriting that sent a thrill of pleasure through and through me. It was Aunt Mary's; and she was the person I loved and honored most in all the world, outside of my own household. She had been my boyhood's idol; maturity, which is fatal to so many enchantments, had not been able to dislodge her from her pedestal; no, it had only justified her right to be there, and placed her dethronement permanently among the impossibilities. To show how strong her influence over me was, I will observe that long after everybody else's "*do*-stop-smoking" had ceased to affect me in the slightest

The Letters of Herman Melville, ed. Merrell R. Davis and William H. Gilman (New Haven and London, 1965), p. 129.

degree, Aunt Mary could still stir my torpid conscience into faint signs of life when she touched upon the matter. But all things have their limit, in this world. A happy day came at last, when even Aunt Mary's words could no longer move me. I was not merely glad to see that day arrive; I was more than glad—I was grateful; for when its sun had set, the one alloy that was able to mar my enjoyment of my aunt's society was gone. The remainder of her stay with us that winter was in every way a delight. Of course she pleaded with me just as earnestly as ever, after that blessed day, to quit my pernicious habit, but to no purpose whatever; the moment she opened the subject I at once became calmly, peacefully, contentedly indifferent—absolutely, adamantinely indifferent. Consequently the closing weeks of that memorable visit melted away as pleasantly as a dream, they were so freighted, for me, with tranquil satisfaction. I could not have enjoyed my pet vice more if my gentle tormentor had been a smoker herself, and an advocate of the practice. Well, the sight of her handwriting reminded me that I was getting very hungry to see her again. I easily guessed what I should find in her letter. I opened it. Good! just as I expected; she was coming! Coming this very day, too, and by the morning train; I might expect her any moment.

I said to myself, "I am thoroughly happy and content, now. If my most pitiless enemy could appear before me at this moment, I would freely right any wrong I may have done him."

Straightway the door opened, and a shriveled, shabby dwarf entered. He was not more than two feet high. He seemed to be about forty years old. Every feature and every inch of him was a trifle out of shape; and so, while one could not put his finger upon any particular part and say, "This is a conspicuous deformity," the spectator perceived that this little person was a deformity as a whole—a vague, general, evenly blended, nicely adjusted deformity. There was a fox-like cunning in the face and the sharp little eyes, and also alertness and malice. And yet, this vile bit of human rubbish seemed to bear a sort of remote and ill-defined resemblance to me! It was dully perceptible in the mean form, the countenance, and even the clothes, gestures, manner, and attitudes of the creature. He was a farfetched, dim suggestion of a burlesque upon me, a caricature of me in little. One thing about him struck me forcibly, and most unpleasantly:

he was covered all over with a fuzzy, greenish mold, such as one sometimes sees upon mildewed bread. The sight of it was nauseating.

He stepped along with a chipper air, and flung himself into a doll's chair in a very free-and-easy way, without waiting to be asked. He tossed his hat into the wastebasket. He picked up my old chalk pipe from the floor, gave the stem a wipe or two on his knee, filled the bowl from the tobacco box at his side, and said to me in a tone of pert command:

"Gimme a match!"

I blushed to the roots of my hair; partly with indignation, but mainly because it somehow seemed to me that this whole performance was very like an exaggeration of conduct which I myself had sometimes been guilty of in my intercourse with familiar friends— but never, never with strangers, I observed to myself. I wanted to kick the pygmy into the fire, but some incomprehensible sense of being legally and legitimately under his authority forced me to obey his order. He applied the match to the pipe, took a contemplative whiff or two, and remarked, in an irritatingly familiar way:

"Seems to me it's devilish odd weather for this time of year."

I flushed again, and in anger and humiliation as before; for the language was hardly an exaggeration of some that I have uttered in my day, and moreover was delivered in a tone of voice and with an exasperating drawl that had the seeming of a deliberate travesty of my style. Now there is nothing I am quite so sensitive about as a mocking imitation of my drawling infirmity of speech. I spoke up sharply and said:

"Look here, you miserable ash-cat! you will have to give a little more attention to your manners, or I will throw you out of the window!"

The manikin smiled a smile of malicious content and security, puffed a whiff of smoke contemptuously toward me, and said, with a still more elaborate drawl:

"Come—go gently, now; don't put on *too* many airs with your betters."

This cool snub rasped me all over, but it seemed to subjugate me, too, for a moment. The pygmy contemplated me awhile with his weasel eyes, and then said, in a peculiarly sneering way:

"You turned a tramp away from your door this morning."

I said crustily:

"Perhaps I did, perhaps I didn't. How do *you* know?"

"Well, I know. It isn't any matter *how* I know."

"Very well. Suppose I *did* turn a tramp away from the door—what of it?"

"Oh, nothing; nothing in particular. Only you lied to him."

"I *didn't!* That is, I—"

"Yes, but you did; you lied to him."

I felt a guilty pang—in truth I had felt it forty times before that tramp had traveled a block from my door—but still I resolved to make a show of feeling slandered; so I said:

"This is a baseless impertinence. I said to the tramp—"

"There—wait. You were about to lie again. *I* know what you said to him. You said the cook was gone downtown and there was nothing left from breakfast. Two lies. You knew the cook was behind the door, and plenty of provisions behind *her.*"

This astonishing accuracy silenced me; and it filled me with wondering speculations, too, as to how this cub could have got his information. Of course he could have culled the conversation from the tramp, but by what sort of magic had he contrived to find out about the concealed cook? Now the dwarf spoke again.

"It was rather pitiful, rather small, in you to refuse to read that poor young woman's manuscript the other day, and give her an opinion as to its literary value; and she had come so far, too, and *so* hopefully. Now *wasn't* it?"

I felt like a cur! And I had felt so every time the thing had recurred to my mind, I may as well confess. I flushed hotly and said:

"Look here, have you nothing better to do than prowl around prying into other people's business? Did that girl tell you that?"

"Never mind whether she did or not. The main thing is, you did that contemptible thing. And you felt ashamed of it afterward. Aha! you feel ashamed of it *now!*"

This was a sort of devilish glee. With fiery earnestness I responded:

"I told that girl, in the kindest, gentlest way, that I could not consent to deliver judgment upon *any*one's manuscript, because an individual's verdict was worthless. It might underrate a work of high merit and lose it to the world, or it might overrate a trashy production and so open the way for its infliction upon the world. I said that the great public was the only tribunal competent to sit in judgment upon a literary effort, and therefore it must be best to lay it before that tribunal in the outset, since in the end it must stand or fall by that mighty court's decision anyway."

"Yes, you said all that. So you did, you juggling, small-souled shuffler! And yet when the happy hopefulness faded out of that poor girl's face, when you saw her furtively slip beneath her shawl the scroll she had so patiently and honestly scribbled at—so ashamed of her darling now—so proud of it before—when you saw the gladness go out of her eyes and the tears come there, when she crept away so humbly who had come so—"

"Oh, peace! peace! peace! Blister your merciless tongue, haven't all these thoughts tortured me enough without *your* coming here to fetch them back again!"

Remorse! Remorse! It seemed to me that it would eat the very heart out of me! And yet that small fiend only sat there leering at me with joy and contempt, and placidly chuckling. Presently he began to speak again. Every sentence was an accusation, and every accusation a truth. Every clause was freighted with sarcasm and derision, every slow-dropping word burned like vitriol. The dwarf reminded me of times when I had flown at my children in anger and punished them for faults which a little inquiry would have taught me that others, and not they, had committed. He reminded me of how I had disloyally allowed old friends to be traduced in my hearing, and been too craven to utter a word in their defense. He reminded me of many dishonest things which I had done; of many which I had procured to be done by children and other irresponsible persons; of some which I had planned, thought upon, and longed to do, and been kept from the performance by fear of consequences only. With exquisite cruelty he recalled to my mind, item by item, wrongs and unkindnesses I had inflicted and humiliations I had put upon friends since dead, "who died thinking of those injuries, maybe, and grieving over them," he added, by way of poison to the stab.

"For instance," said he, "take the case of your younger brother, when you two were boys together, many a long year ago. He always lovingly trusted in you with a fidelity that your manifold treacheries were not able to shake. He followed you about like a dog, content to suffer wrong and abuse if he might only be with you; patient under these injuries so long as it was your hand that inflicted them. The latest picture you have of him in health and strength must be such a comfort to you! You pledged your honor that if he would let you blindfold him no harm should come to him; and then, giggling and choking over the rare fun of the joke, you led him to a brook thinly glazed with ice, and pushed him in; and how you did laugh! Man, you will never forget the gentle, reproachful look he gave you as he struggled shivering out, if you live a thousand years! Oho! you see it now, you see it *now!*"

"Beast, I have seen it a million times, and shall see it a million more! and may you rot away piecemeal, and suffer till doomsday what I suffer now, for bringing it back to me again!"

The dwarf chuckled contentedly, and went on with his accusing history of my career. I dropped into a moody, vengeful state, and suffered in silence under the merciless lash. At last this remark of his gave me a sudden rouse.

"Two months ago, on a Tuesday, you woke up, away in the night, and fell to thinking, with shame, about a peculiarly mean and pitiful act of yours toward a poor ignorant Indian in the wilds of the Rocky Mountains in the winter of eighteen hundred and—"

"Stop a moment, devil! Stop! Do you mean to tell me that even my very *thoughts* are not hidden from you?"

"It seems to look like that. Didn't you think the thoughts I have just mentioned?"

"If I didn't, I wish I may never breathe again! Look here, friend— look me in the eye. Who *are* you?"

"Well, who do you think?"

"I think you are Satan himself. I think you are the devil."

"No."

"No? Then who *can* you be?"

"Would you really like to know?"

"*Indeed* I would."

"Well, I am your *Conscience!*"

In an instant I was in a blaze of joy and exultation. I sprang at the creature, roaring:

"Curse you, I have wished a hundred million times that you were tangible, and that I could get my hands on your throat once! Oh, but I will wreak a deadly vengeance on—"

Folly! Lightning does not move more quickly than my Conscience did! He darted aloft so suddenly that in the moment my fingers clutched the empty air he was already perched on the top of the high bookcase, with his thumb at his nose in token of derision. I flung the poker at him, and missed. I fired the bootjack. In a blind rage I flew from place to place, and snatched and hurled any missile that came handy; the storm of books, inkstands, and chunks of coal gloomed the air and beat about the manikin's perch relentlessly, but all to no purpose; the nimble figure dodged every shot; and not only that, but burst into a cackle of sarcastic and triumphant laughter as I sat down exhausted. While I puffed and gasped with fatigue and excitement, my Conscience talked to this effect.

"My good slave, you are curiously witless—no, I mean characteristically so. In truth, you are always consistent, always yourself, always an ass. Otherwise it must have occurred to you that if you attempted this murder with a sad heart and a heavy conscience, I would droop under the burdening influence instantly. Fool, I should have weighed a ton, and could not have budged from the floor; but instead, you are so cheerfully anxious to kill me that your conscience is as light as a feather; hence I am away up here out of your reach. I can almost respect a mere ordinary sort of fool; but *you*—pah!"

I would have given anything, then, to be heavyhearted, so that I could get this person down from there and take his life, but I could no more be heavyhearted over such a desire than I could have sorrowed over its accomplishment. So I could only look longingly up at my master, and rave at the ill luck that denied me a heavy conscience the one only time that I had ever wanted such a thing in my life. By and by I got to musing over the hour's strange adventure, and of course my human curiosity began to work. I set myself to framing in my mind some questions for this fiend to answer. Just then one of my boys entered, leaving the door open behind him, and exclaimed:

"My! what *has* been going on here? The bookcase is all one riddle of—"

I sprang up in consternation, and shouted:

"Out of this! Hurry! Jump! Fly! Shut the door! Quick, or my Conscience will get away!"

The door slammed to, and I locked it. I glanced up and was grateful, to the bottom of my heart, to see that my owner was still my prisoner. I said:

"Hang you, I might have lost you! Children are the heedlessest creatures. But look here, friend, the boy did not seem to notice you at all; how is that?"

"For a very good reason. I am invisible to all but you."

I made mental note of that piece of information with a good deal of satisfaction. I could kill this miscreant now, if I got a chance, and no one would know it. But this very reflection made me so lighthearted that my Conscience could hardly keep his seat, but was like to float aloft toward the ceiling like a toy balloon. I said, presently:

"Come, my Conscience, let us be friendly. Let us fly a flag of truce for a while. I am suffering to ask you some questions."

"Very well. Begin."

"Well, then, in the first place, why were you never visible to me before?"

"Because you never asked to see me before; that is, you never asked in the right spirit and the proper form before. You were just in the right spirit this time, and when you called for your most pitiless enemy I was that person by a very large majority, though you did not suspect it."

"Well, did that remark of mine turn you into flesh and blood?"

"No. It only made me visible to you. I am unsubstantial, just as other spirits are."

This remark prodded me with a sharp misgiving. If he was unsubstantial, how was I going to kill him? But I dissembled, and said persuasively:

"Conscience, it isn't sociable of you to keep at such a distance. Come down and take another smoke."

This was answered with a look that was full of derision, and with this observation added:

"Come where you can get at me and kill me? The invitation is declined with thanks."

"All right," said I to myself; "so it seems a spirit *can* be killed, after all; there will be one spirit lacking in this world, presently, or I lose my guesss." Then I said aloud:

"Friend—"

"There; wait a bit. I am not your friend, I am your enemy; I am not your equal, I am your master. Call me 'my lord,' if you please. You are too familiar."

"I don't like such titles. I am willing to call you *sir*. That is as far as—"

"We will have no argument about this. Just obey; that is all. Go on with your chatter."

"Very well, my lord—since nothing but my lord will suit you—I was going to ask you how long you will be visible to me?"

"Always!"

I broke out with strong indignation: "This is simply an outrage. That is what I think of it. You have dogged, and dogged, and *dogged* me, all the days of my life, invisible. That was misery enough; now to have such a looking thing as you tagging after me like another shadow all the rest of my days is an intolerable prospect. You have my opinion, my lord; make the most of it."

"My lad, there was never so pleased a conscience in this world as I was when you made me visible. It gives me an inconceivable advantage. *Now,* I can look you straight in the eye, and call you names, and leer at you, jeer at you, sneer at you; and *you* know what eloquence there is in visible gesture and expression, more especially when the effect is heightened by audible speech. I shall always address you henceforth in your o-w-n s-n-i-v-e-l-l-i-n-g d-r-a-w-l—baby!"

I let fly with the coal hod. No result. My lord said:

"Come, come! Remember the flag of truce!"

"Ah, I forgot that. I will try to be civil; and *you* try it, too, for a novelty. The idea of a *civil* conscience! It is a good joke; an excellent joke. All the consciences *I* have ever heard of were nagging, badgering, faultfinding, execrable savages! Yes; and always in a sweat about some poor little insignificant trifle or other—destruction catch the lot of them, *I* say! I would trade mine for the smallpox and seven kinds of consumption, and be glad of the chance. Now tell me, why *is* it that a conscience can't haul a man over the coals once, for an offense, and then let him alone? Why is it that it wants to keep on pegging at him, day and night and night and day, week in and week out, forever and ever, about the same old thing? There is no sense in that, and no reason in it. I think a conscience that will act like that is meaner than the very dirt itself."

"Well, *we* like it; that suffices."

"Do you do it with the honest intent to improve a man?"

That question produced a sarcastic smile, and this reply:

"No sir. Excuse me. We do it simply because it is 'business.' It is our trade. The *purpose* of it *is* to improve the man, but *we* are merely disinterested agents. We are appointed by authority, and haven't anything to say in the matter. We obey orders and leave the consequences where they belong. But I am willing to admit this much: we *do* crowd the orders a trifle when we get a chance, which is most of the time. We enjoy it. We are instructed to remind a man a few times of an error; and I don't mind acknowledging that we try to give pretty good measure. And when we get hold of a man of a peculiarly sensitive nature, oh, but we do haze him! I have known consciences to come all the way from China and Russia to see a person of that kind put through his paces, on a special occasion. Why, I knew a man of that sort who had accidentally crippled a mulatto baby; the news went abroad, and I wish you may never commit another sin if the consciences didn't flock from all over the earth to enjoy the fun and help his master exercise him. That man walked the floor in torture for forty-eight hours, without eating or sleeping, and then blew his brains out. The child was perfectly well again in three weeks."

"Well, you are a precious crew, not to put it too strong. I think I begin to see, now, why you have always been a trifle inconsistent with me. In your anxiety to get all the juice you can out of a sin, you make a man repent of it in three or four different ways. For instance, you found fault with me for lying to that tramp, and I suffered over that. But it was only yesterday that I told a tramp the square truth, to wit, that, it being regarded as bad citizenship to encourage vagrancy, I would give him nothing. What did you do *then?* Why, you made me say to myself, 'Ah, it would have been so much kinder and more blameless to ease him off with a little white lie, and send him away feeling that if he could not have bread, the gentle treatment was at least something to be grateful for!' Well, I suffered all day about *that.* Three days before I had fed a tramp, and fed him freely, supposing it a virtuous act. Straight off you said, 'O false citizen, to have fed a tramp!' and I suffered as usual. I gave a tramp work; you objected to it—*after* the contract was made, of course; you never speak up beforehand. Next, I *refused* a tramp work; you objected to *that.* Next, I proposed to kill a tramp; you kept me awake all night, oozing remorse at every pore. Sure I was going to be right *this* time, I sent the next tramp away with my benediction; and I wish you may live as long as I do, if you didn't make me smart all night again because I didn't kill him. Is there *any* way of satisfying that malignant invention which is called a conscience?"

"Ha, ha! this is luxury! Go on!"

"But come, now, answer me that question. *Is* there any way?"

"Well, none that I propose to tell *you,* my son. Ass! I don't care *what* act you may turn your hand to, I can straightway whisper a word in your ear and make you think you have committed a dreadful meanness. It is my *business*—and my joy—to make you repent of *every*thing you do. If I had fooled away any opportunities it was not intentional; I beg to assure you it was not intentional!"

"Don't worry; you haven't missed a trick that I know of. I never did a thing in all my life, virtuous or otherwise, that I didn't repent of in twenty-four hours. In church last Sunday I listened to a charity sermon. My first impulse was to give three hundred and fifty dollars; I repented of that and reduced it a hundred; repented of that and reduced it another hundred; repented of that and reduced it another hundred; repented of that and reduced the remaining fifty to twenty-five; repented of that and came down to fifteen; repented of that and dropped to two dollars and a half; when the plate came around at last, I repented once more and contributed ten cents. Well, when I got home, I did wish to goodness I had that ten cents back again! You never *did* let me get through a charity sermon without having something to sweat about."

"Oh, and I never shall, I never shall. You can always depend on me."

"I think so. Many and many's the restless night I've wanted to take you by the neck. If I could only get hold of you now!"

"Yes, no doubt. But I am not an ass; I am only the saddle of an ass. But go on, go on. You entertain me more than I like to confess."

"I am glad of that. (You will not mind my lying a little, to keep in practice.) Look here; not to be too personal, I think you are about the shabbiest and most contemptible little shriveled up reptile that can be imagined. I am grateful enough that you are invisible to other people, for I should die with shame to be seen with such a mildewed monkey of a conscience as *you* are. Now if you were five or six feet high, and—"

"Oh, come! who is to blame?"

"*I* don't know."

"Why, you are; nobody else."

"Confound, you, I wasn't consulted about your personal appearance."

"I don't care, you had a good deal to do with it, nevertheless. When you were eight or nine years old, I was seven feet high, and as pretty as a picture."

"I wish you had died young! So you have grown the wrong way, have you?"

"Some of us grow one way and some the other. You had a large conscience once; if you've a small conscience now, I reckon there are reasons for it. However, both of us are to blame, you and I. You see, you used to be conscientious about a great many things; morbidly so, I may say. It was a great many years ago. You probably do not remember it, now. Well, I took a great interest in my work, and I so enjoyed the anguish which certain pet sins of yours afflicted you with, that I kept pelting at you until I rather overdid the matter. You began to rebel. Of course I began to lose ground, then, and shrivel a little—diminish in stature, get moldy, and grow deformed. The more I weakened, the more stubbornly you fastened on to those particular sins; till at last the places on my person that represent those vices became as callous as sharkskin. Take smoking, for instance. I played that card a little too long, and I lost. When people plead with you at this late day to quit that vice, that old callous place seems to enlarge and cover me all over like a shirt of mail. It exerts a mysterious, smothering effect; and presently I, your faithful hater, your devoted Conscience, go sound asleep! Sound? It is no name for it. I couldn't hear it thunder at such a time. You have some few other vices—perhaps eighty, or maybe ninety—that affect me in much the same way."

"This is flattering; you must be asleep a good part of your time."

"Yes, of late years. I should be asleep *all* the time, but for the help I get."

"Who helps you?"

"Other consciences. Whenever a person whose conscience I am acquainted with tries to plead with you about the vices you are callous to, I get my friend to give his client a pang concerning some villainy of his own, and that shuts off his meddling and starts him off to hunt personal consolation. My field of usefulness is about trimmed down to tramps, budding authoresses, and that line of goods, now; but don't you worry—I'll harry you on *them* while they last! Just you put your trust in me."

"I think I can. But if you had only been good enough to mention these facts some thirty years ago, I should have turned my particular attention to sin, and I think that by this time I should not only have had you pretty permanently asleep on the entire list of human vices, but reduced to the size of a homeopathic pill, at that. That is about the style of conscience *I* am pining for. If I only had you shrunk down to a homeopathic pill, and could get my hands on you, would I put you in a glass case for a keepsake? No, sir. I would give you to a yellow dog! That is where *you* ought to be—you and all your tribe. You are not fit to be in society, in my opinion. Now another question. Do you know a good many consciences in this section?"

"Plenty of them."

"I would give anything to see some of them! Could you bring them here? And would they be visible to me?"

"Certainly not."

"I suppose I ought to have known that, without asking. But no matter, you can describe them. Tell me about my neighbor Thompson's conscience, please."

"Very well. I know him intimately; have known him many years. I knew him when he was eleven feet high and of a faultless figure. But he is very rusty and tough and misshapen now, and hardly ever interests himself about anything. As to his present size—well, he sleeps in a cigar box."

"Likely enough. There are few smaller, meaner men in this region than Hugh Thompson. Do you know Robinson's conscience?"

"Yes. He is a shade under four and a half feet high; used to be a blond; is a brunet, now, but still shapely and comely."

"Well, Robinson is a good fellow. Do you know Tom Smith's conscience?"

"I have known him from childhood. He was thirteen inches high, and rather sluggish, when he was two years old—as nearly all of us are, at that age. He is thirty-seven feet high, now, and the stateliest figure in America. His legs are still racked with growing pains, but he has a good time, nevertheless. Never sleeps. He is the most active and energetic member of the New England Conscience Club; is president of it. Night and day you can find him pegging away at Smith, panting with his labor, sleeves rolled up, countenance all alive with enjoyment. He has got his victim splendidly dragooned, now. He can make poor Smith imagine that the most innocent little thing he does is an odious sin; and then he sets to work and almost tortures the soul out of him about it."

"Smith is the noblest man in all this section, and the purest; and yet is always breaking his heart because he cannot be good! Only a conscience *could* find pleasure in heaping agony upon a spirit like that. Do you know my Aunt Mary's conscience?"

"I have seen her at a distance, but am not acquainted with her. She lives in the open air altogether, because no door is large enough to admit her."

"I can believe that. Let me see. Do you know the conscience of that publisher who once stole some sketches of mine for a 'series' of his, and then left me to pay the law expenses I had to incur in order to choke him off?"

"Yes. He has a wide fame. He was exhibited, a month ago, with some other antiquities, for the benefit of a recent Member of the

Cabinet's conscience, that was starving in exile. Tickets and fares were high, but I traveled for nothing by pretending to be the conscience of an editor, and got in for half-price by representing myself to be the conscience of a clergyman. However, the publisher's conscience, which was to have been the main feature of the entertainment, was a failure—as an exhibition. He was there, but what of that? The management had provided a microscope with a magnifying power of only thirty thousand diameters, and so nobody got to see him, after all. There was great and general dissatisfaction, of course, but—"

Just here there was an eager footstep on the stair; I opened the door, and my Aunt Mary burst into the room. It was a joyful meeting, and a cheery bombardment of questions and answers concerning family matters ensued. By and by my aunt said:

"But I am going to abuse you a little now. You promised me, the day I saw you last, that you would look after the needs of the poor family around the corner as faithfully as I had done it myself. Well, I found out by accident that you failed of your promise. *Was* that right?"

In simple truth, I never had thought of that family a second time! And now such a splintering pang of guilt shot through me! I glanced up at my Conscience. Plainly, my heavy heart was affecting him. His body was drooping forward; he seemed about to fall from the bookcase. My aunt continued:

"And think how you have neglected my poor protégé at the almshouse, you dear, hardhearted promise-breaker!"

I blushed scarlet, and my tongue was tied. As the sense of my guilty negligence waxed sharper and stronger, my conscience began to sway heavily back and forth; and when my aunt, after a little pause, said in a grieved tone, "Since you never once went to see her, maybe it will not distress you now to know that that poor child died, months ago, utterly friendless and forsaken!" my Conscience could no longer bear up under the weight of my sufferings, but tumbled headlong from his high perch and struck the floor with a dull, leaden thump. He lay there writhing with pain and quaking with apprehension, but straining every muscle in frantic efforts to get up. In a fever of expectancy I sprang to the door, locked it, placed my back against it, and bent a watchful gaze upon my struggling master. Already my fingers were itching to begin their murderous work.

"Oh, what *can* be the matter!" exclaimed my aunt, shrinking from me, and following with her frightened eyes the direction of mine. My breath was coming in short, quick gasps now, and my excitement was almost uncontrollable. My aunt cried out:

"Oh, do not look so! You appall me! Oh, what can the matter be? What is it you see? Why do you stare so? Why do you work your fingers like that?"

"Peace, woman!" I said, in a hoarse whisper. "Look elsewhere; pay no attention to me; it is nothing—nothing. I am often this way. It will pass in a moment. It comes from smoking too much."

My injured lord was up, wild-eyed with terror, and trying to hobble toward the door. I could hardly breathe, I was so wrought up. My aunt wrung her hands, and said:

"Oh, I knew how it would be; I knew it would come to this at last! Oh, I implore you to crush out that fatal habit while it may yet be time! You must not, you shall not be deaf to my supplications longer!" My struggling Conscience showed sudden signs of weariness! "Oh, promise me you will throw off this hateful slavery of tobacco!" My Conscience began to reel drowsily, and grope with his hands—enchanting spectacle! "I beg you, I beseech you, I implore you! Your reason is deserting you! There is madness in your eye! It flames with frenzy! Oh, hear me, hear me, and be saved! See, I plead with you on my very knees!" As she sank before me my Conscience reeled again, and then drooped languidly to the floor, blinking toward me a last supplication for mercy, with heavy eyes. "Oh, promise, or you are lost! Promise, and be redeemed! Promise! Promise and live!" With a long-drawn sigh my conquered Conscience closed his eyes and fell fast asleep!

With an exultant shout I sprang past my aunt, and in an instant I had my lifelong foe by the throat. After so many years of waiting and longing, he was mine at last. I tore him to shreds and fragments. I rent the fragments to bits. I cast the bleeding rubbish into the fire, and drew into my nostrils the grateful incense of my burnt offering. At last, and forever, my Conscience was dead!

I was a free man! I turned upon my poor aunt, who was almost petrified with terror, and shouted:

"Out of this with your paupers, your charities, your reforms, your pestilent morals! You behold before you a man whose life-conflict is done, whose soul is at peace; a man whose heart is dead to sorrow, dead to suffering, dead to remorse; a man WITHOUT A CONSCIENCE! In my joy I spare you, though I could throttle you and never feel a pang! Fly!"

She fled. Since that day my life is all bliss. Bliss, unalloyed bliss. Nothing in all the world could persuade me to have a conscience again. I settled all my old outstanding scores, and began the world anew. I killed thirty-eight persons during the past two weeks—all of them on account of ancient grudges. I burned a dwelling that interrupted my view. I swindled a widow and some orphans out of their last cow, which is a very good one, though not thoroughbred, I believe. I have also committed scores of crimes, of various kinds, and have enjoyed my work exceedingly, whereas it would formerly have broken my heart and turned my hair gray, I have no doubt.

In conclusion I wish to state, by way of advertisement, that medical colleges desiring assorted tramps for scientific purposes, either by the gross, by cord measurement, or per ton, will do well to examine the lot in my cellar before purchasing elsewhere, as these were all selected and prepared by myself, and can be had at a low rate, because I wish to clear out my stock and get ready for the spring trade.

Angel Levine
Bernard Malamud

Manischevitz, a tailor, in his fifty-first year suffered many reverses and indignities. Previously a man of comfortable means, he overnight lost all he had, when his establishment caught fire and, after a metal container of cleaning fluid exploded, burned to the ground. Although Manischevitz was insured against fire, damage suits by two customers who had been hurt in the flames deprived him of every penny he had collected. At almost the same time, his son, of much promise, was killed in the war, and his daughter, without so much as a word of warning, married a lout and disappeared with him as off the face of the earth. Thereafter Manischevitz was victimized by excruciating backaches and found himself unable to work even as a presser—the only kind of work available to him—for more than an hour or two daily, because beyond that the pain from standing became maddening. His Fanny, a good wife and mother, who had taken in washing and sewing, began before his eyes to waste away. Suffering shortness of breath, she at last became seriously ill and took to her bed. The doctor, a former customer of Manischevitz, who out of pity treated them, at first had difficulty diagnosing her ailment but later put it down as hardening of the arteries at an advanced stage. He took Manischevitz aside, prescribed complete rest for her, and in whispers gave him to know there was little hope.

Throughout his trials Manischevitz had remained somewhat stoic, almost unbelieving that all this had descended upon his head, as if it were happening, let us say, to an acquaintance or some distant relative; it was in sheer quantity of woe incomprehensible. It was also ridiculous, unjust, and because he had always been a religious man, it was in a way an affront to God. Manischevitz believed this in all his suffering. When his burden had grown too crushingly heavy to be borne he prayed in his chair with shut hollow eyes: "My dear God, sweetheart, did I deserve that this should happen to me?" Then recognizing the worthlessness of it, he put aside the complaint and prayed humbly for assistance: "Give Fanny back her health, and to me for myself that I shouldn't feel pain in every step. Help now or tomorrow is too late. This I don't have to tell you." And Manischevitz wept.

Manischevitz's flat, which he had moved into after the disastrous fire, was a meager one, furnished with a few sticks of chairs, a table, and bed, in one of the poorer sections of the city. There were three rooms: a small, poorly-papered living room; an apology for a kitchen, with a wooden icebox; and the comparatively large bedroom where Fanny lay in a sagging secondhand bed, gasping for breath. The bedroom was the warmest room of the house and it was here, after his outburst to God, that Manischevitz, by the light of two small bulbs overhead, sat reading his Jewish newspaper. He was not truly reading, because his thoughts were everywhere; however the print offered a convenient resting place for his eyes, and a word or two, when he permitted himself to comprehend them, had the momentary effect of helping him forget his troubles. After a short while he discovered, to his surprise, that he was actively scanning the news, searching for an item of great interest to him. Exactly what he thought he would read he couldn't say—until he realized, with some astonishment, that he was expecting to discover something about himself. Manischevitz put his paper down and looked up with the distinct impression that someone had entered the apartment, though he could not remember having heard the sound of the door opening. He looked around: the room was very still, Fanny sleeping, for once, quietly. Half-frightened, he watched her until he was satisfied she wasn't dead; then, still disturbed by the thought of an unannounced vistor, he stumbled into the living room and there had the shock of his life, for at the table sat a Negro reading a newspaper he had folded up to fit into one hand.

"What do you want here?" Manischevitz asked in fright.

The Negro put down the paper and glanced up with a gentle expression. "Good evening." He seemed not to be sure of himself, as if he had got into the wrong house. He was a large man, bonily built, with a heavy head covered by a hard derby, which he made no attempt to remove. His eyes seemed sad, but his lips, above which he wore a slight mustache, sought to smile; he was not otherwise prepossessing. The cuffs of his sleeves, Manischevitz noted, were frayed to the lining and the dark suit was badly fitted. He had very large feet. Recovering from his fright, Manischevitz guessed he had left the door open and was being visited by a case worker from the Welfare Department—some came at night—for he had recently applied for relief. Therefore he lowered himself into a chair opposite the Negro, trying, before the man's uncertain smile, to feel comfortable. The former tailor sat stiffly but patiently at the table, waiting for the investigator to take out his pad and pencil and begin asking questions; but before long he became convinced the man intended to do nothing of the sort.

"Who are you?" Manischevitz at last asked uneasily.

"If I may, insofar as one is able to, identify myself, I bear the name of Alexander Levine."

In spite of all his troubles Manischevitz felt a smile growing on his lips. "You said Levine?" he politely inquired.

The Negro nodded. "That is exactly right."

Carrying the jest farther, Manischevitz asked, "You are maybe Jewish?"

"All my life I was, willingly."

The tailor hesitated. He had heard of black Jews but had never met one. It gave an unusual sensation.

Recognizing in afterthought something odd about the tense of Levine's remark, he said doubtfully, "You ain't Jewish anymore?"

Levine at this point removed his hat, revealing a very white part in his black hair, but quickly replaced it. He replied, "I have recently been disincarnated into an angel. As such, I offer you my humble assistance, if to offer is within my province and ability—in the best sense." He lowered his eyes in apology. "Which calls for added explanation: I am what I am granted to be, and at present the completion is in the future."

"What kind of angel is this?" Manischevitz gravely asked.

"A bona fide angel of God, within prescribed limitations," answered Levine, "not to be confused with the members of any particular sect, order, or organization here on earth operating under a similar name."

Manischevitz was thoroughly disturbed. He had been expecting something but not this. What sort of mockery was it—provided

Levine was an angel—of a faithful servant who had from childhood lived in the synagogues, always concerned with the word of God?

To test Levine he asked, "Then where are your wings?"

The Negro blushed as well as he was able. Manischevitz understood this from his changed expression. "Under certain circumstances we lose privileges and prerogatives upon returning to earth, no matter for what purpose, or endeavoring to assist whosoever."

"So tell me," Manischevitz said triumphantly, "how did you get here?"

"I was transmitted."

Still troubled, the tailor said, "If you are a Jew, say the blessing for bread."

Levine recited it in sonorous Hebrew.

Although moved by the familiar words Manischevitz still felt doubt that he was dealing with an angel.

"If you are an angel," he demanded somewhat angrily, "give me the proof."

Levine wet his lips. "Frankly, I cannot perform either miracles or near miracles, due to the fact that I am in a condition of probation. How long that will persist or even consist, I admit, depends on the outcome."

Manischevitz racked his brains for some means of causing Levine positively to reveal his true identity, when the Negro spoke again:

"It was given me to understand that both your wife and you require assistance of salubrious nature?"

The tailor could not rid himself of the feeling that he was the butt of a jokester. Is this what a Jewish angel looks like? he asked himself. This I am not convinced.

He asked a last question. "So if God sends to me an angel, why a black? Why not a white that there are so many of them?"

"It was my turn to go next," Levine explained.

Manischevitz could not be persuaded. "I think you are a faker."

Levine slowly rose. His eyes showed disappointment and worry. "Mr. Manischevitz," he said tonelessly, "if you should desire me to be of assistance to you any time in the near future, or possibly before, I can be found"—he glanced at his fingernails—"in Harlem."

He was by then gone.

The next day Manischevitz felt some relief from his backache and was able to work four hours at pressing. The day after, he put in six hours; and the third day four again. Fanny sat up a little and asked for some halvah to suck. But on the fourth day the stabbing, breaking ache afflicted his back, and Fanny again lay supine, breathing with blue-lipped difficulty.

Manischevitz was profoundly disappointed at the return of his active pain and suffering. He had hoped for a longer interval of easement, long enough to have some thought other than of himself and his troubles. Day by day, hour by hour, minute after minute, he lived in pain, pain his only memory, questioning the necessity of it, inveighing against it, also, though with affection, against God. Why *so much,* Gottenyu? If He wanted to teach His servant a lesson for some reason, some cause—the nature of His nature—to teach him, say, for reasons of his weakness, his pride, perhaps, during his years of prosperity, his frequent neglect of God—to give him a little lesson, why then any of the tragedies that had happened to him, any *one* would have sufficed to chasten him. But *all together*—the loss of both his children, his means of livelihood, Fanny's health and his—that was too much to ask one frail-boned man to endure. Who, after all, was Manischevitz that he had been given so much to suffer? A tailor. Certainly not a man of talent. Upon him suffering was largely wasted. It went nowhere, into nothing: into more suffering. His pain did not earn him bread, nor fill the cracks in the wall, nor lift, in the middle of the night, the kitchen table; only lay upon him, sleepless, so sharply oppressively that he could many times have cried out yet not heard himself through this thickness of misery.

In this mood he gave no thought to Mr. Alexander Levine, but at moments when the pain waivered, slightly diminishing, he sometimes wondered if he had been mistaken to dismiss him. A black Jew and and angel to boot—very hard to believe, but suppose he *had* been sent to succor him, and he, Manischevitz, was in his blindness too blind to comprehend? It was this thought that put him on the knife-point of agony.

Therefore the tailor, after much self-questioning and continuing doubt, decided he would seek the self-styled angel in Harlem. Of course he had great difficulty, because he had not asked for specific directions, and movement was tedious to him. The subway took him to 116th Street, and from there he wandered in the dark world. It was vast and its lights lit nothing. Everywhere were shadows, often moving. Manischevitz hobbled along with the aid of a cane, and not knowing where to seek in the blackened tenement buildings, looked fruitlessly through store windows. In the stores he saw people and *everybody* was black. It was an amazing thing to observe. When he was too tired, too unhappy to go farther, Manischevitz stopped in front of a tailor's store. Out of familiarity with the appearance of it, with some sadness he entered. The tailor, an old skinny Negro with a mop of woolly gray hair, was sitting cross-legged on his work-bench, sewing a pair of full-dress pants that had a razor slit all the way down the seat.

"You'll excuse me, please, gentleman," said Manischevitz, admiring the tailor's deft, thimbled fingerwork, "but you know maybe somebody by the name Alexander Levine?"

The tailor, who Manischevitz thought, seemed a little antagonistic to him, scratched his scalp.

"Cain't say I ever heared dat name."

"Alex-ander Lev-ine," Manischevitz repeated it.

The man shook his head. "Cain't say I heared."

About to depart, Manischevitz remembered to say: "He is an angel, maybe."

"Oh *him*," said the tailor clucking. "He hang out in dat honky tonk down here a ways." He pointed with his skinny finger and returned to the pants.

Manischevitz crossed the street against a red light and was almost run down by a taxi. On the block after the next, the sixth store from the corner was a cabaret, and the name in sparkling lights was Bella's. Ashamed to go in, Manischevitz gazed through the neon-lit window, and when the dancing couples had parted and drifted away, he discovered at a table on the side, towards the rear, Levine.

He was sitting alone, a cigarette butt hanging from the corner of his mouth, playing solitaire with a dirty pack of cards, and Manischevitz felt a touch of pity for him, for Levine had deteriorated in appearance. His derby was dented and had a gray smudge on the side. His ill-fitting suit was shabbier, as if he had been sleeping in it.

His shoes and trouser cuffs were muddy, and his face was covered with an impenetrable stubble the color of licorice. Manischevitz, though deeply disappointed, was about to enter, when a big-breasted Negress in a purple evening gown appeared before Levine's table, and with much laughter through many white teeth, broke into a vigorous shimmy. Levine looked straight at Manischevitz with a haunted expression, but the tailor was too paralyzed to move or acknowledge it. As Bella's gyrations continued, Levine rose, his eyes lit in excitement. She embraced him with vigor, both his hands clasped around her big restless buttocks and they tangoed together across the floor, loudly applauded by the noisy customers. She seemed to have lifted Levine off his feet and his large shoes hung limp as they danced. They slid past the windows where Manischevitz, white-faced, stood staring in. Levine winked slyly and the tailor left for home.

Fanny lay at death's door. Through shrunken lips she muttered concerning her childhood, the sorrows of the marriage bed, the loss of her children, yet wept to live. Manischevitz tried not to listen, but even without ears he would have heard. It was not a gift. The doctor panted up the stairs, a broad but bland, unshaven man (it was Sunday) and soon shook his head. A day at most, or two. He left at once, not without pity, to spare himself Manischevitz's multiplied sorrow; the man who never stopped hurting. He would someday get him into a public home.

Manischevitz visited a synagogue and there spoke to God, but God had absented himself. The tailor searched his heart and found no hope. When she died he would live dead. He considered taking his life although he knew he wouldn't. Yet it was something to consider. Considering, you existed. He railed against God— Can you love a rock, a broom, an emptiness? Baring his chest, he smote the naked bones, cursing himself for having believed.

Asleep in a chair that afternoon, he dreamed of Levine. He was standing before a faded mirror, preening small decaying opalescent wings. "This means," mumbled Manischevitz, as he broke out of sleep, "that it is possible he could be an angel." Begging a neighbor lady to look in on Fanny and occasionally wet her lips with a few drops of water, he drew on his thin coat, gripped his walking stick, exchanged some pennies for a subway token, and rode to Harlem. He knew this act was the last desperate one of his woe: to go without belief, seeking a black magician to restore his wife to invalidism. Yet if there was no choice, he did at least what was chosen.

He hobbled to Bella's but the place had changed hands. It was now, as he breathed, a synagogue in a store. In the front, towards him, were several rows of empty wooden benches. In the rear stood the Ark, its portals of rough wood covered with rainbows of sequins; under it a long table on which lay the sacred scroll unrolled, illuminated by the dim light from a bulb on a chain overhead. Around the table, as if frozen to it and the scroll, which they all touched with their fingers, sat four Negroes wearing skullcaps. Now as they read the Holy Word, Manischevitz could, through the plate glass window, hear the singsong chant of their voices. One of them was old, with a gray beard. One was bubble-eyed. One was humpbacked. The fourth was a boy, no older than thirteen. Their heads moved in rhythmic swaying. Touched by this sight from his childhood and youth, Manischevitz entered and stood silent in the rear.

"Neshoma," said bubble eyes, pointing to the word with a stubby finger. "Now what dat mean?"

"That's the word that means soul," said the boy. He wore glasses.

"Let's git on wid de commentary," said the old man.

"Ain't necessary," said the humpback. "Souls is immaterial substance. That's all. The soul is derived in that manner. The immateriality is derived from the substance, and they both, causally an' otherwise, derived from the soul. There can be no higher."

"That's the highest."

"Over de top."

"Wait a minute," said bubble eyes. "I don't see what is dat immaterial substance. How come de one gits hitched up to de odder?" He addressed the humpback.

"Ask me something hard. Because it is substanceless immateriality. It couldn't be closer together, like all the parts of the body under one skin—closer."

"Hear now," said the old man.

"All you done is switched de words."

"It's the primum mobile, the substanceless substance from which comes all things that were incepted in the idea—you, me and everything and body else."

"Now how did all dat happen? Make it sound simple."

"It de speerit," said the old man. "On de face of de water moved de speerit. An' dat was good. It say so in de Book. From de speerit ariz de man."

"But now listen here. How come it become substance if it all de time a spirit?"

"God alone done dat."

"Holy! Holy! Praise His Name."

"But has dis spirit got some kind of a shade or color?" asked bubble eyes, deadpan.

"Man of course not. A spirit is a spirit."

"Then how come we is colored?" he said with a triumphant glare.

"Ain't got nothing to do wid dat."

"I still like to know."

"God put the spirit in all things," answered the boy. "He put it in the green leaves and the yellow flowers. He put it with the gold in the fishes and the blue in the sky. That's how come it came to us."

"Amen."

"Praise Lawd and utter loud His speechless name."

"Blow de bugle till it bust the sky."

They fell silent, intent upon the next word. Manischevitz approached them.

"You'll excuse me," he said. "I am looking for Alexander Levine. You know him maybe?"

"That's the angel," said the boy.

"Oh, *him*," snuffed bubble eyes.

"You'll find him at Bella's. It's the establishment right across the street," the humpback said.

Manischevitz said he was sorry that he could not stay, thanked them, and limped across the street. It was already night. The city was dark and he could barely find his way.

But Bella's was bursting with the blues. Through the window Manischevitz recognized the dancing crowd and among them sought

Levine. He was sitting loose-lipped at Bella's side table. They were tippling from an almost empty whiskey fifth. Levine had shed his old clothes, wore a shiny new checkered suit, pearl-gray derby, cigar, and big, two-tone button shoes. To the tailor's dismay, a drunken look had settled upon his formerly dignified face. He leaned toward Bella, tickled her ear lobe with his pinky, while whispering words that sent her into gales of raucous laughter. She fondled his knee.

Manischevitz, girding himself, pushed open the door and was not welcomed.

"This place reserved."

"Beat it, pale puss."

"Exit, Yankel, Semitic trash."

But he moved towards the table where Levine sat, the crowd breaking before him as he hobbled forward.

"Mr. Levine," he spoke in a trembly voice. "Is here Manischevitz."

Levine glared blearily. "Speak yo' piece, son."

Manischevitz shuddered. His back plagued him. Cold tremors tormented his crooked legs. He looked around, everybody was all ears.

"You'll excuse me. I would like to talk to you in a private place."

"Speak, Ah is a private pusson."

Bella laughed piercingly. "Stop it, boy, you killin' me."

Manischevitz, no end disturbed, considered fleeing but Levine addressed him:

"Kindly state the pu'pose of yo' communication with yo's truly."

The tailor wet cracked lips. "You are Jewish. This I am sure."

Levine rose, nostrils flaring. "Anythin' else yo' got to say?"

Manischevitz's tongue lay like stone.

"Speak now or fo'ever hold off."

Tears blinded the tailor's eyes. Was ever man so tried? Should he say he believed a half-drunken Negro to be an angel?

The silence slowly petrified.

Manischevitz was recalling scenes of his youth as a wheel in his mind whirred: believe, do not, yes, no, yes, no. The pointer pointed to yes, to between yes and no, to no, no it was yes. He sighed. It moved but one had still to make a choice.

"I think you are an angel from God." He said it in a broken voice, thinking, If you said it it was said. If you believed it you must say it. If you believed, you believed.

The hush broke. Everybody talked but the music began and they went on dancing. Bella, grown bored, picked up the cards and dealt herself a hand.

Levine burst into tears. "How you have humiliated me."

Manischevitz apologized.

"Wait'll I freshen up." Levine went to the men's room and returned in his old clothes.

No one said goodbye as they left.

They rode to the flat via subway. As they walked up the stairs Manischevitz pointed with his cane at his door.

"That's all been taken care of," Levine said. "You best go in while I take off."

Disappointed that it was so soon over but torn by curiosity, Manischevitz followed the angel up three flights to the roof. When he got there the door was already padlocked.

Luckily he could see through a small broken window. He heard an odd noise, as though of a whirring of wings, and when he strained for a wider view, could have sworn he saw a dark figure borne aloft on a pair of magnificent black wings.

A feather drifted down. Manischevitz gasped as it turned white, but it was only snowing.

He rushed downstairs. In the flat Fanny wielded a dust mop under the bed and then upon the cobwebs on the wall.

"A wonderful thing, Fanny," Manischevitz said. "Believe me, there are Jews everywhere."

COMMENTARY
by the Editors

Witty and allegorical in the tradition of Jewish storytelling, Bernard Malamud has contrived a profoundly moral tale. Within a modern context of economic despair and racial suspicion he has given the humble tailor a kind of apocalyptic vision, a miracle—no less—that becomes the basis of his spiritual reaffirmation. Fictionally this is a most bold enterprise, for ours is not an age in which the mystic is ordinarily allowed to challenge the imperfections of rational being. Malamud, well aware of this, has not attempted to argue us out of our skepticism. Nor, on the other hand, does he pretend that Manischevitz is experiencing a sanctified hallucination. Rather, he has ordered his materials in the form of an outwardly simple narrative, making Alexander Levine as palpable and credible as Manischevitz himself. Indeed, he does exist; not only that, unlike the general run of angels, he needs the tailor even as the tailor needs him. "Under certain circumstances [he] lose[s] privileges and prerogatives upon returning to earth, no matter for what purpose, or endeavoring to assist whosoever." Angels, as we all know, have wings; but Angel Levine cannot have his restored to him until Manischevitz asserts his renewed faith.

The allegory works as such because Malamud, though he has subsumed metaphysical meaning within the literal—or at least temporal—elements of his story, intends both the metaphysical and literal to operate simultaneously upon the reader. Superficially, the story is the thing. Nevertheless, he throws out hints that attract us to his deeper purpose. In the initial dialogue, for instance, he turns a joke into a revelation of man's free nature.

"Carrying the jest farther, Manischevitz asked, 'You are maybe Jewish?' "

" 'All my life I was, willingly.' "

That is the word to underscore, *willingly*. For later, still desperate, Manischevitz sees himself as a passive victim, one without options. "Yet if there was no choice, he did at least what was chosen." Immediately thereafter, however, he is prepared for the transformation to inner awareness. He goes to the Negro synagogue where he overhears the debate on the essence of an ineffable divinity. This is his climactic experience, the prelude to a recognition that he finally embraces in the fleshly surroundings of Bella's cabaret.

Manischevitz was recalling scenes of his youth as a wheel in his mind whirred; believe, do not, yes, no, yes, no. The pointer pointed to yes, to between yes and no, to no, no it was yes. He sighed. It moved but one had still to make a choice.
"I think you are an angel from God." He said it in a broken voice, thinking, If you said it it was said. If you believed it you must say it. If you believed, you believed.

Here, finally, is the resolution of doubt and the beginning of redemption. Manischevitz has made his choice.

The allegory, for all its engagingly uninvolved manner, is complex. Manischevitz is not only a disturbed individual bathed in self-pity because of his troubles. Whether he will admit it or not, he is also an inescapably social being linked to all of humanity. Yet even in the midst of his woes, and himself unconsciously symbolic of his own racial oppression, he is guilty of pride as well as doubt when he places a higher value upon his white heritage than the black one of his would-be savior. "So if God sends to me an angel, why a black? Why not a white that there are so many of them?" That pride changes gradually to humility, an enforced change at first because he must turn to his counterpart, the Negro tailor (perhaps an *alter ego*) for help; and then a respectful one as he attends to the discourse in the Negro synagogue. But he must be reduced still more in Bella's cabaret as the members of one oppressed race deride the fellow of another. "Exit, Yankel, Semitic trash."

The language of exclusion could hardly be more cruel—or more familiar or universal. The lesson is driven home poignantly and ironically when "Levine burst into tears. 'How you have humiliated me.' " Manischevitz has been responsible for the angel's decline physically; but this is only symptomatic of Levine's spiritual reduction. Having failed to accept his angelic status, the tailor has in effect diminished Levine's authority and capacity for responsible transcendent duty. This diminution is symbolized by the angel's regression to sensuality, and his cheaply gaudy attire; the shabby clothing he has put off is the outward mark of piety: his no longer tenable divorce from vanity and ostentation. As a further irony, his pompously genteel language becomes the crude talk of a stage Negro.

But the tailor apologizes and the angel assumes once more his dignified shabbiness. His humiliation becomes the humility of service even as Manischevitz's becomes that of gratitude. The story ends with a typical joke that has the ring of truth. " 'A wonderful thing, Fanny,' Manischevitz said. 'Believe me, there are Jews everywhere.' " Misconstrued, this might be taken as the tailor's renewed pride of race. It seems to us, however, that Malamud has instilled in him a new kind of self-valuation: now it is the esteem of belonging, of sharing an elevated destiny with all men. Slyly—and humanly—of course, he places Jews in the forefront, even of moral achievement.

As an allegory, further, "Angel Levine" makes excellent complementary use of setting. The grim domestic environment is a practical reality, but the trip to Harlem suggests departure from normality, a descent into Hell. For Manischevitz, who still clings pathetically to his white separateness, this is an alien "dark world" whose "lights lit nothing" and where *everybody* was black." The strident, garish atmosphere of Bella's cabaret—like a miniature of Joyce's "nighttown"—emphasizes the poverty of spirit and Angel Levine's fallen state. These sinister, mythic effects are countered by the equally unreal ones of the synagogue, significantly the former location of Bella's establishment. Here we find not only the discourse on divinity but the celebration of the warm colors of nature and the renunciation of skin coloration as a test of equality. The return to spiritual reality takes place in Manischevitz's flat where the atmosphere brightens visibly. The liberated black angel ascends, dropping a feather which is whitened by the snow. In this symbolic gesture we discover the revitalized faith in God and humanity of the man who had been "reduced to cursing himself for having believed."

INDEX TO AUTHORS AND TITLES